Math **Diagnosis** and **Intervention** System

Booklet I

Measurement, Geometry,
Data Analysis, and Probability
in Grades 4–6

Scott Foresman·Addison Wesley

enVisionMATH™

Overview of Math Diagnosis and Intervention System

The system can be used in a variety of situations:

- **During School** Use the system for intervention on prerequisite skills at the beginning of the year, the beginning of a topic, or the beginning of a lesson. Use for intervention during the Topic when more is needed beyond the resources already provide for the lesson.

- **After-school, Saturday school, summer-school (intersession) programs** Use the system for intervention offered in special programs.

The system provides resources for:

- **Assessment** Diagnostic Tests are provided. Each Diagnostic Test assesses the content for a grade. Use a test at the start of the year for entry-level assessment or anytime during the year as a summative evaluation.

- **Diagnosis** An item analysis identifies areas where intervention is needed.

- **Intervention** Booklets A–E in Part 1 and Booklets F–J in Part 2 identify specific concepts and assign a number to each concept, for example, A12 or E10. For each concept, there is a two-page Intervention Lesson that provides an instructional activity followed by practice. References for the Intervention Lessons are provided in teacher materials for *enVisionMATH*.

- **Monitoring** The Teacher's Guide provides both Individual Record Forms and Class Record Forms to monitor student progress.

Editorial Offices: Glenview, Illinois • Parsippany, New Jersey • New York, New York

Sales Offices: Boston, Massachusetts • Duluth, Georgia • Glenview, Illinois
Coppell, Texas • Sacramento, California • Mesa, Arizona

ISBN-13: 978-0-328-31124-8
ISBN-10: 0-328-31124-3

Table of Contents

Table of Contents continued

Solid Figures

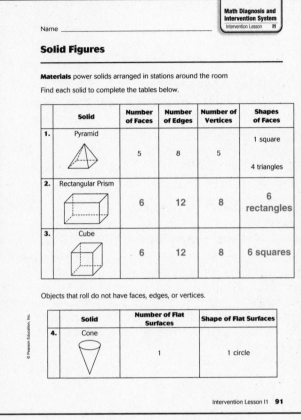

Name _____

Math Diagnosis and Intervention System
Intervention Lesson I1

Solid Figures

Materials power solids arranged in stations around the room

Find each solid to complete the tables below.

	Solid	Number of Faces	Number of Edges	Number of Vertices	Shapes of Faces
1.	Pyramid	5	8	5	1 square 4 triangles
2.	Rectangular Prism	6	12	8	6 rectangles
3.	Cube	6	12	8	6 squares

Objects that roll do not have faces, edges, or vertices.

	Solid	Number of Flat Surfaces	Shape of Flat Surfaces
4.	Cone	1	1 circle

© Pearson Education, Inc.

Intervention Lesson I1 **91**

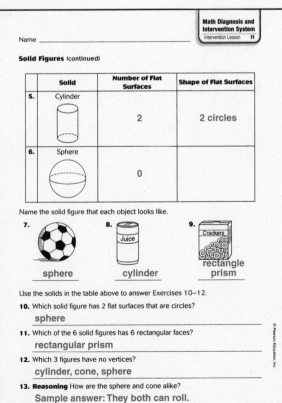

Name _____

Math Diagnosis and Intervention System
Intervention Lesson I1

Solid Figures (continued)

	Solid	Number of Flat Surfaces	Shape of Flat Surfaces
5.	Cylinder	2	2 circles
6.	Sphere	0	

Name the solid figure that each object looks like.

7. sphere   **8.** Juice cylinder   **9.** Crackers rectangle prism

Use the solids in the table above to answer Exercises 10–12.

10. Which solid figure has 2 flat surfaces that are circles?
sphere

11. Which of the 6 solid figures has 6 rectangular faces?
rectangular prism

12. Which 3 figures have no vertices?
cylinder, cone, sphere

13. **Reasoning** How are the sphere and cone alike?
Sample answer: They both can roll.

© Pearson Education, Inc.

92 Intervention Lesson I1

Teacher Notes

Ongoing Assessment

Ask: *Which two solids are the most alike?* Cube and rectangular prism; they have the same number of faces, edges, and vertices.

Error Intervention

If students have trouble naming the shapes of the faces or counting the number of faces, edges, and vertices,

then use D50: Flat Surfaces of Solid Figures, D57: Flat Surfaces and Corners, and D58: Faces, Corners, and Edges.

If You Have More Time

Have a "Solid Bee." Put solids into a bag, including at least one of each discussed in the lesson. Mix in real life objects like a ball, piece of chalk, eraser, and number cube. Have students stand in line. Say: "I need to know the name of this solid." Then pull a solid out of the bag. The first student in line names the solid. If the name is correct, the student goes to the end of the line. If the name is incorrect, the student sits down. Give each student a turn naming a solid. Each round, ask a different question such as:
I need to know how many faces (or flat surfaces) this solid has;
I need to know how many edges this solid has;
I need to know how many vertices this solid has.

Breaking Apart Solids

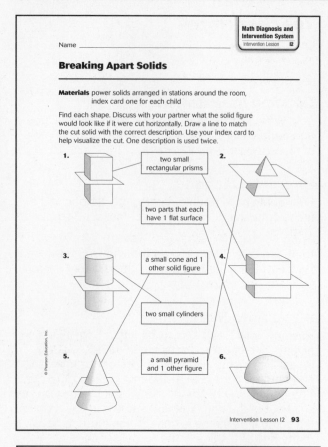

Breaking Apart Solids

Materials power solids arranged in stations around the room, index card one for each child

Find each shape. Discuss with your partner what the solid figure would look like if it were cut horizontally. Draw a line to match the cut solid with the correct description. Use your index card to help visualize the cut. One description is used twice.

1.

two small rectangular prisms

2.

two parts that each have 1 flat surface

3.

a small cone and 1 other solid figure

4.

two small cylinders

5.

a small pyramid and 1 other figure

6.

Teacher Notes

Ongoing Assessment

Ask: *What solid figure do you get if you place two cubes together, one on top of the other?*
Rectangular prism

Error Intervention

If students have trouble naming the solids,

then use D59 or I1: Solid Figures.

If You Have More Time

Put students in pairs or small groups. Have them think of solid items that are cut horizontally or vertically. Example: a loaf of bread resembles a rectangular prism, it is cut into very thin rectangular prisms; a grapefruit is a sphere, it is typically cut into 2 parts that each have 1 flat surface.

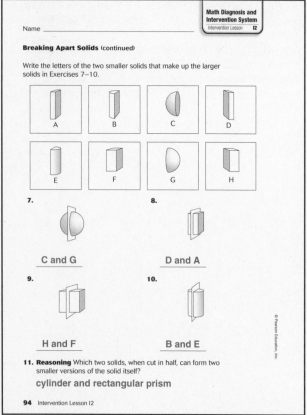

Breaking Apart Solids (continued)

Write the letters of the two smaller solids that make up the larger solids in Exercises 7–10.

A

B

C

D

E

F

G

H

7.

C and G

8.

D and A

9.

H and F

10.

B and E

11. **Reasoning** Which two solids, when cut in half, can form two smaller versions of the solid itself?

cylinder and rectangular prism

Lines and Line Segments

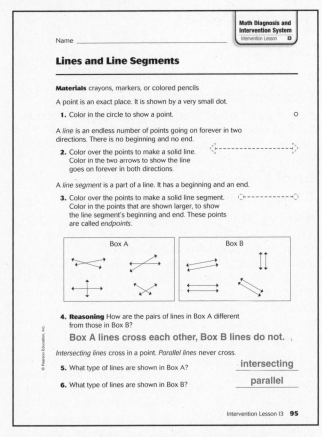

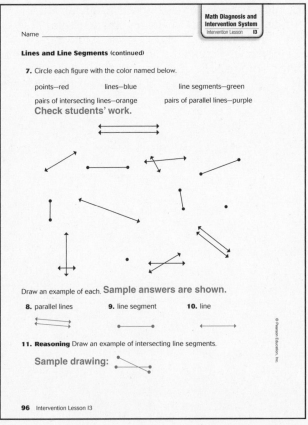

Teacher Notes

Ongoing Assessment

Ask: *Why should teachers say "Please get in a line segment." instead of "Please get in a line"?* When students line up there is a beginning and an end. A line goes on forever in both directions.

Error Intervention

If students confuse parallel and intersecting lines,

then show students that the two L's in the word parallel never cross. So lines that never cross are parallel.

If You Have More Time

Put students in pairs. Give each a copy of a city or neighborhood map. Maps can be printed from the internet. Have students take turns identifying streets that are parallel to each other and ones that intersect.

Acute, Right, and Obtuse Angles

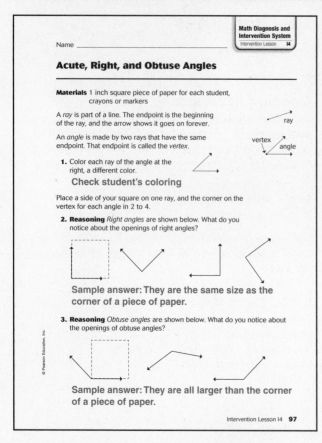

Name _____

Acute, Right, and Obtuse Angles

Materials 1 inch square piece of paper for each student, crayons or markers

A *ray* is part of a line. The endpoint is the beginning of the ray, and the arrow shows it goes on forever.

ray

An *angle* is made by two rays that have the same endpoint. That endpoint is called the *vertex*.

vertex   angle

1. Color each ray of the angle at the right, a different color.

Check student's coloring

Place a side of your square on one ray, and the corner on the vertex for each angle in 2 to 4.

2. Reasoning *Right angles* are shown below. What do you notice about the openings of right angles?

Sample answer: They are the same size as the corner of a piece of paper.

3. Reasoning *Obtuse angles* are shown below. What do you notice about the openings of obtuse angles?

Sample answer: They are all larger than the corner of a piece of paper.

Intervention Lesson I4   **97**

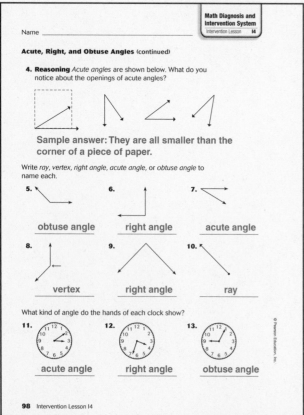

Name _____

Acute, Right, and Obtuse Angles (continued)

4. Reasoning *Acute angles* are shown below. What do you notice about the openings of acute angles?

Sample answer: They are all smaller than the corner of a piece of paper.

Write *ray, vertex, right angle, acute angle,* or *obtuse angle* to name each.

5.
obtuse angle

6.
right angle

7.
acute angle

8.
vertex

9.
right angle

10.
ray

What kind of angle do the hands of each clock show?

11.
acute angle

12.
right angle

13.
obtuse angle

Teacher Notes

Ongoing Assessment
Ask: *What type of angle is formed by the hands on the clock when it shows the time school starts?* Answer will vary by school start times.

Error Intervention
If students confuse acute and obtuse,

then help students by telling them that people often say to a baby "Look how little you are. You are so cute." So, a little baby is "acute". This will help them remember that acute is smaller than a right angle. You can also say the word "acute" with a small, squeaky voice and the word "obtuse" with a big, burly voice.

If You Have More Time
Have students play a math version of "Simon Says". Have a student be Simon, stand in the front of the class room, and say statements such as the following: "Simon says make an obtuse angle." Students can show acute, right, and obtuse angles with both arms. They can also show a ray by pointing with one arm extended in any direction. Those who correctly make an obtuse angle continue. Those who do not must sit down. Students who make the figure when Simon doesn't say "Simon says" must also sit down.

Polygons

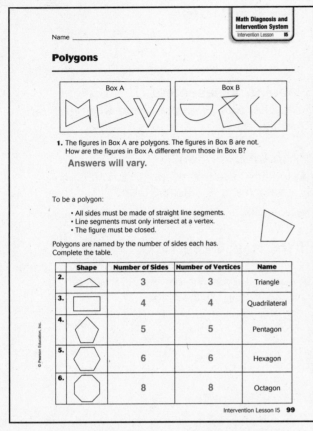

Name _____

Polygons

Box A   Box B

1. The figures in Box A are polygons. The figures in Box B are not. How are the figures in Box A different from those in Box B?

Answers will vary.

To be a polygon:

• All sides must be made of straight line segments.
• Line segments must only intersect at a vertex.
• The figure must be closed.

Polygons are named by the number of sides each has. Complete the table.

	Shape	Number of Sides	Number of Vertices	Name
2.		3	3	Triangle
3.		4	4	Quadrilateral
4.		5	5	Pentagon
5.		6	6	Hexagon
6.		8	8	Octagon

Intervention Lesson I5   **99**

© Pearson Education, Inc.

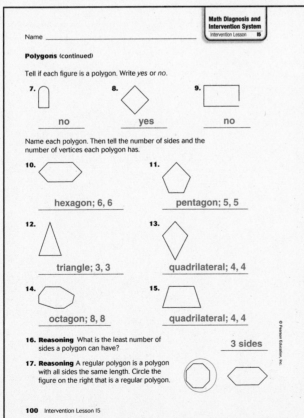

Name _____

Polygons (continued)

Tell if each figure is a polygon. Write *yes* or *no*.

7.   **8.**   **9.**

    no   yes   no

Name each polygon. Then tell the number of sides and the number of vertices each polygon has.

10.   **11.**

   hexagon; 6, 6   pentagon; 5, 5

12.   **13.**

   triangle; 3, 3   quadrilateral; 4, 4

14.   **15.**

   octagon; 8, 8   quadrilateral; 4, 4

16. Reasoning What is the least number of sides a polygon can have?   **3 sides**

17. Reasoning A regular polygon is a polygon with all sides the same length. Circle the figure on the right that is a regular polygon.

© Pearson Education, Inc.

100   Intervention Lesson I5

© Pearson Education, Inc.

Teacher Notes

Ongoing Assessment

Ask: ***Why is a circle not a polygon?*** A polygon must have sides that are line segments. A circle has no line segments.

Error Intervention

If students count the same vertex or side twice,

then have them put an x on each side or vertex as they count it. This will help students to avoid counting a vertex or side more than once.

If You Have More Time

Have students make polygon books. Give each student 3 half-sheets of white paper. With all 3 sheets together, have them fold the papers to make a book. Students should title their book with something having to do with polygons. The first two-page spread should have the heading "Triangles." Let the students use crayons or markers to draw examples of different types of triangles. Also, let them print pictures from the internet or cut out pictures from magazines. Make other two-page spreads for quadrilaterals, pentagons, hexagons, and octagons. The cover, made with construction paper, can be a picture drawn by using only polygons.

Classifying Triangles Using Sides and Angles

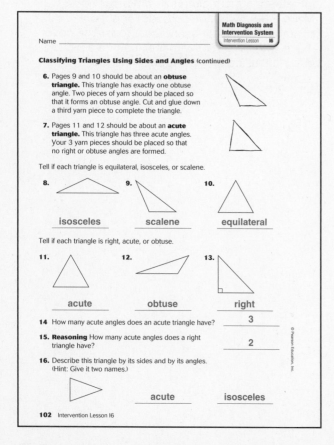

Teacher Notes

Ongoing Assessment

Ask: *What type of angles are in an equilateral triangle?* acute

Error Intervention

If students have trouble identifying right angles, acute angles, and obtuse angles,

then use I4: Acute, Right, and Obtuse Angles.

If You Have More Time

Have students draw a triangle. Trade with a partner and have the partner identify the triangle by its sides and then by its angles.

Quadrilaterals

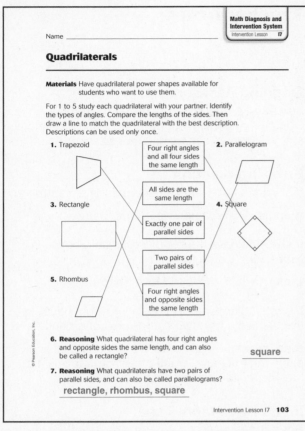

Quadrilaterals

Materials Have quadrilateral power shapes available for students who want to use them.

For 1 to 5 study each quadrilateral with your partner. Identify the types of angles. Compare the lengths of the sides. Then draw a line to match the quadrilateral with the best description. Descriptions can be used only once.

1. Trapezoid
2. Parallelogram
3. Rectangle
4. Square
5. Rhombus

- Four right angles and all four sides the same length
- All sides are the same length
- Exactly one pair of parallel sides
- Two pairs of parallel sides
- Four right angles and opposite sides the same length

6. **Reasoning** What quadrilateral has four right angles and opposite sides the same length, and can also be called a rectangle?

   square

7. **Reasoning** What quadrilaterals have two pairs of parallel sides, and can also be called parallelograms?

   rectangle, rhombus, square

Intervention Lesson I7   **103**

Quadrilaterals (continued)

For Exercises 8–13, circle squares red, rectangles blue, parallelograms green, rhombuses orange and trapezoids purple. Some quadrilaterals may be circled more than once.
See teachers note page.

8.
9.
10.

11.
12.
13.

14. I have two pairs of parallel sides, and all of my sides are equal, but I have no right angles. What quadrilateral am I?   rhombus

15. I have two pairs of parallel sides and 4 right angles, but all 4 of my sides are not equal. What quadrilateral am I?   rectangle

16. Name all of the quadrilaterals in the picture at the right.
    rectangle, rhombus, parallelogram, trapezoid

17. **Reasoning** Why is the quadrilateral on the right a parallelogram, but not a rectangle?
    Sample answer: Both a rectangle and a parallelogram have opposite sides parallel. A rectangle must also have four right angles. This quadrilateral does not have four right angles, so it is a parallelogram, but not a rectangle.

104 Intervention Lesson I7

Teacher Notes

Ongoing Assessment

Ask: *Are all squares rectangles?* yes *Are all rectangles squares?* no

Error Intervention

If students list only one name for rectangles, squares, or rhombuses,

then ask students leading questions so they can discover that other quadrilateral name(s) can also be used.

If You Have More Time

Put students in pairs. Each pair needs five index cards labeled square, rectangle, rhombus, trapezoid, and parallelogram. Have one student shuffle and draw a card. Both students then need to draw an example of the quadrilateral. Students should compare drawings. Tell them to describe the different ways a quadrilateral can be drawn. Help students to discover that quadrilaterals may be different sizes, but they will always have their specific characteristics.

In items 8–13, each quadrilateral should be circled with the color listed below

8. red, blue, green and orange

9. purple

10. green

11. blue, green

12. orange, green

13. purple

Congruent Figures and Motions

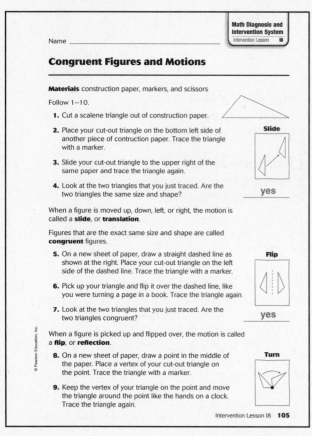

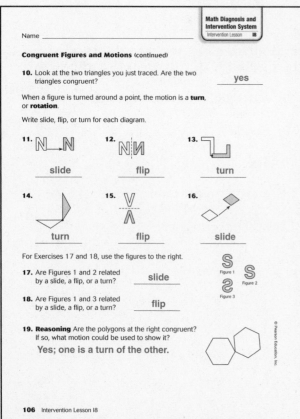

Teacher Notes

Ongoing Assessment

Ask: *Why are all squares not congruent?*
Congruent figures must have the same size and shape. Squares can be different sizes.

Error Intervention

If students have trouble understanding congruency,

then use D54: Same Size, Same Shape.

If students have trouble differentiating between slides, flips, and turns,

then use D55: Ways to Move Shapes.

If students understand congruency, but have trouble deciding if two figures are congruent,

then have students trace one of the figures and place the tracing over the other figure to see if it has the same size and shape.

If You Have More Time

Have students write their name using letters that have been flipped, turned, or slid. Exchange with a partner and have the partner identify what motion was used on each letter. Show the students that some letters can look like a slide and a flip. For example, the letter "I" looks the same when it is flipped and slid to the right.

Line Symmetry

Name _____

Line Symmetry

Materials one sheet of 3″ x 3″ paper, two sheets of 2″ x 4″ paper, for each student

1. How many ways can you fold a rectangular sheet of paper so that the two parts match exactly?

   2

A **line of symmetry** is a line on which a figure can be folded so the two parts match exactly.

2. Fold the square sheet of paper as many ways as you can so the two sides match. One way is shown at the right. How many lines of symmetry does a square have?   **4**

3. Cut a rectangular sheet of paper in half as shown at the right. Cut out one of the triangles formed.

4. Fold the right triangle as many ways as you can so two sides match. How many lines of symmetry does the right triangle have?   **0**

If a figure has at least one line of symmetry, it is **symmetric**.

5. Circle the figures that are symmetric.

To draw a symmetric figure, flip the given half over the line of symmetry.

Intervention Lesson I9   **107**

Name _____

Line Symmetry (continued)

Complete the figure below to make a symmetric figure by answering 6 to 8.

6. Find a vertex that is not on the line of symmetry. Count the number of spaces from the line of symmetry to the vertex.

7. Count the same number of spaces on the other side of the line of symmetry and mark a point.

8. Use line segments to connect the new vertices. Do this until the figure is complete.

line of symmetry

2 spaces   2 spaces

Decide whether or not each figure is symmetric. Write Yes or No

9.   **yes**

10.   **yes**

11.   **no**

Complete each figure so the dotted line segment is the line of symmetry.

12.

13.

Draw all lines of symmetry for each figure.

14.

15.

Teacher Notes

Ongoing Assessment

Ask: ***Do you have letters in your name that are symmetrical? If so, which ones?*** Answers will vary depending on name and handwriting style.

Error Intervention

If students have trouble drawing symmetrical figures,

then use D56: Symmetry.

If students have difficulty visualizing the folding to check for symmetry,

then encourage students to trace and cut out the figure to see if the figure is symmetrical.

If You Have More Time

Give the students a few minutes to look around the room and list as many objects as they can that are symmetrical. Have students share their findings. Help them to discover objects that are not obvious, such as the hand on a clock, has a line of symmetry.

Solids and Nets

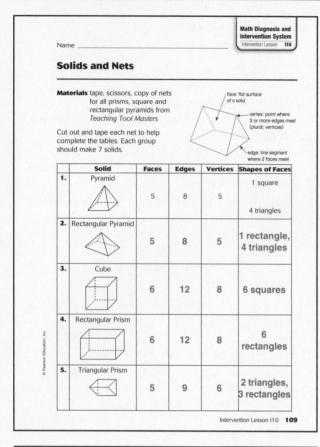

Teacher Notes

Ongoing Assessment

Ask: *What solid best represents a can of corn?*
cylinder

Error Intervention

If students have trouble identifying solids,

then use I1: Solid Figures.

If You Have More Time

In pairs, have students play *Guess My Solid.* One student should select a solid made from the nets; make sure the other student cannot see which solid the partner picks. The second student asks yes-or-no questions such as, *Does it have more than 5 vertices? Does it have at least one square face?* and then tries to guess what the solid is using the clues.

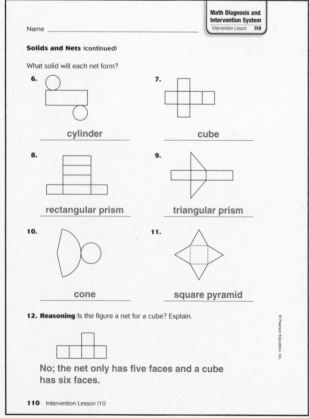

Views of Solid Figures

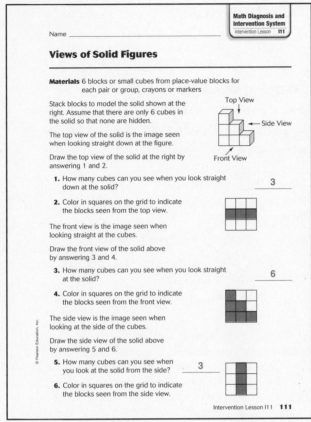

Name _____

Views of Solid Figures

Materials 6 blocks or small cubes from place-value blocks for each pair or group, crayons or markers

Stack blocks to model the solid shown at the right. Assume that there are only 6 cubes in the solid so that none are hidden.

Top View
Side View
Front View

The top view of the solid is the image seen when looking straight down at the figure.

Draw the top view of the solid at the right by answering 1 and 2.

1. How many cubes can you see when you look straight down at the solid? _____ 3

2. Color in squares on the grid to indicate the blocks seen from the top view.

The front view is the image seen when looking straight at the cubes.

Draw the front view of the solid above by answering 3 and 4.

3. How many cubes can you see when you look straight at the solid? _____ 6

4. Color in squares on the grid to indicate the blocks seen from the front view.

The side view is the image seen when looking at the side of the cubes.

Draw the side view of the solid above by answering 5 and 6.

5. How many cubes can you see when you look at the solid from the side? _____ 3

6. Color in squares on the grid to indicate the blocks seen from the side view.

Intervention Lesson I11 **111**

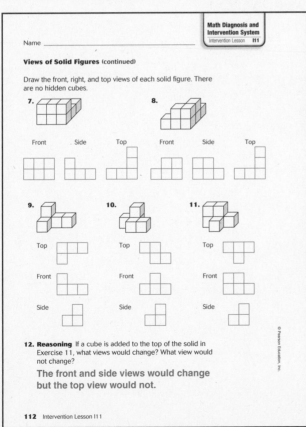

Name _____

Views of Solid Figures (continued)

Draw the front, right, and top views of each solid figure. There are no hidden cubes.

7.   Front   Side   Top

8.   Front   Side   Top

9.   Top   Front   Side

10.   Top   Front   Side

11.   Top   Front   Side

12. **Reasoning** If a cube is added to the top of the solid in Exercise 11, what views would change? What view would not change?

The front and side views would change but the top view would not.

112 Intervention Lesson I11

Teacher Notes

Ongoing Assessment

Ask: *Which views would change if a cube were added behind the far, back, left cube in a solid?* The top view and the side view would change. The front view would not change.

Error Intervention

If students have trouble seeing the views using blocks or small cubes,

then use larger boxes to illustrate the solids in front of the class.

If You Have More Time

Have student work in pairs. One student draws a top, side, or front view and the other student constructs a possible solid having the given view with blocks or small cubes.

Intervention Lesson I11 **11**

© Pearson Education, Inc.

Geometric Ideas

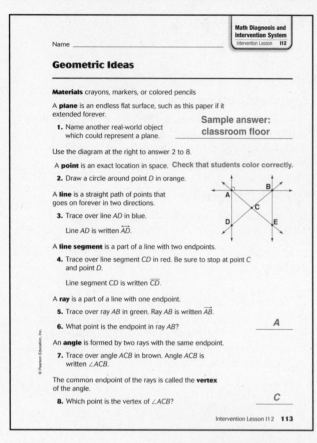

Name _____

Math Diagnosis and Intervention System
Intervention Lesson   I12

Geometric Ideas

Materials crayons, markers, or colored pencils

A **plane** is an endless flat surface, such as this paper if it extended forever.

1. Name another real-world object which could represent a plane. _____

Sample answer: classroom floor

Use the diagram at the right to answer 2 to 8.

A **point** is an exact location in space. Check that students color correctly.

2. Draw a circle around point D in orange.

A **line** is a straight path of points that goes on forever in two directions.

3. Trace over line AD in blue.

   Line AD is written $\overleftrightarrow{AD}$.

A **line segment** is a part of a line with two endpoints.

4. Trace over line segment CD in red. Be sure to stop at point C and point D.

   Line segment CD is written $\overline{CD}$.

A **ray** is a part of a line with one endpoint.

5. Trace over ray AB in green. Ray AB is written $\overrightarrow{AB}$.

6. What point is the endpoint in ray AB? _____ *A*

An **angle** is formed by two rays with the same endpoint.

7. Trace over angle ACB in brown. Angle ACB is written ∠ACB.

The common endpoint of the rays is called the **vertex** of the angle.

8. Which point is the vertex of ∠ACB? _____ *C*

© Pearson Education, Inc.

Intervention Lesson I12   **113**

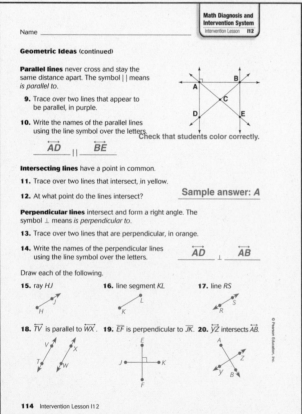

Name _____

Math Diagnosis and Intervention System
Intervention Lesson   I12

Geometric Ideas (continued)

Parallel lines never cross and stay the same distance apart. The symbol || means *is parallel to*.

9. Trace over two lines that appear to be parallel, in purple.

10. Write the names of the parallel lines using the line symbol over the letters. Check that students color correctly.

   $\overleftrightarrow{AD}$ || $\overleftrightarrow{BE}$

Intersecting lines have a point in common.

11. Trace over two lines that intersect, in yellow.

12. At what point do the lines intersect? Sample answer: *A*

Perpendicular lines intersect and form a right angle. The symbol ⊥ means *is perpendicular to*.

13. Trace over two lines that are perpendicular, in orange.

14. Write the names of the perpendicular lines using the line symbol over the letters. $\overleftrightarrow{AD}$ ⊥ $\overleftrightarrow{AB}$

Draw each of the following.

15. ray HJ   16. line segment KL   17. line RS

18. $\overleftrightarrow{TV}$ is parallel to $\overleftrightarrow{WX}$.   19. $\overleftrightarrow{EF}$ is perpendicular to $\overleftrightarrow{JK}$.   20. $\overleftrightarrow{YZ}$ intersects $\overleftrightarrow{AB}$.

© Pearson Education, Inc.

114   Intervention Lesson I12

Teacher Notes

Ongoing Assessment

Ask: *If point C lies on $\overleftrightarrow{AE}$, what are some other ways to name line $\overleftrightarrow{AE}$?* $\overleftrightarrow{AC}$, $\overleftrightarrow{CE}$, $\overleftrightarrow{EA}$, $\overleftrightarrow{CA}$, and $\overleftrightarrow{EC}$ all name the same line.

Error Intervention

If students have trouble understanding concepts involving lines,

then use I3: Lines and Line Segments.

If students have trouble understanding concepts involving rays and angles,

then use I4: Acute, Right, and Obtuse Angles.

If You Have More Time

Give students a drawing showing points and intersecting and parallel lines. Have students name as many points, lines, line segments, rays, and angles as they can. Have students compare their results to see who discovered the most in each category.

© Pearson Education, Inc.

Congruent Figures

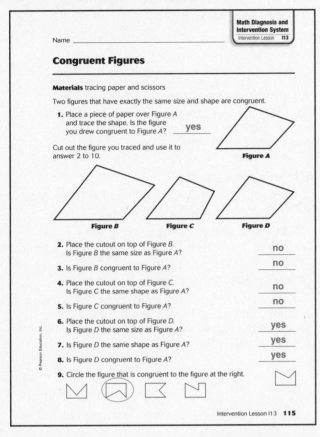

Congruent Figures

Materials tracing paper and scissors

Two figures that have exactly the same size and shape are congruent.

1. Place a piece of paper over Figure *A* and trace the shape. Is the figure you drew congruent to Figure *A*? __yes__

Cut out the figure you traced and use it to answer 2 to 10.

Figure A

Figure B   **Figure C**   **Figure D**

2. Place the cutout on top of Figure *B*. Is Figure *B* the same size as Figure *A*? __no__

3. Is Figure *B* congruent to Figure *A*? __no__

4. Place the cutout on top of Figure *C*. Is Figure *C* the same shape as Figure *A*? __no__

5. Is Figure *C* congruent to Figure *A*? __no__

6. Place the cutout on top of Figure *D*. Is Figure *D* the same size as Figure *A*? __yes__

7. Is Figure *D* the same shape as Figure *A*? __yes__

8. Is Figure *D* congruent to Figure *A*? __yes__

9. Circle the figure that is congruent to the figure at the right.

© Pearson Education, Inc.

Intervention Lesson I13   **115**

Name _____

Congruent Figures (continued)

Tell if the two figures are congruent. Write Yes or No.

10. __yes__

11. __no__

12. __yes__

13. __yes__

14. __no__

15. __no__

16. __yes__

17. __no__

18. __no__

19. Divide the isosceles triangle shown at the right into 2 congruent right triangles.

20. Divide the hexagon shown at the right into 6 congruent equilateral triangles.

21. Divide the rectangle shown at the right into 2 pairs of congruent triangles.

22. **Reasoning** Are the triangles at the right congruent? Why or why not?

   No; the triangles are the same shape, but they are not the same size.

© Pearson Education, Inc.

Teacher Notes

Ongoing Assessment

Ask: ***Do figures have to be facing the same way in order to be considered congruent?*** No, they have to be the same size and the same shape but they can be turned in different directions and still be considered congruent.

Error Intervention

If students have trouble identifying shapes that are the same size,

then have students trace one figure and move the tracing over the other figure.

If You Have More Time

Have student work in pairs to find congruent objects in the classroom.

Circles

Name _____

Math Diagnosis and Intervention System
Intervention Lesson   I14

Circles

Materials crayons, markers, or colored pencils

Use the figure at the right to answer 1 to 10.

Check that students color correctly.

A **circle** is the set of all points in a plane that are the same distance from a point called the **center**.

1. Color the point that is the center of the circle red.

A **radius** is any line that connects the center of the circle to a point on the circle.

2. Color a radius of the circle blue.

3. **Reasoning** Will every radius that is drawn on the circle have same length? Explain your answer.
   Yes; every point on the circle is the same distance from the center.

A **chord** is a line segment that connects any two points on a circle. A chord may or may not go through the center of the circle.

4. Color a chord on the circle that does not include the center of the circle, green.

5. **Reasoning** Will every chord that is drawn on the circle have the same length? Explain your answer.
   No; chords can be different lengths because they do not have to pass through the center of the circle.

A **diameter** is a chord that goes through the center of the circle.

6. Color a diameter of the circle orange.

7. **Reasoning** Will every diameter that is drawn on the circle have the same length? Explain your answer.
   Yes; a diameter is two radii and all radii are the same length. So, diameters of a circle are the same length.

Intervention Lesson I14   **117**

Teacher Notes

Ongoing Assessment

Ask: *Will a chord always be longer than the radii in a circle?* No, a chord may be longer or shorter than a radius.

Error Intervention

If students have trouble answering the Reasoning items on the first page of the worksheet,

then have students use yarn to compare the lengths of the different radii, chords, and diameters.

If You Have More Time

Have students find circular objects in the classroom that they can trace. Have them draw the circle on paper, draw a radius and diameter of the circle and measure both to compare.

Name _____

Math Diagnosis and Intervention System
Intervention Lesson   I14

Circles (continued)

The length of the diameter of a circle is two times the length of the radius.

8. Use a centimeter ruler to measure the length of the radius. What is the length of the radius?   **3** cm

9. Use a centimeter ruler to measure the length of the diameter. What is the length of the diameter?   **6** cm

10. Is the diameter two times the length of the radius?   **yes**

Identify the part of each circle indicated by the arrow.

11.   **center**

12.   **radius**

13.   **chord**

14.   **center**

15.   **diameter**

16.   **chord**

Find the radius or diameter of each circle.

17.   6 in.   radius: **3 in.**

18.   5 ft   diameter: **10 ft**

19.   18 cm   radius: **9 cm**

20. The radius of a circle is 11 centimeters. What is the diameter of the circle?   **22 cm**

© Pearson Education, Inc.

Rotational Symmetry

Rotational Symmetry

Materials paper and scissors

If a figure can be turned less than
a full turn about a point and fit
back on itself, then the figure
has **rotational symmetry.**

All turns in this activity are assumed
to be clockwise. Find the types of
rotational symmetry for the figure
shown at the right by answering
1 to 11.

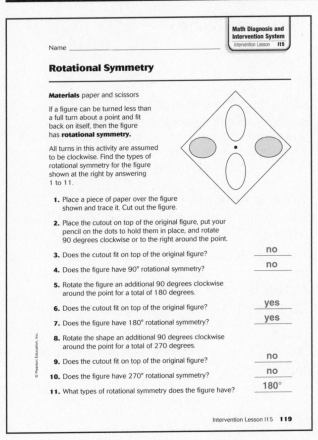

1. Place a piece of paper over the figure
   shown and trace it. Cut out the figure.

2. Place the cutout on top of the original figure, put your
   pencil on the dots to hold them in place, and rotate
   90 degrees clockwise or to the right around the point.

3. Does the cutout fit on top of the original figure?   no

4. Does the figure have 90° rotational symmetry?   no

5. Rotate the figure an additional 90 degrees clockwise
   around the point for a total of 180 degrees.

6. Does the cutout fit on top of the original figure?   yes

7. Does the figure have 180° rotational symmetry?   yes

8. Rotate the shape an additional 90 degrees clockwise
   around the point for a total of 270 degrees.

9. Does the cutout fit on top of the original figure?   no

10. Does the figure have 270° rotational symmetry?   no

11. What types of rotational symmetry does the figure have?   180°

© Pearson Education, Inc.

Intervention Lesson I15   **119**

Rotational Symmetry (continued)

Write 90°, 180°, 270°, or none to describe the rotational
symmetry of each figure.

12.   180°

13.   none

14.   90°, 180°, 270°

15.   none

16.   180°

17.   90°, 180°, 270°

18.   90°, 180°, 270°

19.   none

20.   none

21.   90°, 180°, 270°

22.   180°

23.   90°, 180°, 270°

24. **Reasoning** Draw a figure with
    90°, 180°, and 270° rotational
    symmetry.

Check students' work.

© Pearson Education, Inc.

120   Intervention Lesson I15

Teacher Notes

Ongoing Assessment
Ask: *Does a circle have rotational symmetry?* yes

Error Intervention
If students have trouble deciding if a shape has
rotational symmetry,

then have students trace and rotate the figure on
top of itself.

If You Have More Time
Have students draw an object that has all four
types of rotational symmetry. Then have them
draw an object that has only 180 degree rotational
symmetry. Ask students if it is possible to draw an
object with only 90 degree rotational symmetry.
Challenge them to do so; they will find it is not
possible. Then challenge students to find an object
that has only 270 degree rotational symmetry; this
too is not possible.

Transformations

Name _____

Transformations

Materials paper, scissors, and markers.

Transformations do not change the size or shape of a figure. There are three types of transformations: translation, reflection, and rotation.

Use a piece of paper to trace the house figure shown on the grid. Then, cut it out. Answer 1 to 8.

A **translation** is a slide.

1. Place the cutout shape over the shape on the grid. What are the coordinates of each of the 5 vertices of the pentagon?

   (1, 6), (1, 9), (3, 11), (5, 9), (5, 6)

2. Slide the cutout shape 5 units to the right and trace around it. What are the coordinates of each of the 5 vertices after the translation?

   (6, 6), (6, 9), (8, 11), (10, 9), (10, 6)

3. Now slide the cutout shape 6 units down so that it is 5 units to the right and 6 units down from the original position and trace around it. What are the coordinates of each vertex after the translation?

   (6, 0), (6, 3), (8, 5), (10, 3), (10, 0)

A **reflection** is a flip or a mirror image.

4. Place the cutout shape over the shape shown on the grid. Flip the house over line *m* and trace around it. The left side of the shape in the new position should be the same distance from the line as the right side was in the original position.

5. Place the cutout shape back in the original position. Flip the house over line *n* and trace around it.

© Pearson Education, Inc.

Name _____

Transformations (continued)

A **rotation** is a turn that moves a figure about a point. Each quarter turn is the same as a 90 degree rotation.

6. Place the cutout shape over the shape on the grid. Make a mark on the cutout at the same place as the dot. Turn the shape around the point clockwise so that the roof on the house is now pointing to the right or at 3 o'clock. The mark on the cutout should still be touching the point. Trace around the figure. This is a $\frac{1}{4}$ turn. How many degrees did the figure rotate?

   90 degrees

7. Rotate the shape a total of 180 degrees, or $\frac{1}{2}$ turn, from the original and trace around it. In what direction is the roof of the house now pointing?

   down or 6 o'clock

8. Rotate the shape a total of 270 degrees, or $\frac{3}{4}$ turn, from the original and trace around it. In what direction is the roof pointing?

   left or 9 o'clock

Tell whether the figures in each pair are related by a translation, a reflection, or a rotation.

9.   **reflection**

10.   **rotation**

11.   **translation**

12.   **translation**

13.   **reflection**

14.   **rotation**

© Pearson Education, Inc.

Teacher Notes

Ongoing Assessment

Ask: ***Rotating a figure 270 degrees clockwise is the same as what counter clockwise rotation?*** A counter clockwise rotation 90 degrees is the same as 270 degrees clockwise.

Error Intervention

If students need more practice identifying different transformations,

then use I8: Congruent Figures and Motions.

If You Have More Time

Have students draw a shape of their choice and cut it out. Have students choose one type of transformation and trace their shape repeatedly on a piece of paper to make a design that they can color.

© Pearson Education, Inc.

Measuring and Classifying Angles

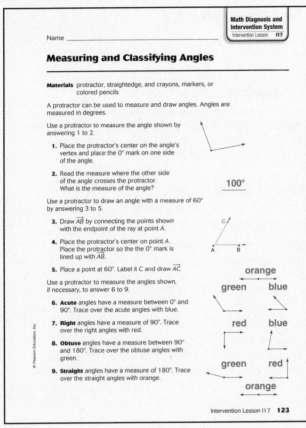

Teacher Notes

Ongoing Assessment

Ask: *Why is there no classification category for angles with measures greater than 180 degrees?* Angles with measures greater than 180 degrees are really angles with measurements that are less than 180 degrees. For example, a 190 degree angle is the same as 170 degree angle.

Error Intervention

If students need more practice identifying angles,

then use I4: Acute, Right, and Obtuse Angles.

If You Have More Time

Have student pairs take turns drawing and measuring angles. One student uses a protractor to draw an angle. Then he or she labels the angle with the correct measurement. The other student uses a protractor to measure the angle to see if the angle is drawn and labeled correctly.

Name _____

Measuring and Classifying Angles (continued)

Classify each angle as acute, right, obtuse, or straight. Then measure the angle.

10.

acute;

30°

11.

acute;

75°

12.

obtuse;

115°

13.

obtuse;

160°

14.

acute;

15°

15.

acute;

45°

Use a protractor to draw an angle with each measure.

16. 120°   17. 35°   18. 70°

19. **Reasoning** If two acute angles are placed next to each other to form one angle, will the result always be an obtuse angle? Explain. Provide a drawing in your explanation.

No; both acute angles could be small enough so that the sum of their measures is less than 90° or equal to 90°. Check student's drawings.

Angle Pairs

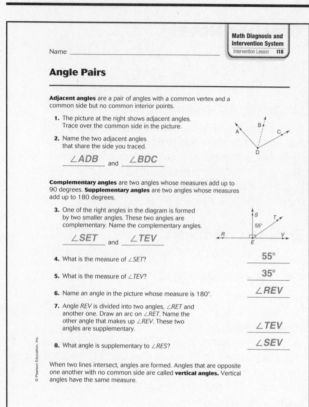

Name _____

Angle Pairs

Adjacent angles are a pair of angles with a common vertex and a common side but no common interior points.

1. The picture at the right shows adjacent angles. Trace over the common side in the picture.

2. Name the two adjacent angles that share the side you traced.

   ∠ADB   and   ∠BDC

Complementary angles are two angles whose measures add up to 90 degrees. **Supplementary angles** are two angles whose measures add up to 180 degrees.

3. One of the right angles in the diagram is formed by two smaller angles. These two angles are complementary. Name the complementary angles.

   ∠SET   and   ∠TEV

4. What is the measure of ∠SET?   55°

5. What is the measure of ∠TEV?   35°

6. Name an angle in the picture whose measure is 180°.   ∠REV

7. Angle REV is divided into two angles, ∠RET and another one. Draw an arc on ∠RET. Name the other angle that makes up ∠REV. These two angles are supplementary.   ∠TEV

8. What angle is supplementary to ∠RES?   ∠SEV

When two lines intersect, angles are formed. Angles that are opposite one another with no common side are called **vertical angles**. Vertical angles have the same measure.

Intervention Lesson I18   **125**

Teacher Notes

Ongoing Assessment

Ask: *If one of two supplementary angles is a right angle, what is the measure of the other angle?* The other angle is a right angle since 180 − 90 is 90 degrees.

Error Intervention

If students have trouble understanding why vertical angles are congruent,

then use two pieces of spaghetti to represent intersecting lines. Change the angles between the pieces of spaghetti to show students that vertical angles are always the same size.

If You Have More Time

Have students draw a clock face on their paper. Then have them find the measure of the angle formed by the hands of their clock at 3:00, (90°) 4:00 (120°), 6:00 (180°), 7:00 (150°), and 10:00 (60°).

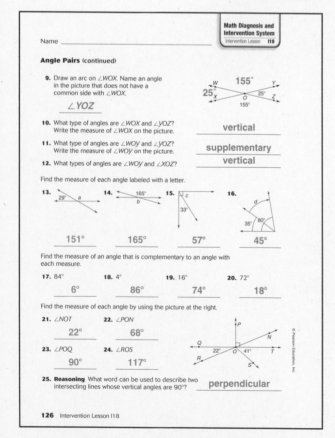

Name _____

Angle Pairs (continued)

9. Draw an arc on ∠WOX. Name an angle in the picture that does not have a common side with ∠WOX.

   ∠YOZ

10. What type of angles are ∠WOX and ∠YOZ? Write the measure of ∠WOX on the picture.   vertical

11. What type of angles are ∠WOY and ∠YOZ? Write the measure of ∠WOY on the picture.   supplementary

12. What types of angles are ∠WOY and ∠XOZ?   vertical

Find the measure of each angle labeled with a letter.

13.   151°

14.   165°

15.   57°

16.   45°

Find the measure of an angle that is complementary to an angle with each measure.

17. 84°   6°

18. 4°   86°

19. 16°   74°

20. 72°   18°

Find the measure of each angle by using the picture at the right.

21. ∠NOT   22°

22. ∠PON   68°

23. ∠POQ   90°

24. ∠ROS   117°

25. **Reasoning** What word can be used to describe two intersecting lines whose vertical angles are 90°?   perpendicular

Missing Angles in Triangles and Quadrilaterals

Math Diagnosis and Intervention System
Intervention Lesson   I19

Name _____

Missing Angles in Triangles and Quadrilaterals

Materials index card and scissors

Find the relationship among angles in a triangle by answering 1 to 9.

1. Draw a triangle on an index card and cut it out.

2. Label each angle in the triangle with A, B, and C.

3. Cut out each corner of your triangle so that angles A, B, and C are separated from the triangle.

4. Start with angle A. Place the vertex on the point shown above and one side of the angle on the dashed line. Trace around the angle.

5. Next place angle B's vertex on the point and one side of the angle so that it is sharing a side with angle A. Trace around the angle.

6. Next place angle C's vertex on the point and one side of the angle so that it is sharing a side with angle B. Trace around the angle.

7. **Reasoning** What do you notice about the angles of a triangle?
   They form a straight line or 180 degrees.

8. Compare your results with that of other students. Do the angles of the triangle have the same relationship?   **yes**

9. What is the sum of the measures of the three angles in any triangle?   **180°**

Find the relationship among angles in a quadrilateral by answering 10 to 16.

10. Draw a quadrilateral, that does not have any right angles, on an index card and cut it out.

11. Label each of the angles in the quadrilateral with A, B, C, and D.

Intervention Lesson I19   **127**

Math Diagnosis and Intervention System
Intervention Lesson   I19

Name _____

Missing Angles in Triangles and Quadrilaterals (continued)

12. Cut out each corner of your quadrilateral so that angles A, B, C, and D are separated from the quadrilateral.

13. Place the vertex of each angle on the point shown. Position the angles so that they are adjacent and share a common side.

14. **Reasoning** What do you notice about the angles of a quadrilateral?
    They form a circle or 360 degrees.

15. Compare your results with that of other students. Do the angles of their quadrilateral have the same relationship?   **yes**

16. What is the sum of the measures of the four angles in a quadrilateral?   **360°**

Find the missing angle measures.

17.   60°, 65°, ?   **55°**

18.   55°, 55°, 125°, ?   **125°**

19.   72°, 68°, 157°, ?   **63°**

20.   34°, 116°, ?   **30°**

21.   115°, ?   **65°**

22.   71°, ?   **19°**

128   Intervention Lesson I19

Teacher Notes

Ongoing Assessment

Ask: *The measures of each angle in an equilateral triangle are the same. What is the measure of each angle?* The measure of each angle is 180 ÷ 3 or 60 degrees.

Error Intervention

If students have trouble cutting and placing the angles of the triangle or quadrilateral,

then have students use a protractor to measure each of the angles and add the angle measures together.

If You Have More Time

Have students draw and cut out quadrilaterals. Then have them draw a diagonal of the quadrilateral and cut the quadrilateral into two triangles. Students should discover that every quadrilateral is made from two triangles so that the sum of the angles in a quadrilateral is two times the sum of those in a triangle.

Constructions

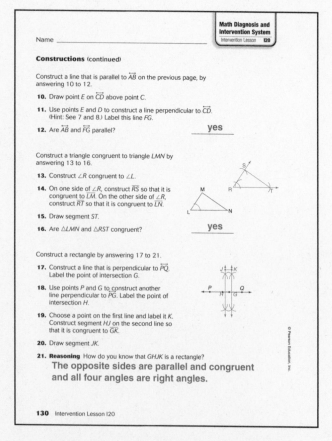

Constructions

Materials compass and straightedge

Construct a segment congruent to $\overline{XY}$ by answering 1 to 3.

1. Use a compass to measure the length of $\overline{XY}$, by placing one point on X and the other on Y.

2. Draw a horizontal ray with endpoint W. Place the compass point on point W. Use the compass measure of $\overline{XY}$ to draw an arc intersecting the ray drawn. Label this intersection J.

3. Are $\overline{XY}$ and $\overline{WJ}$ congruent?   **yes**

Construct an angle congruent to ∠A by answering 4 to 6.

4. Place the compass point on A, and draw an arc intersecting both sides of ∠A. Draw a ray with endpoint S. With the compass point on S, use the same compass setting from ∠A to draw an arc intersecting the ray at point T.

5. Use a compass to measure the length of the arc intersecting both sides of ∠A. Place the compass point on T. Use the same measure from ∠A to draw an arc that intersects the first arc. Label the point of intersection R and draw the $\overline{SR}$.

6. Are ∠A and ∠RST congruent?   **yes**

Construct a line perpendicular to $\overleftrightarrow{AB}$ by answering 7 to 9.

7. Open the compass to more than half the distance between A and B. Place the compass point at A and draw arcs above and below the line.

8. Without changing the compass setting, place the point at B. Draw arcs that intersect the arcs made from point A. Label the point of intersection above the line as C and below the line as D. Draw line CD.

9. Are $\overleftrightarrow{AB}$ and $\overleftrightarrow{CD}$ perpendicular?   **yes**

© Pearson Education, Inc.

Intervention Lesson I20   **129**

Constructions (continued)

Construct a line that is parallel to $\overleftrightarrow{AB}$ on the previous page, by answering 10 to 12.

10. Draw point E on $\overleftrightarrow{CD}$ above point C.

11. Use points E and D to construct a line perpendicular to $\overleftrightarrow{CD}$. (Hint: See 7 and 8.) Label this line FG.

12. Are $\overleftrightarrow{AB}$ and $\overleftrightarrow{FG}$ parallel?   **yes**

Construct a triangle congruent to triangle LMN by answering 13 to 16.

13. Construct ∠R congruent to ∠L.

14. On one side of ∠R, construct $\overline{RS}$ so that it is congruent to $\overline{LM}$. On the other side of ∠R, construct $\overline{RT}$ so that it is congruent to $\overline{LN}$.

15. Draw segment ST.

16. Are △LMN and △RST congruent?   **yes**

Construct a rectangle by answering 17 to 21.

17. Construct a line that is perpendicular to $\overleftrightarrow{PQ}$. Label the point of intersection G.

18. Use points P and G to construct another line perpendicular to $\overleftrightarrow{PG}$. Label the point of intersection H.

19. Choose a point on the first line and label it K. Construct segment HJ on the second line so that it is congruent to $\overline{GK}$.

20. Draw segment JK.

21. **Reasoning** How do you know that GHJK is a rectangle?
    The opposite sides are parallel and congruent and all four angles are right angles.

© Pearson Education, Inc.

130   Intervention Lesson I20

Teacher Notes

Ongoing Assessment

Ask: ***Can any compass opening be used to draw the first arc on an angle when constructing an angle congruent to it?*** Yes, the first arc can be any size as long as the same opening is used to draw the first arc on the construction of the angle.

Error Intervention

If students are not convinced that their constructions are accurate,

then have them measure angles using a protractor, and side lengths using a ruler, after they complete their constructions.

If You Have More Time

Challenge student pairs to find a way to construct an isosceles right triangle using the construction techniques they have learned. Students should begin by constructing two perpendicular lines and then constructing two congruent legs on the lines.

© Pearson Education, Inc.

Measuring Length to $\frac{1}{2}$ and $\frac{1}{4}$ Inch

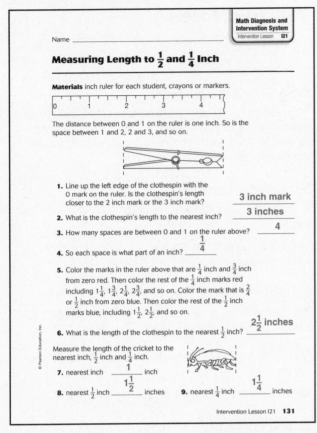

Teacher Notes

Ongoing Assessment

Ask: *How long is your finger to the nearest $\frac{1}{4}$ inch?* Answers will vary.

Error Intervention

If students have trouble measuring to the nearest inch,

then use D25: Inches.

If You Have More Time

Have students choose 5 different objects in the classroom. Have them measure each to the nearest inch, $\frac{1}{2}$ inch, and $\frac{1}{4}$ inch. If time allows, have students take turns reporting their findings for one of the items they measured.

Worksheet 1 (page 131)

Name _____

Math Diagnosis and Intervention System
Intervention Lesson   I21

Measuring Length to $\frac{1}{2}$ and $\frac{1}{4}$ Inch

Materials inch ruler for each student, crayons or markers.

The distance between 0 and 1 on the ruler is one inch. So is the space between 1 and 2, 2 and 3, and so on.

1. Line up the left edge of the clothespin with the 0 mark on the ruler. Is the clothespin's length closer to the 2 inch mark or the 3 inch mark?   **3 inch mark**

2. What is the clothespin's length to the nearest inch?   **3 inches**

3. How many spaces are between 0 and 1 on the ruler above?   **4**

4. So each space is what part of an inch?   **$\frac{1}{4}$**

5. Color the marks in the ruler above that are $\frac{1}{4}$ inch and $\frac{3}{4}$ inch from zero red. Then color the rest of the $\frac{1}{4}$ inch marks red including $1\frac{1}{4}$, $1\frac{3}{4}$, $2\frac{1}{4}$, $2\frac{3}{4}$, and so on. Color the mark that is $\frac{2}{4}$ or $\frac{1}{2}$ inch from zero blue. Then color the rest of the $\frac{1}{2}$ inch marks blue, including $1\frac{1}{2}$, $2\frac{1}{2}$, and so on.

6. What is the length of the clothespin to the nearest $\frac{1}{2}$ inch?   **$2\frac{1}{2}$ inches**

Measure the length of the cricket to the nearest inch, $\frac{1}{2}$ inch and $\frac{1}{4}$ inch.

7. nearest inch   **1** inch

8. nearest $\frac{1}{2}$ inch   **$1\frac{1}{2}$** inches

9. nearest $\frac{1}{4}$ inch   **$1\frac{1}{4}$** inches

Intervention Lesson I21   **131**

Worksheet 2 (page 132)

Name _____

Math Diagnosis and Intervention System
Intervention Lesson   I21

Measuring Length to $\frac{1}{2}$ and $\frac{1}{4}$ Inch (continued)

Measure each object to the nearest inch, $\frac{1}{2}$ inch, and $\frac{1}{4}$ inch.

10. Nearest inch: **3** inches

11. Nearest $\frac{1}{2}$ inch: **3** inches

Nearest $\frac{1}{4}$ inch: **$2\frac{3}{4}$** inches

12. Nearest inch: **3** inches

13. Nearest $\frac{1}{2}$ inch: **$2\frac{1}{2}$** inches

Nearest $\frac{1}{4}$ inch: **$2\frac{3}{4}$** inches

14. Nearest inch: **1** inch

15. Nearest $\frac{1}{2}$ inch: **$1\frac{1}{2}$** inches

Nearest $\frac{1}{4}$ inch: **$1\frac{1}{4}$** inches

16. **Reasoning** Which gives the closest measurement, measuring to the nearest inch, $\frac{1}{2}$ inch, or $\frac{1}{4}$ inch? Explain.

Sample answer: Measuring to the nearest $\frac{1}{4}$ inch gives the closest measurement because there are more $\frac{1}{4}$ marks than $\frac{1}{2}$ inch or inch marks.

132 Intervention Lesson I21

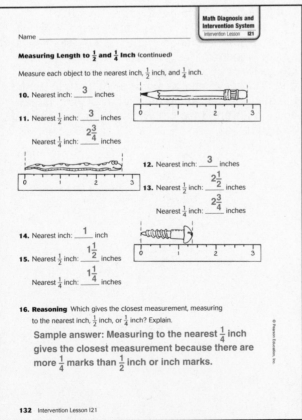

Using Customary Units of Length

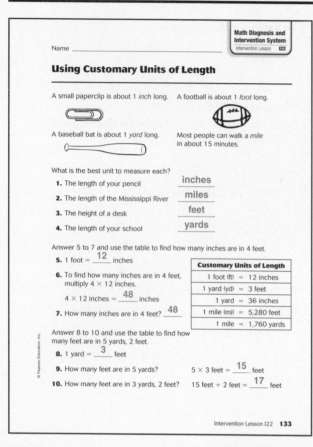

Name _____

Math Diagnosis and
Intervention System
Intervention Lesson **I22**

Using Customary Units of Length

A small paperclip is about 1 *inch* long.   A football is about 1 *foot* long.

A baseball bat is about 1 *yard* long.   Most people can walk a *mile* in about 15 minutes.

What is the best unit to measure each?

1. The length of your pencil   <u>inches</u>

2. The length of the Mississippi River   <u>miles</u>

3. The height of a desk   <u>feet</u>

4. The length of your school   <u>yards</u>

Answer 5 to 7 and use the table to find how many inches are in 4 feet.

5. 1 foot = <u>12</u> inches

6. To find how many inches are in 4 feet, multiply 4 × 12 inches.

   4 × 12 inches = <u>48</u> inches

7. How many inches are in 4 feet? <u>48</u>

Customary Units of Length	
1 foot (ft)	= 12 inches
1 yard (yd)	= 3 feet
1 yard	= 36 inches
1 mile (mi)	= 5,280 feet
1 mile	= 1,760 yards

Answer 8 to 10 and use the table to find how many feet are in 5 yards, 2 feet.

8. 1 yard = <u>3</u> feet

9. How many feet are in 5 yards?   5 × 3 feet = <u>15</u> feet

10. How many feet are in 3 yards, 2 feet?   15 feet + 2 feet = <u>17</u> feet

Intervention Lesson I22   **133**

Name _____

Math Diagnosis and
Intervention System
Intervention Lesson **I22**

Using Customary Units of Length (continued)

Which unit would you use to measure each item?
Write *inch*, *foot*, *yard*, or *mile*.

11. The length of a gerbil   <u>inch</u>

12. The length of a football field   <u>yard</u>

13. The height of a door   <u>foot</u>

14. The distance to the sun   <u>mile</u>

Circle the better estimate.

15. The distance you travel on an airplane

   560 yards   or   (560 miles)

16. The height of a full grown adult giraffe

   6 feet   or   (6 yards)

17. The length of a bar of soap

   (3 inches)   or   7 inches

18. The length of your bed

   (7 feet)   or   7 yards

Find each missing number.

19. 2 yards = <u>6</u> feet

20. 3 feet = <u>36</u> inches

21. 4 yards = <u>144</u> inches

22. 3 yards, 2 feet = <u>11</u> feet

23. 1 foot, 9 inches = <u>21</u> inches

24. 2 yards, 2 feet = <u>96</u> inches

25. Reasoning What unit would you use to measure the length of an earthworm? Explain why your choice is the best unit.

   Inches; An earthworm is less than a foot long, so any unit other than inches would be too large.

134   Intervention Lesson I22

Teacher Notes

Ongoing Assessment

Ask: *Why would you not measure the length of your school in inches?* Sample answer: My school is very long. It would be hard to give an accurate measurement in inches.

Error Intervention

If students have trouble visualizing an inch, foot, or yard,

then draw and label each length on the board. Students could also cut each length out of yarn.

If students have trouble visualizing a mile,

then give them an example of a building located about 1 mile from the school.

If students have trouble estimating inches, feet or yards,

then use D24: Inches, Feet, and Yards.

If You Have More Time

Cut 8 pieces of yarn the following lengths: 10 inches, 1 foot 2 inches, 1 foot 8 inches, 2 feet, 2 feet 3 inches, 2 feet 6 inches, 2 feet 9 inches, and 2 feet 11 inches. Put the yarn pieces in stations labeled A through H. Each student needs paper, pencil, and a ruler. Have groups of 3 rotate through the stations measuring the pieces of yarn in feet and inches and then converting the measurement to inches.

Using Metric Units of Length

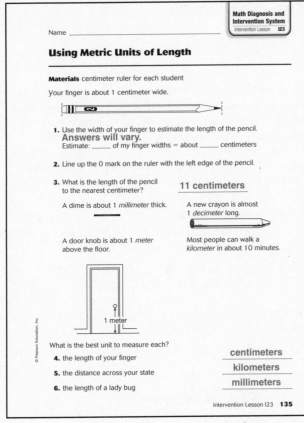

Name _____

**Math Diagnosis and
Intervention System**
Intervention Lesson   I23

Using Metric Units of Length

Materials centimeter ruler for each student

Your finger is about 1 centimeter wide.

1. Use the width of your finger to estimate the length of the pencil.
   Answers will vary.
   Estimate: _____ of my finger widths = about _____ centimeters

2. Line up the 0 mark on the ruler with the left edge of the pencil.

3. What is the length of the pencil
   to the nearest centimeter?   **11 centimeters**

A dime is about 1 *millimeter* thick.   A new crayon is almost
                                          1 *decimeter* long.

A door knob is about 1 *meter*   Most people can walk a
above the floor.   *kilometer* in about 10 minutes.

1 meter

What is the best unit to measure each?

4. the length of your finger   **centimeters**

5. the distance across your state   **kilometers**

6. the length of a lady bug   **millimeters**

Intervention Lesson I23   **135**

Name _____

Using Metric Units of Length (continued)

Answer 7 to 9 and use the table to find how many centimeters
are in 4 meters, 76 centimeters.

7. 1 meter = **100** centimeters

Metric Units of Length		
1 centimeter (cm)	=	10 millimeters
1 decimeter (dm)	=	10 centimeters
1 meter (m)	=	100 centimeters
1 kilometer (km)	=	1,000 meters

8. How many centimeters are
   in 4 meters?

   4×100 cm = **400** cm

9. How many centimeters are in
   4 meters, 76 centimeters?

   400 cm + 76 cm = **476** cm

Estimate the length of the spoon. Then measure to the
nearest centimeter.

10.

13 centimeters

What unit would you use to measure each item?
Write *millimeter, centimeter, decimeter, meter,* or *kilometer.*

11. An adult's height   12. Distance traveled on vacation
        meter   **kilometer**

Choose the best estimate.

13. Length of a car   14. Length of a calculator

    5 decimeters or ⟨5 meters⟩   ⟨12 centimeters⟩ or 12 decimeters

Find each missing number.

15. 3 meters 18 centimeters = **318** centimeters

16. 6 meters 3 centimeters = **603** centimeters

136 Intervention Lesson I23

© Pearson Education, Inc.

Teacher Notes

Ongoing Assessment

Ask: *Jane and Tela measured the distance
their turtles crawled. Jane wrote down 654
centimeters. Tela wrote down 8 meters and then
her pencil broke. Do you need to know what
else Tela was going to write to tell whose turtle
crawled farther?* No; Tela's turtle crawled farther
because 8 meters equals 800 centimeters and 800
is greater than 653. It doesn't matter how many
more centimeters Tela's turtle might have crawled.

Error Intervention

If students have trouble measuring to the nearest
centimeter,

then use D27: Centimeters.

If students have trouble estimating centimeters or
meters,

then use D26: Centimeters and Meters.

If You Have More Time

Have students draw an 8-sided irregular polygon on
their paper. Then trade with a partner and measure
each side to the nearest centimeter.

Using Customary Units of Capacity

Using Customary Units of Capacity

Materials 6 stations each equipped with the following: cup, pint, quart, and gallon measuring containers labeled with their units; one of 6 different sized containers to be measured labeled A, B, C, D, E, and F; enough rice to fill the container at least one and a half times; a piece of paper taped into a funnel for containers with small openings

The **capacity** of a container is the amount the container can hold.

Go to each station. Find the row in the table which matches the letter on the container. Complete the table by doing the following.

Customary Units of Capacity		
1 pint (pt)	=	2 cups (c)
1 quart (qt)	=	2 pints
1 gallon (gal)	=	4 quarts

- Decide what unit to use to measure the lettered container.
- Estimate the capacity of the container.
- Then measure the capacity of the container by filling the cup, pint, quart, or gallon container with rice and pouring it into the container until that container is full.

	Container	Best Unit	Estimate	Capacity
1.	A			
2.	B			
3.	C			
4.	D			
5.	E			
6.	F			

Answers will vary depending on containers.

Intervention Lesson I24 **137**

Using Customary Units of Capacity (continued)

What unit would you use to measure the capacity of each item?
Write *cup, pint, quart,* or *gallon.*

7. A pond
gallon

8. A watering can
quart

9. A juice box
cup

10. A kitchen sink
gallon

11. A coffee mug
cup

12. A pitcher of water
quart or pint

13.
1 pt or (gal)

14.
1 c or (1 qt)

15.
25 c or (25 gal)

16.
2 c or (2 qt)

17. Reasoning Martin bought a pint of grape juice. Franco bought a gallon of orange juice. Seth bought a quart of apple juice. List the type of juice in order from least to greatest capacities.
grape juice, apple juice, orange juice

18. Reasoning Romona is making spaghetti. Explain why the better estimate for the amount of water boiling in the pot is 2 quarts and not 2 cups.
Sample answer: A pot large enough to boil spaghetti needs to hold much more than 2 cups of water.

138 Intervention Lesson I24

Teacher Notes

Ongoing Assessment
Ask: *If you measured the capacity of a container in cups and then in gallons, which measure would have the lesser number?* Sample answer: The gallons would have the lesser number because the gallon is much larger and it would take fewer gallons to fill the container.

Error Intervention
If students have trouble understanding the concept of capacity,

then use D19: Comparing and Ordering by Capacity and D28: Exploring Capacity.

If students have trouble distinguishing with cups, pints, and quarts,

then use D29: Cups, Pints, and Quarts.

If You Have More Time
Have students list other items that would be measured in cups, pints, quarts, and gallons.

Using Metric Units of Capacity

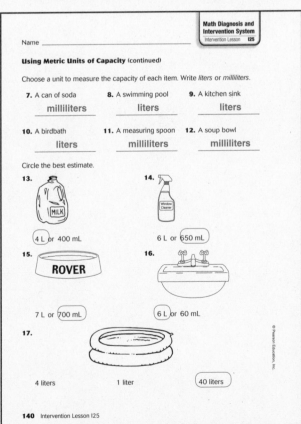

Student Worksheet (page 139):

Math Diagnosis and
Intervention System
Intervention Lesson   I25

Name _____

Using Metric Units of Capacity

A water bottle holds about 1 liter.   A medicine dropper holds about 1 milliliter.

1 liter   1 milliliter

Garrison wants to find out how much a small bottle of perfume holds. Decide whether he should measure the amount in liters or milliliters by answering 1 and 2.

Metric Units of Capacity
1 liter (L) = 1,000 milliliters (mL)

1. Would the perfume bottle hold more than a medicine dropper?   **yes**

2. Would the perfume bottle hold more than a water bottle?   **no**

Since the perfume bottle holds less than 1 liter, it should be measured in milliliters.

Decide whether 2 milliliters or 2 liters is a better estimate for the amount of soup the bowl holds by answering 3 to 5.

3. Would 2 medicine droppers fill the bowl?   **no**

4. Would 2 water bottles fill the bowl?   **yes**

5. Which is better estimate?   **2 liters**

6. Reasoning Explain why the better estimate for the amount of water a bucket holds is 8 liters and not 8 milliliters.

Sample answer: A bucket holds much more than 8 medicine droppers. It could hold as much as 8 water bottles.

Intervention Lesson I25   **139**

© Pearson Education, Inc.

Student Worksheet (page 140):

Math Diagnosis and
Intervention System
Intervention Lesson   I25

Name _____

Using Metric Units of Capacity (continued)

Choose a unit to measure the capacity of each item. Write *liters* or *milliliters*.

7. A can of soda   **milliliters**

8. A swimming pool   **liters**

9. A kitchen sink   **liters**

10. A birdbath   **liters**

11. A measuring spoon   **milliliters**

12. A soup bowl   **milliliters**

Circle the best estimate.

13.   MILK   (4 L) or 400 mL

14.   Window Cleaner   6 L or (650 mL)

15.   ROVER   7 L or (700 mL)

16.   6 L or 60 mL

17.   4 liters   1 liter   (40 liters)

140   Intervention Lesson I25

© Pearson Education, Inc.

Teacher Notes

Ongoing Assessment

Ask: *If you measured the capacity of a container in milliliters and then in liters, which measure would have the greater number?* Sample answer: The number of milliliters would be greater because the milliliter is much smaller and it would take many more milliliters to fill the container.

Error Intervention

If students have trouble understanding the concept of capacity,

then use D19: Comparing and Ordering by Capacity and D28: Exploring Capacity.

If students have trouble estimating with liters,

then use D30: Liters.

If You Have More Time

Have students list other items that would be measured in milliliters and liters. Encourage them to be creative with their ideas for milliliters. For example, a screw top from a soda bottle that was left outside and filled with rainwater would be measured in millimeters.

Using Customary Units of Weight

Using Customary Units of Weight

The **weight** of an object is the measure of how heavy the object is.

A key weighs about 1 ounce.

A football weighs about 1 pound.

A bull weighs about 1 ton.

Lucy wants to find out how much her cat weighs. Decide whether she should use ounces, pounds, or tons by answering 1 to 3.

Customary Units of Weight
1 pound (lb) = 16 ounces (oz)
1 ton (T) = 2,000 pounds

1. Would the cat be heavier than a key? **yes**

2. Would the cat be heavier than a football? **yes**

3. Would the cat be heavier than a bull? **no**

Since the cat would weigh more than a key, and more than a football, but less than a bull, it should be measured in pounds.

When measuring the weight of light objects, use ounces. When measuring the weight of heavier objects, use pounds. When measuring the weight of very heavy objects, like a bull, use tons.

Decide whether 4 pounds or 4 ounces is a better estimate for the weight of a carrot by answering 4 to 6.

4. Would a carrot feel as heavy as 4 footballs? **no**

5. Would a carrot feel as heavy as 4 keys? **yes**

6. Which is a better estimate for the weight of a carrot, 4 ounces or 4 pounds? **4 ounces**

Using Customary Units of Weight (continued)

Choose a unit to measure the weight of each item. Write *ounces, pounds,* or *tons.*

7. Eyeglasses ounces

8. An adult whale tons

9. A dog pounds

10. A tomato ounces

11. An eraser ounces

12. A school bus tons

13. A ship tons

14. A guitar pounds

15. A desk pounds

16. A mouse ounces

17. A motor scooter pounds

18. A feather ounces

Circle the best estimate for the weight of each item.

19. The space shuttle
45 lb or (45 T)

20. A bowling ball
10 oz or (10 lb)

21. A slice of bread
(1 oz) or 1 lb

22. A turkey
15 oz or (15 lb)

23. A chicken
7 oz or (7 lb)

24. A hippopotamus
5 lb or (5 T)

25. Reasoning Explain why the better estimate for the weight of a pencil is 1 ounce and not 1 pound.
Sample answer: A football weighs about 1 pound and a key weighs about 1 ounce. A pencil weighs much less than a football, but about the same as a key.

26. Reasoning If you had a bag of apples that weighed a pound and a bag of marshmallows that weighed a pound, which bag would have more items in it? Explain.
Sample answer: There would be more marshmallows. Each marshmallows weighs less than each apple, so it would take more marshmallows than apples to equal a pound.

Teacher Notes

Ongoing Assessment

Ask: *Which item would you not measure in ounces: strawberry, orange, pumpkin, kiwi?* pumpkin

Error Intervention

If students have trouble understanding customary units of weight,

then use D32: Pounds and D33: Pounds and Ounces.

If You Have More Time

Have students list 10 objects in their classroom they would weigh in pounds and 10 objects they would weigh in ounces.

Using Metric Units of Mass

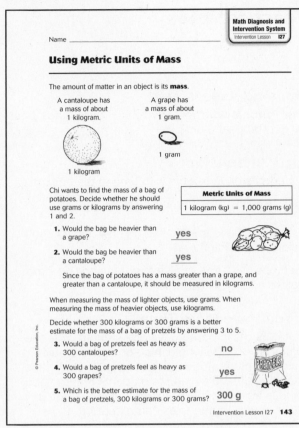

Teacher Notes

Ongoing Assessment

Ask: ***Does a larger object always have a greater mass than a smaller object? Explain why or why not.*** No; An empty box large enough for a television is much larger than a brick, but the brick would have a greater mass.

Error Intervention

If students have trouble understanding metric units of mass,

then use D34: Grams and Kilograms.

If You Have More Time

Have students list 10 food items that would be measured in kilograms and 10 food items that would be measured in grams.

Time to the Quarter Hour

Worksheet (page 145)

Name _____

Time to the Quarter Hour

Use the clocks at the right to answer 1 to 6.

1. What two numbers is the hour hand between?
   __12__ and __1__

2. Since the hour hand has not reached the 1, it is after 12:00. Write 12 for the hours in the digital clock.

   12:15
   hours minutes

3. What number is the minute hand on? __3__

4. Each number on the clock represents 5 minutes after the hour. Count by 5s. How many minutes is it after 12? __15__

5. Write 15 for the minutes in the digital clock.

The clock shows 12:15 or twelve fifteen.

6. Write 12:15 in two other ways.
   15 minutes past __12__;   quarter past __12__

Use the clock at the right to answer 7 to 11.

7. What two numbers is the hour hand between?
   __1__ and __2__

8. What is the hour? __1__

9. What number is the minute hand on? __6__

10. Count by 5s. How many minutes is it after the hour? __30__

11. Write the time in three ways.
    __1__ : __30__; __30__ minutes past __1__; __half__ past __1__

Intervention Lesson I28 **145**

Worksheet (page 146)

Name _____

Time to the Quarter Hour (continued)

For Exercises 12 to 15, use the clock at the right.

12. What time is shown on the clock? __1__ : __45__

13. What hour is it about to be? **2:00**

14. Count by 5s. How many minutes is it before 2 o'clock? __15__

15. Write the time in two other ways.
    15 minutes to __2__;   quarter to __2__

Write the hour and then the minutes after the hour. Then circle the two correct times.

16. hour __2__ minutes __45__
    (2:45)   3:45   1:45
    quarter to 2   (15 minutes to 3)   quarter past 2

17. hour __5__ minutes __15__
    4:15   6:15   (5:15)
    quarter past 6   (quarter past 5)   15 minutes to 5

18. hour __8__ minutes __30__
    7:30   (8:30)   9:30
    (half past 8)   quarter past 8   30 minutes past 9

19. hour __11__ minutes __45__
    (11:45)   11:15   12:45
    quarter to 11   15 minutes to 11   (quarter to 12)

146 Intervention Lesson I28

Teacher Notes

Ongoing Assessment

Ask: *What is another way to say 15 minutes past 4?* quarter past 4 or 4:15

Error Intervention

If students have trouble with time to the half hour,

then use D5: Time to the Half Hour.

If students have trouble finding how many minutes before or after an hour,

then use D8: Time to Five Minutes and D9: Time Before and After the Hour.

If You Have More Time

Put students in pairs. Have one student write the digital time to the whole, half, or quarter hours. Have the other student use the pupil's clock face to show the time. Remind the students that the hour hand is between two numbers when it is not an exact hour. Change roles and repeat.

Telling Time

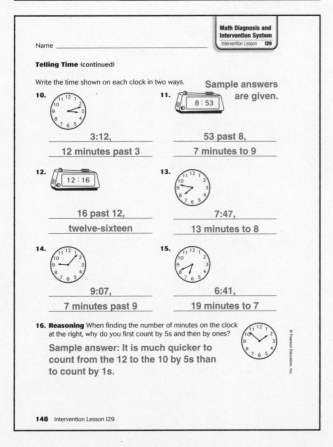

Name _____

Telling Time

Find the time on the clock by answering 1 to 8.

1. What two numbers is the hour hand between?

   __5__ and __6__

2. Since the hour hand has not reached the 6, it is after 5:00. Write 5 for the hours in the digital clock.

3. It takes the minute hand 5 minutes to move from one number to the next. To find the minutes, first count by 5s from the 12 to the 7. Then count by 1s for each small mark after the 7.

4. How many minutes is it after 5? __37__
Write the minutes in the digital clock above.

5. Write the time in three different ways.

   __5__ : __37__ ;

   __five__ thirty-seven;

   __37__ minutes past 5

6. To find how many minutes before the next hour, count the other way. Count by 5s from the 12 to the 8, then count by 1s for each small mark after the 8.

7. How many minutes is it before 6? __23__

8. Write the time another way.

   __23__ minutes to 6

9. Write the time shown on the clock at the right in two different ways.

   __two__ twenty- __four__ ; __24__ minutes past 2

5 : 37
hours minutes

2 : 24

© Pearson Education, Inc.

Intervention Lesson I29 **147**

Name _____

Telling Time (continued)

Write the time shown on each clock in two ways.

Sample answers are given.

10.

   3:12,
   12 minutes past 3

11. 8 : 53

   53 past 8,
   7 minutes to 9

12. 12 : 16

   16 past 12,
   twelve-sixteen

13.

   7:47,
   13 minutes to 8

14.

   9:07,
   7 minutes past 9

15.

   6:41,
   19 minutes to 7

16. Reasoning When finding the number of minutes on the clock at the right, why do you first count by 5s and then by ones?

Sample answer: It is much quicker to count from the 12 to the 10 by 5s than to count by 1s.

© Pearson Education, Inc.

148 Intervention Lesson I29

Teacher Notes

Ongoing Assessment

Ask: *Why do you count by 5s when you move from one number to the next on a clock?* It takes the minute hand 5 minutes to move from one number to the next, so there are 5 minutes between each number.

Error Intervention

If students have trouble differentiating the minute hand from the hour hand,

then use D4: Time to the Hour.

If students have trouble telling time to five minutes,

then use D8: Time to Five Minutes.

If You Have More Time

Write 3:16, 8:22, 10:37, and 11:52 on the board. Have students draw the analog clock face for each time. Remind students that the hour hand is between two numbers when it is not an exact hour.

Units of Time

Name _____

Math Diagnosis and Intervention System
Intervention Lesson I30

Units of Time

Benny spent 3 weeks at his cousin's house. Find how many days Benny spent at his cousin's by using the table and answering 1 to 3.

1. 1 week = __7__ days

Relating Units of Time	
1 week	=	7 days
1 day	=	24 hours
1 hour	=	60 minutes

2. To find how many days are in 3 weeks, multiply 3 × 7 days.

   3 × 7 days = __21__ days

3. How many days did Benny spend at his cousin's? __21__ days

The talent show lasted 2 hours and 17 minutes. Find how many minutes the talent show lasted by using the table and answering 4 to 6.

4. 1 hour = __60__ minutes

5. First, find the number of minutes in 2 hours. Then add the 17 minutes.

   2 × 60 minutes = __120__ minutes

   120 minutes + 17 minutes = __137__ minutes

6. How many minutes did the talent show last? __137__ minutes

Cindy left her radio on for 4 days, 5 hours. Find how many hours Cindy's radio stayed on by using the table and answering 7 to 9.

7. 1 day = __24__ hours

8. First find the number of hours in 4 days. Then add the 5 hours.

   4 × 24 hours = __96__ hours

   96 hours + 5 hours = __101__ hours

9. How many hours did Cindy's radio stay on? __101__ hours

© Pearson Education, Inc.

Intervention Lesson I30 **149**

Name _____

Math Diagnosis and Intervention System
Intervention Lesson I30

Units of Time (continued)

Find the missing numbers.

10. 6 hours = __360__ minutes   11. 8 days = __192__ hours

12. 9 weeks = __63__ days   13. 5 hours = __300__ minutes

14. 5 days, 3 hours = __123__ hours   15. 1 hour, 2 minutes = __62__ minutes

16. 6 weeks, 6 days = __48__ days   17. 3 days, 16 hours = __88__ hours

18. The first space flight when humans orbited the earth lasted 1 hour, 48 minutes. How many minutes did the flight last?   __108 minutes__

19. The first space flight when humans orbited the moon lasted 6 days, 3 hours. How many hours did the mission last?   __147 hours__

20. It normally takes a duck egg 4 weeks, 2 days to hatch. How many days is 4 weeks, 2 days?   __30 days__

21. It normally takes a pigeon egg 2 weeks, 4 days to hatch. How many days is 2 weeks, 4 days?   __18 days__

22. **Reasoning** A chicken egg normally hatches in 21 days. A turkey egg normally hatches in 3 weeks, 5 days. How many more days does it normally take a turkey egg to hatch than a chicken egg? Explain how you solved.

    5 more days; 3 weeks is 3 × 7 = 21 days, 3 weeks 5 days is 21 + 5 = 26 days. 26 days − 21 days = 5 days.

23. Eddie ran a marathon in 4 hours and 7 minutes. His goal was to finish the race in less than 250 minutes. Did Eddie achieve his goal? Explain your reasoning.

    Yes; 4 hours 7 minutes is 240 + 7 = 247 minutes. He finished the race 3 minutes faster than his goal.

© Pearson Education, Inc.

150 Intervention Lesson I30

Teacher Notes

Ongoing Assessment

Ask: *Explain how you change 5 weeks, 3 days to days.* First multiply 5 x 7 days to find the number of days in 5 weeks. Then add the 3 days.

Error Intervention

If students cannot find the number of days in 3 weeks,

then have them color 3 weeks on a calendar.

If You Have More Time

Have students make up silly word problems that involve time. For example: Mandy jumped and sang Mary Had a Little Lamb for 2 hours and 13 minutes. How many minutes did Mandy jump and sing? Have students trade problems with a partner to solve.

© Pearson Education, Inc.

Elapsed Time

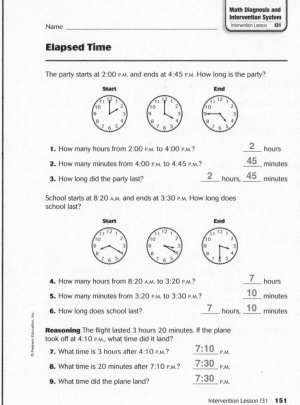

Name _____

Math Diagnosis and
Intervention System
Intervention Lesson   I31

Elapsed Time

The party starts at 2:00 P.M. and ends at 4:45 P.M. How long is the party?

Start   End

1. How many hours from 2:00 P.M. to 4:00 P.M.?   __2__ hours
2. How many minutes from 4:00 P.M. to 4:45 P.M.?   __45__ minutes
3. How long did the party last?   __2__ hours, __45__ minutes

School starts at 8:20 A.M. and ends at 3:30 P.M. How long does school last?

Start   End

4. How many hours from 8:20 A.M. to 3:20 P.M.?   __7__ hours
5. How many minutes from 3:20 P.M. to 3:30 P.M.?   __10__ minutes
6. How long does school last?   __7__ hours, __10__ minutes

Reasoning The flight lasted 3 hours 20 minutes. If the plane took off at 4:10 P.M., what time did it land?

7. What time is 3 hours after 4:10 P.M.?   __7:10__ P.M.
8. What time is 20 minutes after 7:10 P.M.?   __7:30__ P.M.
9. What time did the plane land?   __7:30__ P.M.

Intervention Lesson I31   **151**

Teacher Notes

Ongoing Assessment

Ask: *Why do you not count hours first when finding the elapsed time from 8:40 A.M. to 9:10 A.M.?* Sample answer: If you counted hours you would go from 8:40 to 9:40, but the ending time is before 9:40, so you only count minutes.

Error Intervention

If students have trouble finding elapsed time mentally,

then encourage them to draw a clock face.

If You Have More Time

Print off flight schedules (that have minutes in multiples of 5) from an airport nearby showing departing and arrival times. Have students find the flight time (elapsed time) for each flight. Be sure to use flights in the same time zone.

Name _____

Math Diagnosis and
Intervention System
Intervention Lesson   I31

Elapsed Time (continued)

Find the elapsed time.

10. Start Time: 1:00 P.M.
    End Time: 8:00 P.M.

    _____7 hours_____

11. Start Time: 7:00 A.M.
    End Time: 10:35 A.M.

    ___3 hours, 35 minutes___

12. Start Time: 11:35 A.M.
    End Time: 3:50 P.M.

    ___4 hours, 15 minutes___

13. Start Time: 6:10 P.M.
    End Time: 12:25 A.M.

    ___6 hours, 15 minutes___

14. Start Time: 2:00 P.M.
    End Time: 6:05 P.M.

    ___4 hours, 5 minutes___

15. Start Time: 9:20 A.M.
    End Time: 2:40 P.M.

    ___5 hours, 20 minutes___

16. Start Time: 4:35 P.M.
    End Time: 5:15 P.M.

    ___40 minutes___

17. Start Time: 8:15 A.M.
    End Time: 2:55 A.M.

    ___6 hours, 40 minutes___

18. **Reasoning** The baseball game started at 3:00 P.M. It lasted 2 hours and 45 minutes. What time did the baseball game end?   5:45 P.M.

19. **Reasoning** Erin got home from the soccer match at 5:20 P.M. She went to bed 3 hours and 45 minutes later. What time did she go to bed?   9:05 P.M.

20. **Reasoning** The rainstorm began at 1:15 P.M. Marco's class came in from recess 25 minutes earlier. What time did the class come in from recess?   12:50 P.M.

21. **Reasoning** What is 30 minutes before 12:25 P.M.?   11:55 P.M.

152   Intervention Lesson I31

© Pearson Education, Inc.

Temperature

Name _____

Temperature

Temperature is the measure of how hot or how cold something is.

Temperature can be measured in **degrees Fahrenheit** (°F) or **degrees Celsius** (°C).

1. Look at the thermometer at the right. Does the right side show °F or °C?   **°C**

2. What is the temperature in °C?   **20°C**

Find the temperature in °F by answering 3 to 7.

3. Which side shows °F?   **left**

4. Look at the left side of the thermometer. How many spaces are between 30° and 40°?   **5**

5. What is 40° − 30°?   **10°**

6. Each space on the left side of the thermometer equals how many degrees? 10° ÷ 5 = **2°**

7. Start at 60°F. Then count up by 2s to where the dark bar stops.

60, 62, **64** , **66** , **68**

The top of the dark bar is at 68, so the temperature is 68°F.

8. Reasoning Would you build a snowman in 34°F or 64°F weather? Use the table to decide and explain your reasoning.

34°F; 34°F is close to the temperature water freezes and 64°F is close to room temperature. You would build a snowman in freezing weather not at room temperature.

	°F	°C
Water boils	212	100
Normal body temperature	98.6	37
Room temperature	68	20
Water Freezes	32	0

Teacher Notes

Ongoing Assessment

Ask: ***Would you wear a coat outside if the temperature were 40°C? Why?*** No, 40°C is very hot, swimming weather.

Error Intervention

If students have trouble reading a thermometer,

then use D12: Measuring Temperature.

If You Have More Time

Put students in pairs. Give the students a recent weather report for 6 places around the world, and a copy of a thermometer. Have partners mark and label each location's temperature. A map or globe may help students see how the weather is in different parts of the world.

Name _____

Temperature (continued)

Choose the better temperature for each activity.

9. bicycle riding   **10.** camping   **11.** ice skating   **12.** wearing shorts

30°F or (70°F)   0°C or (30°C)   (32°F) or 72°F   (35°C) or 100°C

Choose the better estimate for the temperature.

13. hot pizza   **14.** ice cream   **15.** bathwater   **16.** cold drink

80°F or (160°F)   (0°C) or 30°C   45°F or (95°F)   0°C or (10°C)

Write each temperature in °F and °C.

17. **76** °F   **24** °C

18. **50** °F   **10** °C

19. **64** °F   **18** °C

20. **46** °F   **8** °C

21. **54** °F   **12** °C

22. **86** °F   **30** °C

23. One cold morning, the temperature was 35°F. The temperature rose to 53°F later in the day. How many degrees had the temperature increased?   **18°F**

24. Reasoning This morning the temperature was 65°F. Then it rose 3°. Then the temperature dropped 10°. What was the final temperature?   **58°F**

Converting Customary Units of Length

Name _____

Math Diagnosis and Intervention System
Intervention Lesson I33

Converting Customary Units of Length

Mayla bought 6 yards of ribbon. How many feet of ribbon did she buy?

Answer 1 to 4 to change 6 yards to feet.

To change larger units to smaller units, multiply. To change smaller units to larger units, divide.

Customary Units of Length
1 foot (ft) = 12 inches (in.)
1 yard (yd) = 36 (in.)
1 yard (yd) = 3 feet (ft)
1 mile (mi) = 5,280 feet (ft)
1 mile (mi) = 1,760 yards (yd)

1. 1 yard = __3__ feet

2. Do you need to multiply or divide to change from yards to feet? __multiply__

3. What is 6 × 3 feet? __18__ feet

4. How many feet of ribbon did Mayla buy? __18 ft__

Deidra bought 60 inches of ribbon. How many feet of ribbon did she buy? Change 60 inches to feet by answering 5 to 8.

5. 1 foot = __12__ inches

6. Do you need to multiply or divide to change from feet to inches? __divide__

7. What is 60 ÷ 12? __5__

8. How many feet of ribbon did Deidra buy? __5 ft__

Troy ran 4 miles. How many yards did he run? Change 4 miles to yards by answering 9 to 11.

9. 1 mile = __1,760__ yards

10. Do you need to multiply or divide to change from miles to yards? __multiply__

11. 4 miles = __7,040__ yards

12. How many yards did Troy run? __7,040 yd__

© Pearson Education, Inc.

Intervention Lesson I33   **155**

Name _____

Math Diagnosis and Intervention System
Intervention Lesson I33

Converting Customary Units of Length (continued)

Find each missing number.

13. 1 yd = __3__ ft   **14.** 72 in. = __6__ ft   **15.** 3 mi = __15,840__ ft

16. 5,280 ft = __1__ mi   **17.** 5 mi = __8,800__ yd   **18.** 4 yd = __12__ ft

19. 48 in. = __4__ ft   **20.** 1 yd = __36__ in.   **21.** 6 mi = __31,680__ ft

22. 5 yd = __15__ ft   **23.** 3 mi = __5,280__ yd   **24.** 2 ft = __24__ in.

25. 21 ft = __7__ yd   **26.** 3 yd = __108__ in.   **27.** 4 yd = __144__ in.

For Exercises 28 to 32 use the information in the table.

28. How many inches did Speedy crawl?

__36__ inches

29. How many inches did Pokey crawl?

__72__ inches

30. How many inches did Pickles crawl?

__48__ inches

Turtle Crawl Results	
Turtle	**Distance**
Snapper	38 inches
Speedy	3 feet
Pokey	2 yards
Pickles	4 feet

31. Reasoning Which turtle crawled the greatest distance? __Pokey__

32. Reasoning Which turtle crawled the least distance? __Speedy__

33. Reasoning Explain how you could use addition to find how many yards are in 72 inches.

Sample answer: I know 36 in. = 1 yd.
If I add 36 + 36, I get 72.
Since I added 36 two times, 72 in. = 2 yd.

© Pearson Education, Inc.

156   Intervention Lesson I33

Teacher Notes

Ongoing Assessment

Ask: *Would you multiply or divide to change miles to inches?* Multiply

Error Intervention

If students have trouble remembering the size of each unit,

then use I22: Using Customary Units of Length to familiarize students with relative sizes. This will help them decide whether they are changing from a smaller unit to a larger unit or a larger unit to a smaller unit.

If You Have More Time

Write the following in one column on the board: feet to inches, yards to inches, yards to feet, miles to feet, and miles to yards. Have students make up fun word problems that involve the conversions on the board. Exchange stories with a partner and solve. For example: Yazmine's dog's tail is 2 yards long. How many inches long is the dog's tail?

Converting Customary Units of Capacity

Math Diagnosis and
Intervention System
Intervention Lesson   I34

Name _____

Converting Customary Units of Capacity

The bread recipe calls for 2 cups of milk. How many fluid ounces (fl oz) is that? Change 2 cups to fluid ounces by answering 1 to 3.

To change larger units to smaller units, multiply. To change smaller units to larger units, divide.

Customary Units of Capacity
1 tablespoon (tbsp) = 3 teaspoons (tsp)
1 cup (c) = 8 fluid ounces (fl oz)
1 pint (pt) = 2 cups (c)
1 quart (qt) = 2 pints (pt)
1 gallon (gal) = 4 quarts (qt)

1. 1 cup = __8__ fluid ounces

2. Do you need to multiply or divide to change from cups to fluid ounces?   _divide_

3. What is 2 × 8 fluid ounces? __16__ fluid ounces

4. How many fluid ounces of milk is 2 cups? __16 fl oz__

Change 18 teaspoons to tablespoons by answering 5 to 8.

5. 1 tablespoon = __3__ teaspoons

6. Do you need to multiply or divide to change from teaspoons to tablespoons?   _divide_

7. What is 18 ÷ 3? __6__

8. 18 teaspoons = __6__ tablespoons

Javier made 5 quarts of punch. How many pints did he make? Change 5 quarts to pints by answering 9 to 12.

9. 1 quart = __2__ pints

10. Do you need to multiply or divide to change from quarts to pints?   _multiply_

11. 5 quarts = __10__ pints

12. How many pints of punch did Javier make? __10 pts__

© Pearson Education, Inc.

Intervention Lesson I34   **157**

Name _____

Converting Customary Units of Capacity (continued)

Find each missing number.

13. 40 fl oz = __5__ c   **14.** 3 gal = __12__ qt   **15.** 15 tsp = __5__ tbsp

16. 4 qt = __8__ pt   **17.** 12 pt = __6__ qt   **18.** 8 c = __64__ fl oz

19. 3 tbsp = __9__ tsp   **20.** 18 c = __9__ pt   **21.** 14 gal = __56__ qt

22. 24 fl oz = __3__ c   **23.** 16 qt = __32__ pt   **24.** 32 qt = __8__ gal

25. 3 pt = __6__ c   **26.** 8 qt = __2__ gal   **27.** 4 c = __2__ pt

Lee has the supplies listed in the table to use in his science fair project. Use the table for Exercises 28 to 32.

28. How many cups of orange juice does Lee have?   __4__ cups

29. How many cups of milk does Lee have?   __2__ cups

30. How many cups of water does Lee have?   __6__ cups

Science Project Supplies	
Liquid	Amount
Orange Juice	32 fl oz
Milk	1 pt
Vinegar	3 c
Water	3 pt

31. Reasoning Which liquid does Lee have the most of?   _water_

32. Reasoning Which liquid does Lee have the least of?   _milk_

33. Reasoning Lee also needs 4 tablespoons of baking soda, but he can only find a teaspoon to measure with. How many teaspoons of baking soda does he need?   __12 tsp__

34. Reasoning Explain how to convert 6 pints to quarts.

2 pt = 1 qt, so I would divide 6 by 2.
6 pt = 3 qt

© Pearson Education, Inc.

158 Intervention Lesson I34

Teacher Notes

Ongoing Assessment

Ask: *Would you multiply or divide to change pints to gallons?* Divide

Error Intervention

If students have trouble deciding whether to multiply or divide to convert units,

then write a diagram like the one below on the board.

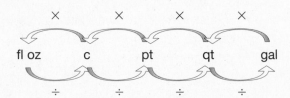

Explain that when changing gallons to quarts, quarts to pints, and so on, multiply. When changing fluid ounces to cups, cups to pints, and so on, divide.

If You Have More Time

Show a bottle or carton with two customary units of capacity. For example, a milk carton might have both 1 pt and 16 fl oz on its label. Have students work in pairs to explain why the two measures are equal. For the milk example, 1 pt = 2 c and 2 c = 2 × 8 = 16 fl oz, so 1 pt = 16 fl oz.

© Pearson Education, Inc.

Converting Customary Units of Weight

Name _____

Converting Customary Units of Weight

An average size ostrich egg weighs 3 pounds. How many ounces does an average size ostrich egg weigh?

Change 3 pounds to ounces by answering 1 to 4.

To change larger units to smaller units, multiply. To change smaller units to larger units, divide.

Customary Units of Weight
1 pound (lb) = 16 ounces (oz)
1 ton (T) = 2,000 pounds (lb)

1. 1 pound = __16__ ounces

2. Do you need to multiply or divide to change from pounds to ounces?   multiply

3. What is 3 × 16 ounces? __48__ ounces

4. How many ounces does an average size ostrich egg weigh?   48 oz

An African elephant can weigh up to 22,000 pounds. How many tons can an African elephant weigh? Change 22,000 pounds to tons by answering 5 to 8.

5. 1 ton = __2,000__ pounds

6. Do you need to multiply or divide to change from pounds to tons?   divide

7. What is 22,000 ÷ 2,000? Hint: Think 22 ÷ 2. __11__

8. How many tons can an African elephant weigh? __11 T__

An Asian elephant can grow to a little more than 5 tons. How many pounds can the Asian elephant weigh? Change 5 tons to pounds by answering 9 to 12.

9. 1 ton = __2,000__ pounds

10. Do you need to multiply or divide to change from tons to pounds?   multiply

Intervention Lesson I35   **159**

Name _____

Converting Customary Units of Weight (continued)

11. 5 tons = __10,000__ pounds

12. How many pounds can an Asian elephant weigh? __10,000 lbs__

Find each missing number.

13. 8 lb = __128__ oz   **14.** 12 T = __24,000__ lb   **15.** 48 oz = __3__ lb

16. 24,000 lb = __12__ T   **17.** 80 oz = __5__ lb   **18.** 22 T = __44,000__ lb

19. 64 oz = __4__ lb   **20.** 4,000 lb = __2__ T   **21.** 22 lb = __352__ oz

22. 14,000 lb = __7__ T   **23.** 160 oz = __10__ lb   **24.** 10 T = __20,000__ lb

25. 4 T = __8,000__ lb   **26.** 32 oz = __2__ lb   **27.** 16,000 lb = __8__ T

For Exercises 28 to 32, use the information in the table.

28. How many pounds of carrots were shipped? __8,000__ pounds

29. How many pounds of peas were shipped? __4,000__ pounds

30. Reasoning Which vegetable shipment was the heaviest?
    potatoes

31. Reasoning Which vegetable shipment was the lightest?   peas

32. Reasoning Five tons of corn were shipped. Explain how to find how many more pounds of potatoes than corn were shipped.

Sample answer: Change 5 tons to pounds by multiplying 5 × 2,000. So 10,000 pounds of corn were shipped. Subtract: 16,000 − 10,000 = 6,000. So, 6,000 more pounds of potatoes than corn were shipped.

Vegetable Shipments

Vegetable	Amount
Carrots	4 T
Celery	12,000 lb
Peas	2 T
Potatoes	16,000 lb

© Pearson Education, Inc.

Teacher Notes

Ongoing Assessment

Ask: *How do you convert 9 tons to pounds?* 1 ton = 2,000 pounds, so I would multiply 9 × 2,000. 9 tons = 18,000 pounds

Error Intervention

If students have trouble converting pounds to tons,

then explain that when dividing by multiples of 10, the same number of zeros can be removed from each number without effecting the quotient. For example, 16,000 ÷ 2,000 is the same as 16 ÷ 2.

If You Have More Time

Write the following information on the board: Basset hound—22 pounds, Boxer—65 pounds, Chihuahua—5 pounds, Golden Retriever—73 pounds, and Great Dane—110 pounds. Have students convert the weight of each dog to ounces.

Converting Metric Units

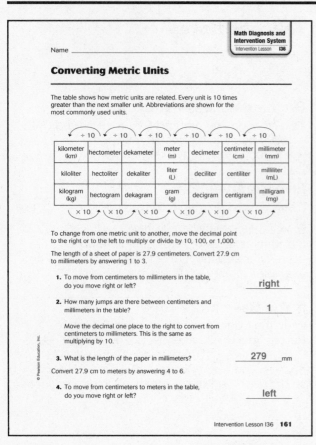

Name _____

**Math Diagnosis and
Intervention System**
Intervention Lesson I36

Converting Metric Units

The table shows how metric units are related. Every unit is 10 times greater than the next smaller unit. Abbreviations are shown for the most commonly used units.

÷ 10 ÷ 10 ÷ 10 ÷ 10 ÷ 10 ÷ 10

kilometer (km)	hectometer	dekameter	meter (m)	decimeter	centimeter (cm)	millimeter (mm)
kiloliter	hectoliter	dekaliter	liter (L)	deciliter	centiliter	milliliter (mL)
kilogram (kg)	hectogram	dekagram	gram (g)	decigram	centigram	milligram (mg)

× 10 × 10 × 10 × 10 × 10 × 10

To change from one metric unit to another, move the decimal point to the right or to the left to multiply or divide by 10, 100, or 1,000.

The length of a sheet of paper is 27.9 centimeters. Convert 27.9 cm to millimeters by answering 1 to 3.

1. To move from centimeters to millimeters in the table, do you move right or left?   **right**

2. How many jumps are there between centimeters and millimeters in the table?   **1**

Move the decimal one place to the right to convert from centimeters to millimeters. This is the same as multiplying by 10.

3. What is the length of the paper in millimeters?   **279** mm

Convert 27.9 cm to meters by answering 4 to 6.

4. To move from centimeters to meters in the table, do you move right or left?   **left**

Intervention Lesson I36 **161**

Name _____

**Math Diagnosis and
Intervention System**
Intervention Lesson I36

Converting Metric Units (continued)

5. How many jumps are there between centimeters and meters in the table?   **2**

Move the decimal two places to the left to convert from centimeters to meters. This is the same as dividing by 100.

6. What is the length of the paper in meters?   **0.279** m

Tell the direction and number of jumps in the table for each conversion. Then convert.

7. 742 cm to meters
2 jumps **left**
7.42 m

8. 12.4 kg to g
3 jumps **right**
12,400 g

9. 0.62 L to mL
3 jumps **left**
620 mL

Write the missing numbers.

10. 150 mg = **0.15** g   **11.** 2,600 m = **2.6** km   **12.** 0.4 L = **400** mL

13. 300 mL = **0.3** L   **14.** 4 kg = **4,000,000** mg   **15.** 2.6 m = **2,600** mm

16. 2,670 mg = **2.67** g   **17.** 34 cm = **340** mm   **18.** 16 L = **16,000** mL

For Exercises 19 to 21 use the table at the right.

19. What is the height of the Petronas Towers in centimeters?
45,200 cm

20. What is the height of the CN Tower in meters?
553 m

21. What is the height of the John Hancock Center in km?
0.344 km

Building	Height
John Hancock Center	344 m
Petronas Towers	452 m
Sears Tower	44,200 cm
CN Tower	553,000 mm

22. Reasoning Which is shorter, 15 centimeters or 140 millimeters? Explain.
15 centimeters is equal to 150 millimeters and 140 < 150, so 140 millimeters is shorter.

162 Intervention Lesson I36

Teacher Notes

Ongoing Assessment

Ask: *When changing from smaller units to larger units, do you multiply or divide?* Divide

Error Intervention

If students do not understand the relationship between moving the decimal and multiplying or dividing a number by 10,

then use H59: Multiplying Decimals by 10, 100, or 1,000 and H64: Dividing Decimals by 10, 100, or 1,000.

If You Have More Time

Have student pairs measure their heights in centimeters and convert the measurements into meters and into millimeters.

Converting Between Measurement Systems

Name _____

Math Diagnosis and Intervention System
Intervention Lesson   I37

Converting Between Measurement Systems

The table shows the relationships between customary and metric units. Only the equivalent for inches and centimeters is exact. All other equivalents are approximate. The symbol ≈ means "approximately equal to."

A standard CD has a diameter of 4.75 inches. How many centimeters is the diameter of the CD?

Convert 4.75 inches to centimeters by answering 1 to 4.

Customary and Metric Unit Equivalent
Length
1 in. = 2.54 cm
1 m ≈ 39.97 in.
1 mi ≈ 1.61 km
Weight and Mass
1 oz ≈ 28.35 g
1 kg ≈ 2.2 lb
1 metric ton (t) ≈ 1.102 tons (T)
Capacity
1 L ≈ 1.06 qt
1 gal ≈ 3.79 L

1. How many centimeters equal one inch?   **2.54**

To change larger units to smaller units multiply. To change smaller units to larger units, divide.

2. Do you need to multiply or divide to change from inches to centimeters?   **multiply**

3. What is 4.75 × 2.54 to the nearest tenth?   **12.1**

4. How many centimeters is the diameter of the CD?   **12.1** cm

The average golden retriever weighs 65 pounds. What is the approximate mass in kilograms of an average golden retriever?

Convert 65 pounds to kilograms by answering 5 to 8.

5. According to the table, how many pounds equal about one kilogram?   **2.2**

6. Do you need to multiply or divide to change from pounds to kilograms?   **divide**

7. What is 65 ÷ 2.2 rounded to the nearest tenth?   **29.5**

8. What is the approximate mass in kilograms of an average golden retriever?   **29.5** kg

Intervention Lesson I37   **163**

Name _____

Math Diagnosis and Intervention System
Intervention Lesson   I37

Converting Between Measurement Systems (continued)

Complete. Round to the nearest tenth, if necessary.

9. 3.8 m ≈ ▓ in.   **151.9**

10. 50 g ≈ ▓ oz   **1.8**

11. 3 L ≈ ▓ gal   **0.8**

12. 44 in. ≈ ▓ cm   **111.8**

13. 2.5 t ≈ ▓ T   **2.8**

14. $3\frac{1}{2}$ kg ≈ ▓ lb   **7.7**

15. $5\frac{1}{4}$ qt ≈ ▓ L   **5.0**

16. 100 km ≈ ▓ mi   **62.1**

17. 10 cm ≈ ▓ in.   **3.9**

18. 2 cm ≈ ▓ in.   **0.8**

19. 2.4 t ≈ ▓ T   **2.6**

20. $8\frac{2}{3}$ m ≈ ▓ yd   **9.6**

21. $3\frac{1}{2}$ yd ≈ ▓ m   **3.2**

22. 500 lb ≈ ▓ kg   **227.3**

23. 11 in. ≈ ▓ m   **0.3**

24. Rewrite the materials list at the right using meters for fabric, inches for thread, and kilograms for stuffing. Write your conversions to the nearest tenth below:

Materials List
$1\frac{1}{2}$ yd fabric
65 cm thread
$1\frac{3}{4}$ lb stuffing

fabric: **1.4** m   thread: **25.6** in.   stuffing: **0.8** kg

25. **Reasoning** A necklace measures $16\frac{1}{2}$ inches.

About how many centimeters is this to the nearest tenth?   **41.9 cm**

164 Intervention Lesson I37

Math Diagnosis and Intervention System

Intervention Lesson   **I37**

Converting Between Measurement Systems

Teacher Notes

Ongoing Assessment

Ask: *How can you convert inches to millimeters?* First convert the inches to centimeters by multiplying by 2.54 and then convert the centimeters to millimeters by moving the decimal point to the right one place.

Error Intervention

If students have trouble multiplying and dividing decimals,

then use H62: Multiplying Decimals by Decimals and H67: Dividing a Decimal by a Decimal.

If You Have More Time

Have students look up the dimensions of a football field, a soccer field, or a baseball field. Have students convert the measurements to metric units.

Units of Measure and Precision

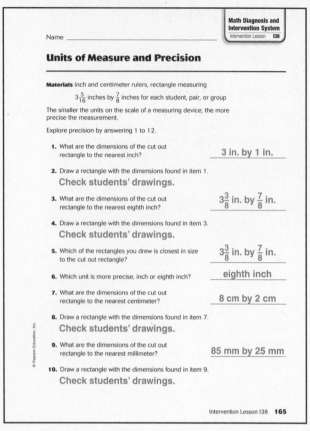

Name _____

Math Diagnosis and Intervention System
Intervention Lesson I38

Units of Measure and Precision

Materials inch and centimeter rulers, rectangle measuring $3\frac{5}{16}$ inches by $\frac{7}{8}$ inches for each student, pair, or group

The smaller the units on the scale of a measuring device, the more precise the measurement.

Explore precision by answering 1 to 12.

1. What are the dimensions of the cut out rectangle to the nearest inch?   **3 in. by 1 in.**

2. Draw a rectangle with the dimensions found in item 1.
   Check students' drawings.

3. What are the dimensions of the cut out rectangle to the nearest eighth inch? $3\frac{3}{8}$ in. by $\frac{7}{8}$ in.

4. Draw a rectangle with the dimensions found in item 3.
   Check students' drawings.

5. Which of the rectangles you drew is closest in size to the cut out rectangle? $3\frac{3}{8}$ in. by $\frac{7}{8}$ in.

6. Which unit is more precise, inch or eighth inch?   **eighth inch**

7. What are the dimensions of the cut out rectangle to the nearest centimeter?   **8 cm by 2 cm**

8. Draw a rectangle with the dimensions found in item 7.
   Check students' drawings.

9. What are the dimensions of the cut out rectangle to the nearest millimeter?   **85 mm by 25 mm**

10. Draw a rectangle with the dimensions found in item 9.
    Check students' drawings.

© Pearson Education, Inc.

Intervention Lesson I38   **165**

Teacher Notes

Ongoing Assessment
Ask: *Which is more precise, 2.3 centimeters or 23 millimeters?* They have the same precision. When centimeters are measured to the nearest tenth, the measurement is to the nearest millimeter.

Error Intervention

If students have trouble measuring to the nearest fraction of an inch or to the nearest centimeter,

then use I21: Measuring Length to $\frac{1}{2}$ and $\frac{1}{4}$ Inch and I23: Using Metric Units of Length.

If You Have More Time
Have student pairs play a guessing game. One student cuts out a polygon and describes it using its measurements. The other student draws the polygon based on the description given. Have students compare the cut out polygon to the drawn one. Then, have them change roles and repeat.

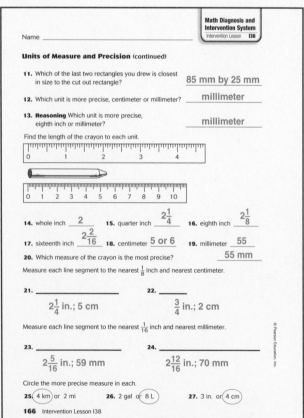

Name _____

Math Diagnosis and Intervention System
Intervention Lesson I38

Units of Measure and Precision (continued)

11. Which of the last two rectangles you drew is closest in size to the cut out rectangle?   **85 mm by 25 mm**

12. Which unit is more precise, centimeter or millimeter?   **millimeter**

13. **Reasoning** Which unit is more precise, eighth inch or millimeter?   **millimeter**

Find the length of the crayon to each unit.

14. whole inch   **2**   15. quarter inch $2\frac{1}{4}$ 16. eighth inch $2\frac{1}{8}$

17. sixteenth inch $2\frac{2}{16}$ 18. centimeter   **5 or 6**   19. millimeter   **55**

20. Which measure of the crayon is the most precise?   **55 mm**

Measure each line segment to the nearest $\frac{1}{8}$ inch and nearest centimeter.

21. _____   22. _____
    $2\frac{1}{4}$ in.; 5 cm $\frac{3}{4}$ in.; 2 cm

Measure each line segment to the nearest $\frac{1}{16}$ inch and nearest millimeter.

23. _____   24. _____
    $2\frac{5}{16}$ in.; 59 mm $2\frac{12}{16}$ in.; 70 mm

Circle the more precise measure in each.

25. **4 km** or 2 mi   26. 2 gal or **8 L**   27. 3 in. or **4 cm**

166 Intervention Lesson I38

© Pearson Education, Inc.

More Units of Time

Teacher Notes

Name _____

More Units of Time

Natalia, one of the finalists at a dance marathon, danced 1,740 minutes. Tony, the other finalist, danced 28 hours and 20 minutes. Which finalist danced the longest?

Solve by answering 1 to 6.

To change a smaller unit to a larger unit, divide. To change a larger unit to a smaller unit, multiply.

Units of Time
1 minute = 60 seconds
1 hour = 60 minutes
1 day = 24 hours
1 week = 7 days
1 month = about 4 weeks
1 year = 52 weeks
1 year = 12 months
1 year = 365 days
1 leap year = 366 days
1 decade = 10 years
1 century = 100 years
1 millennium = 1,000 years

1. How many minutes are in an hour?   **60**

2. Do you need to multiply or divide to change from minutes to hours?   **divide**

3. What is 1,740 ÷ 60?   **29**

4. How many hours equal 1,740 minutes?   **29**

5. Compare. Write >, <, or =.

   1,740 min $\boxed{>}$ 28 h 20 min

6. Which finalist danced the longest?   **Natalia**

Fred is two years and ten days older than Ron. Alfonzo is 745 days older than Ron. Who is older, Fred or Alfonzo?

Solve by answering 7 to 12.

7. How many days are in a year?   **365**

8. Do you need to multiply or divide to change years to days?   **multiply**

9. What is (2 × 365) + 10?   **740**

10. How many days are two years and ten days?   **740**

Intervention Lesson I39   **167**

Name _____

More Units of Time (continued)

11. Compare. Write >, <, or =.   2 years 10 days $\boxed{<}$ 745 days

12. Who is older, Fred or Alfonzo?   **Alfonzo**

13. **Reasoning** Find the missing numbers.

   75 minutes = **1** hour, **15** minutes

Compare. Write >, <, or =.

14. 2 minutes $\boxed{<}$ 126 seconds
15. 4 weeks $\boxed{=}$ 28 days

16. 2 weeks and 3 days $\boxed{>}$ 16 days
17. 50 weeks $\boxed{=}$ 350 days

18. 50 hours $\boxed{>}$ 2 days
19. 208 minutes $\boxed{<}$ 4 hours

20. 2 decades $\boxed{<}$ 34 years
21. 28 months $\boxed{>}$ 2 years

22. 23 weeks $\boxed{=}$ 161 days
23. 6 hours $\boxed{>}$ 150 minutes

Find each missing number.

24. 420 seconds = **7** minutes
25. 156 weeks = **3** years

26. 105 days = **15** weeks
27. 3 hours = **10,800** seconds

28. **Reasoning** Jerome slept 8 hours and 35 minutes on Tuesday night while Manuel slept 525 minutes. Who slept longer? Explain how you solved.

   Manuel; Sample answer: 8 hours and 35 minutes equal 515 minutes and 515 < 525.

Ongoing Assessment

Ask: *How do you change 360 minutes to hours?* Divide 360 by 60.

Error Intervention

If students have trouble multiplying large numbers,

then use G70: Multiplying by Two-Digit Numbers and G71: Multiplying Greater Numbers.

If students have trouble dividing large numbers,

then use G75: Dividing by Two-Digit Divisors, G76: One- and Two-Digit Quotients and G77: Dividing Greater Numbers.

If You Have More Time

Have students find their age in years, months and days. For example, a student might be 10 years 3 months and 9 days old. Then have them convert their age into months and days and then into approximate number of days.

More Elapsed Time

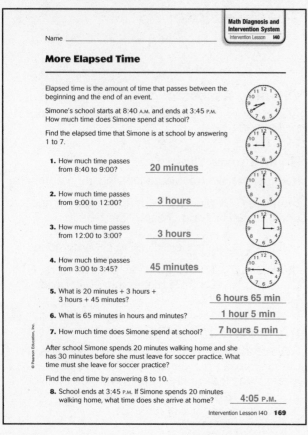

Name _____

More Elapsed Time

Elapsed time is the amount of time that passes between the beginning and the end of an event.

Simone's school starts at 8:40 A.M. and ends at 3:45 P.M. How much time does Simone spend at school?

Find the elapsed time that Simone is at school by answering 1 to 7.

1. How much time passes from 8:40 to 9:00? ___20 minutes___

2. How much time passes from 9:00 to 12:00? ___3 hours___

3. How much time passes from 12:00 to 3:00? ___3 hours___

4. How much time passes from 3:00 to 3:45? ___45 minutes___

5. What is 20 minutes + 3 hours + 3 hours + 45 minutes? ___6 hours 65 min___

6. What is 65 minutes in hours and minutes? ___1 hour 5 min___

7. How much time does Simone spend at school? ___7 hours 5 min___

After school Simone spends 20 minutes walking home and she has 30 minutes before she must leave for soccer practice. What time must she leave for soccer practice?

Find the end time by answering 8 to 10.

8. School ends at 3:45 P.M. If Simone spends 20 minutes walking home, what time does she arrive at home? ___4:05 P.M.___

Intervention Lesson I40   **169**

Name _____

More Elapsed Time (continued)

9. Simone must leave for practice 30 minutes later. What time is it 30 minutes after 4:05? ___4:35 P.M.___

10. What time must Simone leave for soccer practice? ___4:35 P.M.___

11. Start: 3:05 A.M. Finish: 5:37 A.M. ___2 h 32 min___

12. Start: 10:45 A.M. Finish: 3:07 P.M. ___4 h 22 min___

13. Start: 4:58 P.M. Finish: 6:56 P.M. ___1 h 58 min___

Write the time each clock will show in 38 minutes.

14. 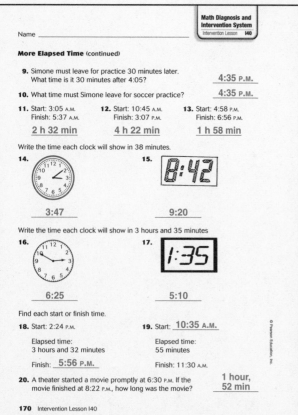 ___3:47___

15. ⟦8:42⟧ ___9:20___

Write the time each clock will show in 3 hours and 35 minutes

16. ___6:25___

17. ⟦1:35⟧ ___5:10___

Find each start or finish time.

18. Start: 2:24 P.M.

Elapsed time: 3 hours and 32 minutes

Finish: ___5:56 P.M.___

19. Start: 10:35 A.M.

Elapsed time: 55 minutes

Finish: 11:30 A.M.

20. A theater started a movie promptly at 6:30 P.M. If the movie finished at 8:22 P.M., how long was the movie? ___1 hour, 52 min___

170   Intervention Lesson I40

Teacher Notes

Ongoing Assessment

Ask: **How do the times that Simone starts and ends school compare with the times that you start and end?** Sample answer: I start 10 minutes earlier and end 15 minutes later. **How does the length of time you are in school compare with the length of time Simone is in school?** Sample answer: I am in school 25 minutes longer than Simone.

Error Intervention

If students have trouble reading the clocks,

then use I28: Time to the Quarter Hour and I29: Telling Time.

If students do not understand elapsed time,

then use I31: Elapsed Time.

If You Have More Time

Have students make two decks of cards. One deck has starting times written on each card and the other deck has elapsed time. Students take turns drawing a card from each deck and finding the ending time.

Elapsed Time in Other Units

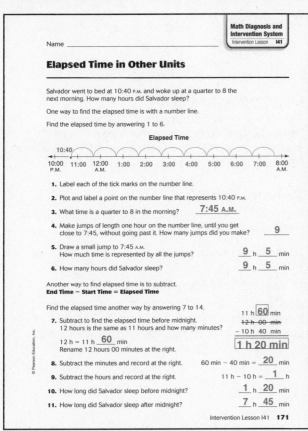

Name _____

Elapsed Time in Other Units

Salvador went to bed at 10:40 P.M. and woke up at a quarter to 8 the next morning. How many hours did Salvador sleep?

One way to find the elapsed time is with a number line.

Find the elapsed time by answering 1 to 6.

Elapsed Time

```
10:40
 ↓
├───┼───┼───┼───┼───┼───┼───┼───┼───┼───┤
10:00 11:00 12:00 1:00 2:00 3:00 4:00 5:00 6:00 7:00 8:00
P.M.                                              A.M.
```

1. Label each of the tick marks on the number line.

2. Plot and label a point on the number line that represents 10:40 P.M.

3. What time is a quarter to 8 in the morning?   **7:45** A.M.

4. Make jumps of length one hour on the number line, until you get close to 7:45, without going past it. How many jumps did you make?   **9**

5. Draw a small jump to 7:45 A.M. How much time is represented by all the jumps?   **9** h **5** min

6. How many hours did Salvador sleep?   **9** h **5** min

Another way to find elapsed time is to subtract.
End Time − Start Time = Elapsed Time

Find the elapsed time another way by answering 7 to 14.

7. Subtract to find the elapsed time before midnight. 12 hours is the same as 11 hours and how many minutes?

    11 h **60** min
    ~~12 h 00 min~~
   − 10 h 40 min
    1 h 20 min

12 h = 11 h **60** min
Rename 12 hours 00 minutes at the right.

8. Subtract the minutes and record at the right.   60 min − 40 min = **20** min

9. Subtract the hours and record at the right.   11 h − 10 h = **1** h

10. How long did Salvador sleep before midnight?   **1** h **20** min

11. How long did Salvador sleep after midnight?   **7** h **45** min

---

Name _____

Elapsed Time in Other Units (continued)

12. Add the elapsed time before midnight to the elapsed time after midnight to find the total elapsed time. Record at the right.

    1 h 20 min
  + 7 h 45 min
   8 h 65 min

20 min + 45 min = **65** min   1 h + 7 h = **8** h

13. Rename 8 hours 65 minutes.

65 minutes = **1** h **5** min   8 hours 65 minutes = **9** h **5** min

14. How many hours did Salvador sleep?   **9** h **5** min

Find each elapsed time.

15. 9:15 A.M. to 4:05 P.M.
   6 h 50 min

16. Quarter to 8 in the evening to 2:30 A.M.
   6 h 45 min

17. 1:26 P.M. to 5:56 A.M.
   16 h 30 min

18. Quarter after 12 noon to 9:30 P.M.
   9 h 15 min

Find each start or end time.

19. Start: 10:24 P.M.

Elapsed time: 3 h and 41 min

Finish: **2:05** A.M.

20. Start: **3:35** P.M.

Elapsed time: 12 h 55 min

Finish: 4:30 A.M.

Add or subtract.

21.   6 h 20 min
  − 3 h 40 min
   2 h 40 min

22.   3 h 38 min
  + 6 h 47 min
  10 h 25 min

23.   2 h 39 min
  +   56 min
   3 h 35 min

24.   5 h 10 min
  − 2 h 55 min
   2 h 15 min

25.   5 h 24 min
  + 3 h 41 min
   9 h 5 min

26.   1 h 35 min
  −   56 min
    39 min

27. **Reasoning** An airplane takes off at 11:50 P.M. and lands at 8:12 A.M. How long was the plane in the air?   **8 h 22 min**

Teacher Notes

Ongoing Assessment

Ask: **How can you rename 7 hours and 70 minutes?** 8 hours and 10 minutes

Error Intervention

If students have trouble converting units of time when renaming,

then use I30: Units of Time and I39: More Units of Time.

If You Have More Time

Have students write down the times of events in a typical school day. Students can then find the elapsed time for each activity in a 24 hour period. Activities could include sleeping, eating, class work, homework, and extracurricular activities.

Temperature Changes

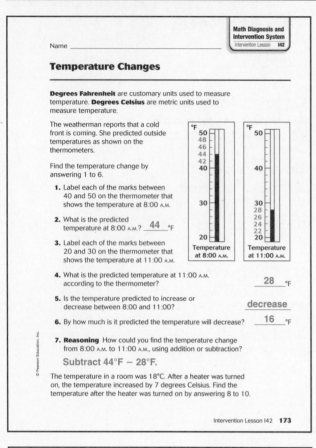

Name _____

Math Diagnosis and Intervention System
Intervention Lesson   I42

Temperature Changes

Degrees Fahrenheit are customary units used to measure temperature. **Degrees Celsius** are metric units used to measure temperature.

The weatherman reports that a cold front is coming. She predicted outside temperatures as shown on the thermometers.

Find the temperature change by answering 1 to 6.

1. Label each of the marks between 40 and 50 on the thermometer that shows the temperature at 8:00 A.M.

2. What is the predicted temperature at 8:00 A.M.? __44__ °F

3. Label each of the marks between 20 and 30 on the thermometer that shows the temperature at 11:00 A.M.

4. What is the predicted temperature at 11:00 A.M. according to the thermometer? __28__ °F

5. Is the temperature predicted to increase or decrease between 8:00 and 11:00? __decrease__

6. By how much is it predicted the temperature will decrease? __16__ °F

7. Reasoning How could you find the temperature change from 8:00 A.M. to 11:00 A.M., using addition or subtraction?

Subtract 44°F − 28°F.

The temperature in a room was 18°C. After a heater was turned on, the temperature increased by 7 degrees Celsius. Find the temperature after the heater was turned on by answering 8 to 10.

Intervention Lesson I42   **173**

Teacher Notes

Ongoing Assessment
Ask: *If water is heated, does the water's temperature increase or decrease?* increase *If water is placed in the freezer, does the water's temperature increase or decrease?* decrease

Error Intervention
If students have trouble reading temperatures on the thermometer,

then I32: Temperature.

If You Have More Time
Use a newspaper to find the record high and low temperatures for the current day as well as temperature predictions for the week. Find the difference between the temperatures.

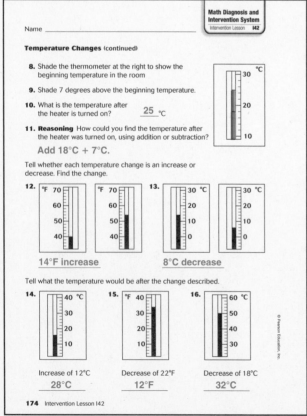

Name _____

Math Diagnosis and Intervention System
Intervention Lesson   I42

Temperature Changes (continued)

8. Shade the thermometer at the right to show the beginning temperature in the room

9. Shade 7 degrees above the beginning temperature.

10. What is the temperature after the heater is turned on? __25__ °C

11. Reasoning How could you find the temperature after the heater was turned on, using addition or subtraction?

Add 18°C + 7°C.

Tell whether each temperature change is an increase or decrease. Find the change.

12.   14°F increase

13.   8°C decrease

Tell what the temperature would be after the change described.

14. Increase of 12°C   __28°C__

15. Decrease of 22°F   __12°F__

16. Decrease of 18°C   __32°C__

174   Intervention Lesson I42

Perimeter

Name _____

Perimeter

Materials crayons or markers, centimeter ruler for each student.

Find the perimeter of the figure at the right by answering 1 to 3. **Perimeter** is the distance around a figure. Each space between lines equals 1 unit.

1 unit   2 units

scale: |—| = 1 unit

1. Trace the figure with a crayon or marker. Count the number of spaces as you trace.

2. How many spaces did you trace? __12__

3. What is the perimeter of the figure? __12__ units

You can also find the perimeter by adding the lengths of the sides.

Find the perimeter of the figure to the right by answering 4 to 6.

4. How many sides does this figure have? __6__

5. Trace over the sides as you count and record the length of each side.

Order of answers may vary.

scale: |– –| = 1 meter

__3__ + __5__ + __5__ + __3__ + __2__ + __2__ = __20__

6. What is the perimeter of the figure? __20__ meters

Find the perimeter of the rectangle by answering 7 to 8.

Opposite sides of a rectangle have equal lengths.

7. Record the length of the sides. Find the sum.

10 cm

10 + 3 + __10__ + __3__ = __16__

3 cm

8. What is the perimeter of the rectangle? __16__ cm

Intervention Lesson I43   **175**

Teacher Notes

Ongoing Assessment

Ask: *What are some real world examples that use the measure of the perimeter to solve a problem?* Sample answers: fencing, borders, picture frames, landscaping

Error Intervention

If students have trouble understanding the concept of perimeter,

then use D35: Perimeter.

If You Have More Time

Have students draw their names on a grid using block letters. They must only use vertical or horizontal lines, no diagonals. Have students find the perimeter of each letter in their names.

Name _____

Perimeter (continued)

9. **Reasoning** Use a ruler to measure each side of the figure in inches. What is the perimeter of the figure?

__10 in.__

Find the perimeter of each figure.

10.

__18 units__

11.

__30 units__

12.
3 in.   5 in.
4 in.

__12 in.__

13.
5 cm
1 cm   1 cm
5 cm

__12 cm__

14.
9 cm
9 cm

__36 cm__

15.
5 cm   5 cm
6 cm
6 cm   6 cm

__28 cm__

16. **Reasoning** If the length of one side of a square is 3 inches, what is the perimeter of the square? Explain your answer.

The lengths of the sides of a square are all the same. Therefore the perimeter is
3 + 3 + 3 + 3 = 12 inches.

176   Intervention Lesson I43

Finding Area on a Grid

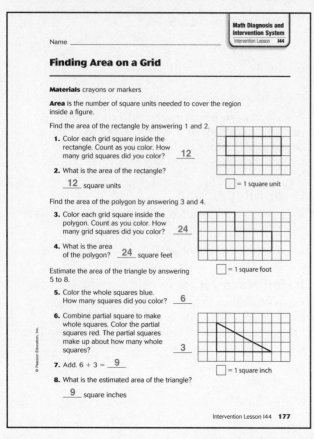

Name _____

Finding Area on a Grid

Materials crayons or markers

Area is the number of square units needed to cover the region inside a figure.

Find the area of the rectangle by answering 1 and 2.

1. Color each grid square inside the rectangle. Count as you color. How many grid squares did you color?   __12__

2. What is the area of the rectangle?
   __12__ square units

☐ = 1 square unit

Find the area of the polygon by answering 3 and 4.

3. Color each grid square inside the polygon. Count as you color. How many grid squares did you color?   __24__

4. What is the area of the polygon?   __24__ square feet

☐ = 1 square foot

Estimate the area of the triangle by answering 5 to 8.

5. Color the whole squares blue. How many squares did you color?   __6__

6. Combine partial square to make whole squares. Color the partial squares red. The partial squares make up about how many whole squares?   __3__

7. Add. 6 + 3 = __9__

8. What is the estimated area of the triangle?
   __9__ square inches

☐ = 1 square inch

Intervention Lesson I44   **177**

Teacher Notes

Ongoing Assessment

Ask: *How is the area of a rectangle different than the perimeter of a rectangle?* The area of a rectangle is the number of square units needed to cover the rectangle. The perimeter is the distance around the rectangle.

Error Intervention

If students have trouble understanding the concept of area,

then use D36: Exploring Area.

If You Have More Time

Give each pair of students an area in square units. Have the pairs of students draw as many rectangular figures on a grid as they can with that area. For example, if students are given an area of 10 square units, then the students could draw figures that are 1 unit by 10 units or 2 units by 5 units long. Have the students share their figures with the class. Encourage students to find the relationship between the sides of the rectangular figure and the area of the figure. ($A = L \times W$)

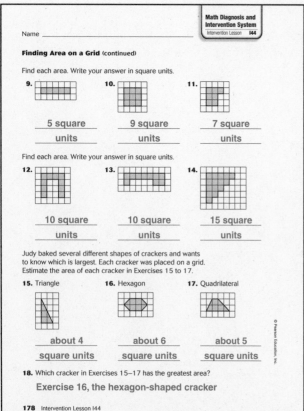

Name _____

Finding Area on a Grid (continued)

Find each area. Write your answer in square units.

9.   5 square units

10.   9 square units

11.   7 square units

Find each area. Write your answer in square units.

12.   10 square units

13.   10 square units

14.   15 square units

Judy baked several different shapes of crackers and wants to know which is largest. Each cracker was placed on a grid. Estimate the area of each cracker in Exercises 15 to 17.

15. Triangle   about 4 square units

16. Hexagon   about 6 square units

17. Quadrilateral   about 5 square units

18. Which cracker in Exercises 15–17 has the greatest area?
   Exercise 16, the hexagon-shaped cracker

178   Intervention Lesson I44

© Pearson Education, Inc.

More Perimeter

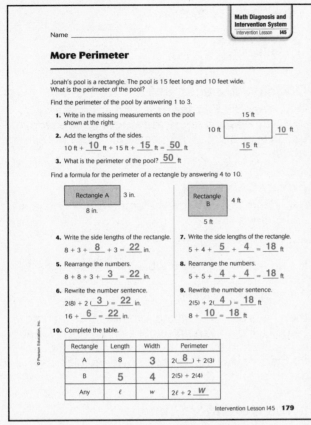

Math Diagnosis and Intervention System
Intervention Lesson I45

Name _____

More Perimeter

Jonah's pool is a rectangle. The pool is 15 feet long and 10 feet wide. What is the perimeter of the pool?

Find the perimeter of the pool by answering 1 to 3.

1. Write in the missing measurements on the pool shown at the right.

   15 ft

   10 ft   10 ft

   15 ft

2. Add the lengths of the sides.

   10 ft + __10__ ft + 15 ft + __15__ ft = __50__ ft

3. What is the perimeter of the pool? __50__ ft

Find a formula for the perimeter of a rectangle by answering 4 to 10.

Rectangle A   3 in.
8 in.

Rectangle B   4 ft
5 ft

4. Write the side lengths of the rectangle.

   8 + 3 + __8__ + 3 = __22__ in.

5. Rearrange the numbers.

   8 + 8 + 3 + __3__ = __22__ in.

6. Rewrite the number sentence.

   2(8) + 2 (__3__) = __22__ in.

   16 + __6__ = __22__ in.

7. Write the side lengths of the rectangle.

   5 + 4 + __5__ + __4__ = __18__ ft

8. Rearrange the numbers.

   5 + 5 + __4__ + __4__ = __18__ ft

9. Rewrite the number sentence.

   2(5) + 2(__4__) = __18__ ft

   8 + __10__ = __18__ ft

10. Complete the table.

Rectangle	Length	Width	Perimeter
A	8	3	2(__8__) + 2(3)
B	5	4	2(5) + 2(4)
Any	ℓ	w	$2\ell + 2$ __w__

© Pearson Education, Inc.

Intervention Lesson I45   **179**

Math Diagnosis and Intervention System
Intervention Lesson I45

Name _____

More Perimeter (continued)

The formula for the perimeter of a rectangle is $P = 2\ell + 2w$

11. **Reasoning** Use the formula to find the perimeter of Jonah's pool.

   $P = 2\ell + 2w$

   $P = 2(\underline{15}) + 2(\underline{10}) = \underline{30} + \underline{20} = \underline{50}$ ft

12. Is the perimeter the same as you found on the previous page? __yes__

A square is a type of rectangle where all of the side lengths are equal.

Find a formula for the perimeter of the square by answering 13 to 15.

13. Add to find the perimeter of the square shown at the right.

   __5__ + __5__ + __5__ + __5__ = __20__

   5 cm

14. What could you multiply to find the perimeter of the square? __4 × 5__

15. If s equals the length of a side of a square, how could you find the perimeter? $P =$ __4s__

Find the perimeter of the rectangle with the given dimensions.

16. $\ell = 9$ mm, $w = 12$ mm

   __42 mm__

17. $\ell = 13$ in., $w = 14$ in.

   __54 in.__

18. $\ell = 2$ ft, $w = 15$ ft

   __34 ft__

19. $\ell = 17$ cm, $w = 25$ cm

   __84 cm__

Find the perimeter of the square with the given side.

20. $s = 2$ yd   __8 yd__

21. $s = 10$ in.   __40 in.__

22. $s = 31$ km   __124 km__

23. $s = 11$ m   __44 m__

24. **Reasoning** Could you use the formula for the perimeter of a rectangle to find the perimeter of a square? Explain your reasoning.

   Yes; the formula for the perimeter of a rectangle can be used to find the perimeter of a square because a square is a rectangle.

180   Intervention Lesson I45

© Pearson Education, Inc.

Math Diagnosis and Intervention System

Teacher Notes

Ongoing Assessment

Ask: **Why is the formula for the perimeter of a square P = 4s?** Because all of the sides of a square are equal, you can just multiply one side by 4 instead of adding each side.

Error Intervention

If students do not know the properties of rectangles,

then use I7: Quadrilaterals.

If students are having trouble remembering the formula for the perimeter of a square and the formula of the perimeter of a rectangle,

then have students create formula cards on note cards including examples of how to use the formula correctly.

If You Have More Time

Have students work in pairs to create a stack of 16 index cards with numbers 2 to 9 each written on cards. Have students draw two cards from the deck. The first card represents the length and the second card represents the width. The students work together to find the perimeter of a rectangle with the given dimensions. Have the students draw from the deck at least five different times and record their work.

Area of Rectangles and Squares

Worksheet 1

Name _____

Area of Rectangles and Squares

Maria's flower garden is in the shape of rectangle that measures 6 feet long and 4 feet wide. What is the area of the garden?

Find a formula for area of a rectangle by answering 1 to 6.

1. The rectangle at the right is a model of the garden. How many squares are in the model? **24**

2. What is the area of the garden? **24** square feet

3. What is the length of the garden? **6** feet

4. What is the width of the garden? **4** feet

5. What could you multiply to find the area of the garden? **6 × 4**

6. Find the area of each rectangle by counting squares. Write the area in the table below. Complete the table.

Rectangle A — 7 cm, 4 cm
Rectangle B — 6 in., 3 in.

Rectangle	Area	Length	Width	Product
Maria's garden	24	6	4	6 × 4
A	28	7	4	7 × **4**
B	18	6	3	**6** × **3**
Any	Any	ℓ	w	$\ell \times$ **w**

Intervention Lesson I46 **181**

Worksheet 2

Name _____

Area of Rectangles and Squares (continued)

The formula for the area of a rectangle is $A = \ell \times w$ or $A = \ell w$.

7. **Reasoning** Use the formula to find the area of a rectangle that is 8 meters long and 5 meters wide.

$A = \quad \ell \quad \times \quad w$

$A = (\underline{8}) \times (\underline{5}) = \underline{40}$ square meters

A square is a type of rectangle where all of the side lengths are equal.

Find a formula for the area of the square shown by answering 8 and 9.

8. Use the formula $A = \ell w$ to find the area of the square.

$\underline{8} \times \underline{8} = \underline{64}$ mm² — 8 mm

9. If s equals the length of a side of a square, how could you find the area of any square? $A = \quad s \times s$

Find the area of each figure.

10. 7 in., 7 in., 7 in., 7 in.
49 in.²

11. 5 cm, 3 cm
15 cm²

12. 2 km, 14 km
28 km²

Find the area of the rectangle with the given dimensions.

13. $\ell = 15$ mm, $w = 4$ mm
60 mm²

14. $\ell = 3$ cm, $w = 10$ cm
30 cm²

15. **Reasoning** The area of a square is 81 square feet. What is the length of each side? **9 ft**

16. **Reasoning** Using only whole numbers, what are all the possible dimensions of a rectangle with an area of 12 square centimeters?
1 cm by 12 cm; 2 cm by 6 cm; 3 cm by 4 cm

182 Intervention Lesson I46

Teacher Notes

Ongoing Assessment

Ask: **When finding the area of a square, why do you only need to know the length of one side?** Because all of the sides of a square have the same length.

Error Intervention

If students do not know the properties of squares and rectangles,

then use I7: Quadrilaterals.

If students are having trouble remembering the formula for the area of a square and the formula of the area of a rectangle,

then have students create formula cards on note cards including examples of how to use the formula correctly. Add these note cards to cards made for the formulas for perimeter of rectangles and squares

If You Have More Time

Give each student one index card. On the card have students write a number from 2 to 50. This number represents a dimension of a rectangle or square. First have students use their value to find the area of square with that side length. Students should record this area. Next have each student pair up with another student to find the area of a rectangle given the dimensions on the cards. Have students pair up with other students to find the areas of five different rectangles. Students should record the dimensions and the area of each rectangle. Have students share their results.

Area of Irregular Figures

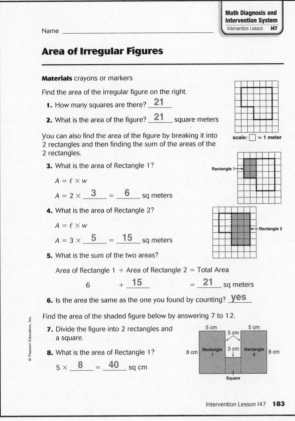

Name _____

Area of Irregular Figures

Materials crayons or markers

Find the area of the irregular figure on the right.

1. How many squares are there? __21__

2. What is the area of the figure? __21__ square meters

You can also find the area of the figure by breaking it into 2 rectangles and then finding the sum of the areas of the 2 rectangles.

3. What is the area of Rectangle 1?

$A = \ell \times w$

$A = 2 \times \underline{3} = \underline{6}$ sq meters

4. What is the area of Rectangle 2?

$A = \ell \times w$

$A = 3 \times \underline{5} = \underline{15}$ sq meters

scale: ☐ = 1 meter

Rectangle 1 →

← Rectangle 2

5. What is the sum of the two areas?

Area of Rectangle 1 + Area of Rectangle 2 = Total Area

6 + __15__ = __21__ sq meters

6. Is the area the same as the one you found by counting? __yes__

Find the area of the shaded figure below by answering 7 to 12.

7. Divide the figure into 2 rectangles and a square.

8. What is the area of Rectangle 1?

$5 \times \underline{8} = \underline{40}$ sq cm

5 cm   5 cm   5 cm
        5 cm
8 cm Rectangle 3 cm Rectangle 8 cm
         1   2
              Square

© Pearson Education, Inc.

Intervention Lesson I47   **183**

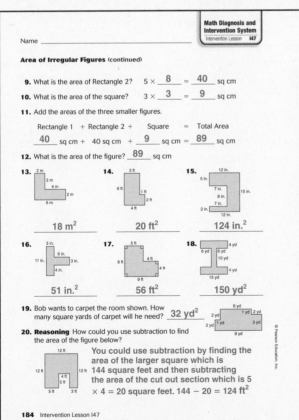

Name _____

Area of Irregular Figures (continued)

9. What is the area of Rectangle 2? $5 \times \underline{8} = \underline{40}$ sq cm

10. What is the area of the square? $3 \times \underline{3} = \underline{9}$ sq cm

11. Add the areas of the three smaller figures.

Rectangle 1 + Rectangle 2 + Square = Total Area

__40__ sq cm + 40 sq cm + __9__ sq cm = __89__ sq cm

12. What is the area of the figure? __89__ sq cm

13.   14.   15.

2 m   3 ft   12 in.
  3 m   5 in.
    4 m   6 ft   1 ft   7 in.
      2 m   8 in.   15 in.
  6 m   4 ft   7 in.
                              2 in.
                                 12 in.

__18 m²__   __20 ft²__   __124 in.²__

16.   17.   18.

3 in.   5 ft   4 yd
  6 in.   6 yd 6 yd
11 in.   3 in.   8 ft   4 ft   10 yd
  4 in.   4 yd
              9 ft   15 yd

__51 in.²__   __56 ft²__   __150 yd²__

19. Bob wants to carpet the room shown. How many square yards of carpet will he need? __32 yd²__

            6 yd
        2 yd   1 yd 2 yd
   2 yd 1 yd   3 yd
   2 yd
           9 yd

20. **Reasoning** How could you use subtraction to find the area of the figure below?

12 ft
12 ft   12 ft
      4 ft
  5 ft   3 ft

You could use subtraction by finding the area of the larger square which is 144 square feet and then subtracting the area of the cut out section which is 5 × 4 = 20 square feet. 144 − 20 = 124 ft²

© Pearson Education, Inc.

© Pearson Education, Inc.

184 Intervention Lesson I47

Teacher Notes

Ongoing Assessment

Ask: *A rectangle and a square make up an irregular figure. If the area of the figure is 15 square inches and the area of the square is 9 square inches, what is the area of the rectangle?* 6 square inches

Error Intervention

If students are having problems finding areas of rectangles and squares

then use I46: Area of Rectangles and Squares.

If students are not finding the area of all the parts of the irregular figure,

then have students redraw the figure on grid paper and count the squares that make up the irregular figure.

If You Have More Time

Give each student a piece of drawing paper. Have students draw an irregular figure on the paper and give the dimensions of the figure. No diagonals are allowed. Have students exchange papers with a partner and find the area of their partner's irregular figure.

Rectangles with the Same Area or Perimeter

Name _____

Rectangles with the Same Area or Perimeter

Materials colored pencils or crayons.

Ms. Arellano's class is making a sand box shaped like a rectangle for the kindergarten class. They have 16 feet of wood to put around the sand box. What length and width should the sand box be so it has the greatest area?

Each of the rectangles in the grid at the right has a perimeter of 16 feet. Find which rectangle has the greatest area by answering 1 to 3.

1. Complete the table. The formula for area of a rectangle is $A = \ell \times w$.

Rectangle	Length	Width	Area (square units)
W	7	1	7
X	2	6	12
Y	3	5	15
Z	4	4	16

2. What are the length and width of the rectangle with the greatest area?   **4 ft by 4 ft**

3. What length and width should Ms. Arellano's class use for the sand box?   **4 ft by 4 ft**

4. **Reasoning** Tracy told Tomas that if a two rectangles have the same perimeter, they have the same area. Is Tracy correct? Explain your reasoning.

   Tracy is not correct. All of the rectangles in the grid above have the same perimeter, but none have the same area.

Mr. Katz has 30 carpet squares to make a reading area in his classroom. Each square is one foot on a side. He wants to make the area in the shape of a rectangle with the least possible border. How should he arrange the carpet squares?

Intervention Lesson I48   **185**

Name _____

Rectangles with the Same Area or Perimeter (continued)

Each of the rectangles on the grid at the right has an area of 30 square feet. Find which one has the least perimeter by answering 5 to 8.

Rectangle 1
Rectangle 2

5. What is the perimeter of Rectangle 1?

   $P = 2\ell + 2w = 2(\underline{6}) + 2(5)$

   $= \underline{12} + \underline{10} = \underline{22}$ feet

6. What is the perimeter of Rectangle 2?

   $P = 2\ell + 2w = 2(\underline{10}) + 2(3) = \underline{20} + \underline{6} = \underline{26}$ feet

7. What is the length and width of the rectangle with the least perimeter?   **5 ft by 6 ft**

8. How should Mr. Katz arrange the carpet squares?   **in a 5 by 6 array**

Draw a rectangle with the same area as the one shown. **Answers may vary.** Then find the perimeter of each.   **Possible answers are given.**

9.   P = 12 in.
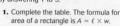
2 in.
4 in.

10.   P = 18 cm
3 cm
6 cm

11.   P = 22 m
4 m
7 m

 8 in. by 1 in.;
$P = 18$ in.

 9 cm by 2 cm;
$P = 22$ cm

 14 m by 2 m;
$P = 32$ m

12. **Reasoning** Marco has 36 feet of fencing, what is the greatest area that he can can fence?   **81 ft^2**

186   Intervention Lesson I48

Teacher Notes

Ongoing Assessment

Ask: *Can two or more rectangles or squares have the same area but have different perimeters?* Yes *Can they have the same perimeter but different areas?* Yes

Error Intervention

If students are having trouble finding the perimeter of a rectangle or square,

then use I43: Perimeter and I45: More Perimeter.

If the students are having trouble finding the area of a rectangle or square,

then use I44: Finding Area on a Grid and I46: Area of Rectangles and Squares.

If You Have More Time

Put students in groups of three or four. Each group needs to chose a person to record the data. Give each group a value for an area such as 36, 72, 64, 81, and 100. Then, give each group enough colored tiles to equal the value they are assigned. Each group needs to create as many different rectangles with that area as possible and find the perimeter of each rectangle. The recorder records the dimensions of each rectangle and the perimeter. Have the groups share their results with the class. Repeat with assigned perimeters, if time allows.

Area of Parallelograms

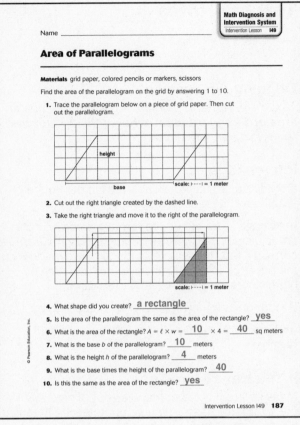

Name _____

Math Diagnosis and Intervention System
Intervention Lesson I49

Area of Parallelograms

Materials grid paper, colored pencils or markers, scissors

Find the area of the parallelogram on the grid by answering 1 to 10.

1. Trace the parallelogram below on a piece of grid paper. Then cut out the parallelogram.

height

base   scale: ⊢---⊣ = 1 meter

2. Cut out the right triangle created by the dashed line.

3. Take the right triangle and move it to the right of the parallelogram.

scale: ⊢---⊣ = 1 meter

4. What shape did you create? __a rectangle__

5. Is the area of the parallelogram the same as the area of the rectangle? __yes__

6. What is the area of the rectangle? $A = \ell \times w = $ __10__ $\times 4 = $ __40__ sq meters

7. What is the base b of the parallelogram? __10__ meters

8. What is the height h of the parallelogram? __4__ meters

9. What is the base times the height of the parallelogram? __40__

10. Is this the same as the area of the rectangle? __yes__

© Pearson Education, Inc.

Intervention Lesson I49   **187**

Name _____

Math Diagnosis and Intervention System
Intervention Lesson I49

Area of Parallelograms (continued)

The formula for the area of a parallelogram is $A = bh$.

11. Use the formula to find the area of a parallelogram with a base of 9 ft and a height of 6 feet.

$A = \quad b \quad \times \quad h$

$A = ($ __9__ $) \times ($ __6__ $) = $ __54__ square feet

Find the area of each figure.

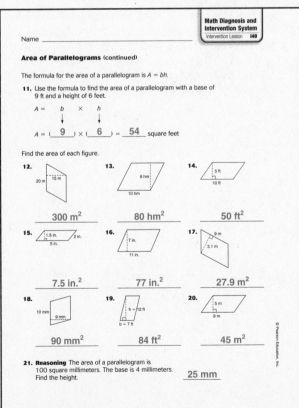

12. 20 m, 15 m

__300 m²__

13. 8 hm, 10 hm

__80 hm²__

14. 5 ft, 10 ft

__50 ft²__

15. 1.5 in., 2 in., 5 in.

__7.5 in.²__

16. 7 in., 11 in.

__77 in.²__

17. 9 m, 3.1 m

__27.9 m²__

18. 10 mm, 9 mm

__90 mm²__

19. $h = 12$ ft, $b = 7$ ft

__84 ft²__

20. 5 m, 9 m

__45 m²__

21. Reasoning The area of a parallelogram is 100 square millimeters. The base is 4 millimeters. Find the height.

__25 mm__

© Pearson Education, Inc.

188   Intervention Lesson I49

Teacher Notes

Ongoing Assessment

Ask: *How is the formula for the area of a parallelogram similar to the formula for the area of a rectangle? How is it different?*
Sample answer: To find the area of a rectangle or a parallelogram you multiply two dimensions. In a rectangle you multiply the length by the width, but in a parallelogram you multiply the base by the height.

Error Intervention

If students do not know the properties of parallelograms,

then use I7: Quadrilaterals.

If students are having trouble remembering the formula for the area of a parallelogram,

then have students create formula cards on note cards including examples of how to use the formula correctly. Add these note cards to cards made for the formulas for perimeter and area of rectangles and squares

If You Have More Time

Give each student three index cards. Have them label card 1 Base, card 2 Height, and card 3 Area. Have students write a value for the base of a parallelogram on card 1, the height of a parallelogram on card 2, and area of that parallelogram on card 3. Collect all the cards and shuffle them. Have students draw 3 cards from the pile. They need to actively trade their cards in order to have a base, height, and area card with values that make the formula for the area of a parallelogram true. As soon as they have a matching set of cards, they need to sit down.

Area of Triangles

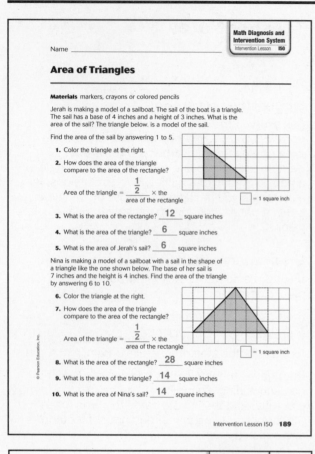

Name _____

Area of Triangles

Materials markers, crayons or colored pencils

Jerah is making a model of a sailboat. The sail of the boat is a triangle. The sail has a base of 4 inches and a height of 3 inches. What is the area of the sail? The triangle below. is a model of the sail.

Find the area of the sail by answering 1 to 5.

1. Color the triangle at the right.

2. How does the area of the triangle compare to the area of the rectangle?

Area of the triangle = $\frac{1}{2}$ × the area of the rectangle

☐ = 1 square inch

3. What is the area of the rectangle? __12__ square inches

4. What is the area of the triangle? __6__ square inches

5. What is the area of Jerah's sail? __6__ square inches

Nina is making a model of a sailboat with a sail in the shape of a triangle like the one shown below. The base of her sail is 7 inches and the height is 4 inches. Find the area of the triangle by answering 6 to 10.

6. Color the triangle at the right.

7. How does the area of the triangle compare to the area of the rectangle?

Area of the triangle = $\frac{1}{2}$ × the area of the rectangle

☐ = 1 square inch

8. What is the area of the rectangle? __28__ square inches

9. What is the area of the triangle? __14__ square inches

10. What is the area of Nina's sail? __14__ square inches

Intervention Lesson I50   **189**

Name _____

Area of Triangles (continued)

11. Complete the table.

Triangle	Base	Height	Area
Jerah's sail	4	3	6
Nina's sail	7	4	14
Any	b	h	$\frac{1}{2} \times b \times$ __h__

The formula for the area of a triangle is $A = \frac{1}{2} \times b \times h$ or $A = \frac{1}{2}bh$.

12. Reasoning Use the formula to find the area of Jerah's sail.

$A = \frac{1}{2} \times \quad b \quad \times \quad h$

$A = \frac{1}{2} \times$ __4__ $\times$ __3__ = __6__ square inches

13. Is the area the same as you found on the previous page? __yes__

Find the area of each figure.

14. 6 cm, 7 cm

__21 cm²__

15. 7 in., 16 in.

__56 in.²__

16. 9 yd, 15 yd, 12 yd

__54 yd²__

Find the area of the triangle with the measurements shown below. Give the correct units.

17. $b = 22$ yd
$h = 20$ yd

__220 yd²__

18. $b = 8$ mm
$h = 4$ mm

__16 mm²__

19. $b = 12$ cm
$h = 4$ cm

__24 cm²__

20. The front of a tent is in the shape of a triangle with a height of 6 feet and a base of 10 feet. What is the area of the front of the tent?

__30 ft²__

190   Intervention Lesson I50

Teacher Notes

Ongoing Assessment

Ask: *If the rectangle enclosing a triangle has an area of 14 square units, what is the area of the triangle?* 7 square units

Intervention

If students are having trouble remembering the formula for the area of a triangle,

then have students create formula cards on note cards including examples of how to use the formula correctly. Add these note cards to cards made for the previous formulas for perimeter and area of parallelograms, rectangles, and squares.

If students are having problems multiplying by $\frac{1}{2}$,

then use H45: Multiplying Fractions by Whole Numbers.

If You Have More Time

Make different sizes of triangles out of card stock or cardboard. Pass a triangle out to each student. Have students measure the base and the height of their triangle using a ruler. Have them write the formula for the area of a triangle on the triangle. Then using the formula and the dimensions of that triangle, have students work out the steps of the formula on their triangle to find the area. Display the triangles around the room.

Circumference

Name _____

Circumference

Materials Round objects, at least 3 for each group; tape measure or
ruler and string for each student.

Circumference (*C*) is the distance around a circle.

1. Complete the table for 3 different round objects.

**Answers will vary but last column should be close
to 3.14.**

Object	Circumference (*C*)	Diameter (*d*)	*C* ÷ *d*

The last column should be close to π, ≈ 3.14, every time.

If *C* ÷ *d* = π, then *C* = π*d*.

2. What is the relationship between the diameter (*d*)
and radius (*r*) of any circle? $d = \underline{2r}$

3. If *C* = π*d* and *d* = 2*r*, what is a formula for
the circumference using the radius (*r*)? $C = 2\pi \underline{r}$

Use a formula to find the circumference of each circle to the nearest
whole number.

4.

(10 in.)

$C = 2 \quad \pi \quad r$
       ↓   ↓

$C \approx 2 \times 3.14 \times \underline{10}$

$C \approx \underline{63}$ inches

5.

(9 in.)

$C = \quad \pi \quad d$
     ↓   ↓

$C \approx \underline{3.14} \times \underline{9}$

$C \approx \underline{28}$ inches

Name _____

Circumference (continued)

Find the circumference of each circle to the nearest whole number.
Use 3.14 or $\frac{22}{7}$ for π.

6. (12 m)   **75 m**

7. (14 ft)   **88 ft**

8. (16 cm)   **50 cm**

9. (28 yd)   **88 yd**

10. (2 in.)   **6 in.**

11. (13 mm)   **82 mm**

12. (15 ft)   **47 ft**

13. (35 m)   **110 m**

14. (3.6 cm)   **11 cm**

15. (5.7 yd)   **18 yd**

16. (1½ in.)   **9 in.**

17. (9.7 ft)   **61 ft**

18. Miranda wants to sew lace around the outside of a pillow.
The pillow has a diameter of 35 centimeters. How much
lace does Miranda need?   **about 110 cm**

19. **Reasoning** Find the distance around the figure at the right.
Round your answer to the nearest whole number   **33 in.**

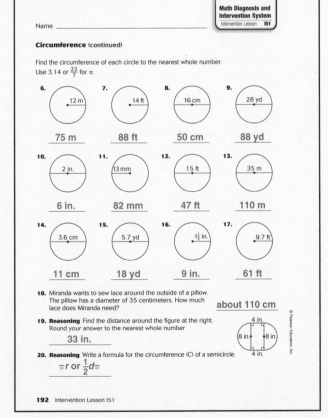

(figure: 4 in. / 8 in. 8 in. / 4 in.)

20. **Reasoning** Write a formula for the circumference (*C*) of a semicircle.
   πr or $\frac{1}{2}d\pi$

Teacher Notes

Ongoing Assessment
Ask: *What is the circumference divided by the
diameter of any circle?* pi

Error Intervention
If students have trouble using formulas,

then use F45: Formulas and Equations.

If students multiply decimals incorrectly,

then use H58: Multiplying with Decimals and
Whole Numbers and H62: Multiplying Decimals by
Decimals.

If You Have More Time
Have students measure the circumference and
diameter of a very large circle, like the cement
ring around a flag pole. Have them divide the
circumference by the diameter to see that the result
is close to pi.

Area of a Circle

Name _____

Math Diagnosis and Intervention System
Intervention Lesson   I52

Area of a Circle

Materials crayons, markers, or colored pencils, grid paper, compass

Sue places a water sprinkler in her yard. It sprays water 5 feet in every direction. What is the area of the lawn the sprinkler waters?

Find a formula for the area of a circle and find the area of the lawn by answering 1 to 8.

1. The sprinkler sprays in a circle. What is the radius of the circle? **5 ft**

Estimated areas may vary, but should be close to the sample answers given.

2. The grid at the right is a diagram of the sprinkler. Color all the whole squares within the circle one color. How many whole squares did you color?

 68 whole squares

3. Combine partial squares to estimate whole squares. Color the partial squares, using a different color. The partial squares make up about how many whole squares?

 12 whole squares

4. Add. What is a good estimate of the area of the circle? **80** units

5. Draw circles on grid paper with each radius listed in the table. Estimate the area and complete the table. Use 3.14 for π. Round πr^2 to the nearest whole number.

Estimated Area	Radius (r)	r^2	πr^2
80	5	25	**79**
26	3	**9**	28
106	6	**36**	113

6. Is the estimated area close to πr^2 each time? **yes**

Name _____

Math Diagnosis and Intervention System
Intervention Lesson   I52

Area of a Circle (continued)

The formula for the area of a circle is $A = \pi r^2$.

7. Use the formula to find the area of a circle with radius 5 feet by filling in the blanks at the right. Round to the nearest whole number.

8. What is the approximate area of lawn watered by the sprinkler? Include the correct units.

about **79 sq ft**

$A = \pi \qquad r^2$
$\qquad \downarrow \qquad \downarrow$
$A \approx 3.14 \times \underline{25}$
$A \approx \underline{79}$

Find the area of each circle to the nearest whole number.
Use either 3.14 or $\frac{22}{7}$ for π.

9. (28 yd)   **615 yd²**

10. (12 m)   **452 m²**

11. (16 cm)   **201 cm²**

12. (2 in.)   **3 in.²**

13. (14 ft)   **615 ft²**

14. (15 ft)   **177 ft²**

15. (13 mm)   **531 mm²**

16. (35 m)   **962 mm²**

17. A cement ring the shape of a circle surrounds a flag pole. The ring is 6 meters across. How much sod, to the nearest whole square meter, does it take to cover the area inside the ring? **28 m²**

18. Reasoning Chase used 3.14 for π and found the circumference of a circle to be 47.1 feet. Find the area of the circle to the nearest whole number. **177 ft²**

Teacher Notes

Ongoing Assessment

Ask: *If the radius of a circle is 7 centimeters, what units would you use for the area of the circle?* square centimeters *What units would you use for the circumference?* centimeters

Error Intervention

If students have trouble using formulas,

F45: Formulas and Equations.

If students do not know how to find r^2,

then use G62: Exponents.

If You Have More Time

Have students measure the diameter of various real circular-shaped objects. Then have them compute the area of each object.

© Pearson Education, Inc.

Surface Area of Rectangular Prisms

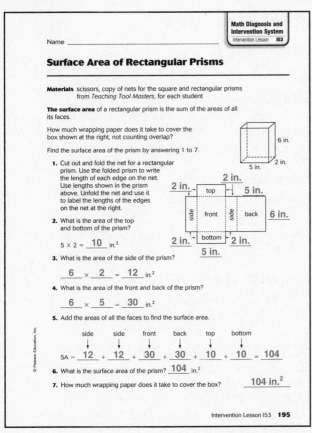

Name _____

Surface Area of Rectangular Prisms

Materials scissors, copy of nets for the square and rectangular prisms from *Teaching Tool Masters*, for each student

The surface area of a rectangular prism is the sum of the areas of all its faces.

How much wrapping paper does it take to cover the box shown at the right, not counting overlap?

Find the surface area of the prism by answering 1 to 7.

1. Cut out and fold the net for a rectangular prism. Use the folded prism to write the length of each edge on the net. Use lengths shown in the prism above. Unfold the net and use it to label the lengths of the edges on the net at the right.

2. What is the area of the top and bottom of the prism?

$5 \times 2 = \underline{10}$ in.²

3. What is the area of the side of the prism?

$\underline{6} \times \underline{2} = \underline{12}$ in.²

4. What is the area of the front and back of the prism?

$\underline{6} \times \underline{5} = \underline{30}$ in.²

5. Add the areas of all the faces to find the surface area.

	side	side	front	back	top	bottom
SA =	12	+ 12	+ 30	+ 30	+ 10	+ 10	= 104

6. What is the surface area of the prism? __104__ in.²

7. How much wrapping paper does it take to cover the box? __104 in.²__

© Pearson Education, Inc.

Intervention Lesson I53 **195**

Name _____

Surface Area of Rectangular Prisms (continued)

8. Cut out and fold the net for the square prism and use it to find the surface area of the prism at the right.

	side	side	front	back	top	bottom
SA =	6	+ 6	+ 6	+ 6	+ 4	+ 4	= 32 yd²

Find the surface area of each figure.

9. (3 in., 10 in., 4)
__164 in.²__

10. (9 ft, 2 ft, 3 ft)
__102 ft²__

11. (5 in., 4 in., 6 in.)
__148 in.²__

12. (7 cm, 4 cm, 4 cm)
__144 cm²__

13. (8 in., 3 in., 4 in.)
__136 in.²__

14. (15 m, 12 m, 5 m)
__630 m²__

15. What is the surface area of a rectangular prism that is 9 yards wide, 10 yards long, and 11 yards high?
__598 yd²__

16. How much wood does it take to make a storage box that is 4 feet square on the bottom and 3 feet high, with a lid? Do not count overlap.
__80 ft²__

17. **Reasoning** What is the surface area of the cube shown at the right? How could you find the surface area without using addition?
384 m²; Multiply 6 × 8 × 8. (8 m, 8 m, 8 m)

© Pearson Education, Inc.

196 Intervention Lesson I53

Teacher Notes

Ongoing Assessment

Ask: *What is the surface area of a prism?* The sum of the areas of all the faces of a prism is its surface area.

Error Intervention

If students have trouble relating the solid and its net,

then use I10: Solids and Nets.

If students do not know how to find the area of the faces,

then use I46: Area of Rectangles and Squares.

If You Have More Time

Give pairs of students a ruler and an empty cardboard box, such as a cereal or cracker box. Have them measure the dimensions and find how much cardboard it takes to make the box, not counting overlap. If students have difficulty, encourage them to take the box apart to form a net.

Surface Area

Math Diagnosis and Intervention System
Intervention Lesson I54

Name _____

Surface Area

Materials scissors, copy of nets for the cylinder, square pyramid, and triangular prism from *Teaching Tool Masters*, for each student

How much aluminum does it take to make a juice can, not counting overlap, if the diameter is 6 centimeters and the height is 12 centimeters?

$d = $ **6 cm**

$h = $ **12 cm**

$\ell = $ **18.85 cm**

Find the surface area of a cylinder by answering 1 to 8.

1. Cut out and fold the net for a cylinder. Use the folded cylinder to write the diameter and height of the can, on the net. Unfold the net and use it to label those dimensions on the net at the right.

In any prism or cylinder, the top and bottom are bases. The remaining area is called the **lateral surface area**.

2. The lateral surface area of a cylinder makes a rectangle in the net. The width of the rectangle is the height of the cylinder. What is the length of the rectangle in the cylinder? Fold the net to see.

The length of the rectangle = the **circumference** of the base.

3. Use the formula for the circumference of a circle to find the length of the rectangle. Write the length in the net above.

$C = \pi d \approx$ **3.14** $\times$ **6** $\approx$ **18.84 cm**

4. What is the lateral surface area of the cylinder, to the nearest whole number?

12 $\times 18.84 \approx$ **226 cm²**

5. What is the radius of the base of the cylinder? $r = $ **3**

6. What is the area of each base of the cylinder, to the nearest whole number?

$A = \pi r^2 \approx$ **3.14** $\times$ **9** $\approx$ **28 cm²**

7. What is the approximate surface area of the cylinder?

base   base   lateral SA

$SA \approx$ **28** + **28** + **226** $\approx$ **282** cm²

Intervention Lesson I54   **197**

Math Diagnosis and Intervention System
Intervention Lesson I54

Name _____

Surface Area (continued)

8. How much aluminum does it take to make a juice can?

282 cm²

How much canvas does it take to make the pup tent shown, not counting overlap? Answer 9 to 12 to find the surface area of the triangular prism.

9. Cut out and fold the net for a triangular prism. Use the folded prism to write the lengths on the net. Unfold the net and use it to label the lengths on the net at the right.

5 ft   4 ft   8 ft   6 ft

10. Find the area of each face and write the areas below.

front   back   bottom   side   side

$SA = $ **12** + 12 + **48** + **40** + 40

4 ft   6 ft   8 ft   5 ft   5 ft

11. What is the surface area of the triangular prism? **152** ft²

12. How much canvas does it take to make the tent? **152 ft²**

Answer 13 to 15 to find the surface area of the pyramid at the right.

13. Cut out and fold the net for a square pyramid to label the lengths on the net at the right.

10 m   12 m   12 m

14. Find the area of each face and write the areas below.

bottom   side   side   side   side

$SA = $ **144** + 60 + **60** + 60 + **60**

10 m   12 m

15. What is the surface area of the pyramid? **384 m²**

Find the surface area of each solid. Use 3.14 for π.

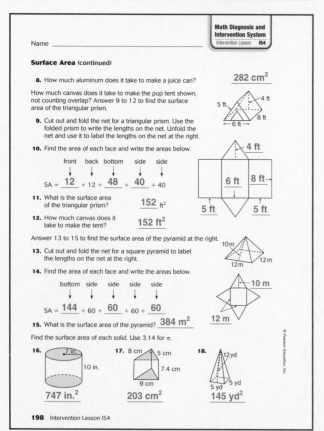

16. 7 in.   10 in.
747 in.²

17. 8 cm   5 cm   7.4 cm   9 cm
203 cm²

18. 12 yd   5 yd   5 yd
145 yd²

Teacher Notes

Ongoing Assessment

Ask: *How do you find the lateral surface area of a cylinder?* Multiply the circumference of the base times the height of the cylinder.

Error Intervention

If students do not know how to find the circumference or area of a circle,

then use I51: Circumference and I52: Area of a Circle.

If students do not know how to find the area of a triangle,

then use I50: Area of Triangles.

If You Have More Time

Give pairs of students a ruler and a can of soup or vegetables. Have them measure the dimensions of the can and find how much aluminum it takes to make the can, not counting overlap. If students have difficulty, encourage them to use paper to cover the can to create a net.

Counting Cubes to Find Volume

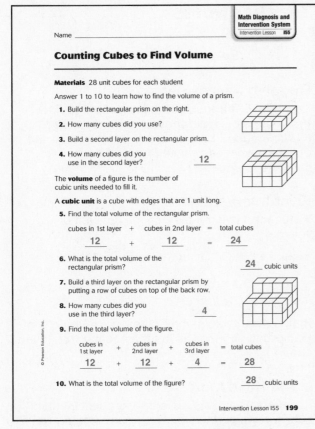

Name _____

Math Diagnosis and
Intervention System
Intervention Lesson I55

Counting Cubes to Find Volume

Materials 28 unit cubes for each student

Answer 1 to 10 to learn how to find the volume of a prism.

1. Build the rectangular prism on the right.

2. How many cubes did you use?

3. Build a second layer on the rectangular prism.

4. How many cubes did you use in the second layer?   **12**

The **volume** of a figure is the number of cubic units needed to fill it.

A **cubic unit** is a cube with edges that are 1 unit long.

5. Find the total volume of the rectangular prism.

   cubes in 1st layer + cubes in 2nd layer = total cubes
         12   +   **12**   =   **24**

6. What is the total volume of the rectangular prism?   **24** cubic units

7. Build a third layer on the rectangular prism by putting a row of cubes on top of the back row.

8. How many cubes did you use in the third layer?   **4**

9. Find the total volume of the figure.

   cubes in 1st layer + cubes in 2nd layer + cubes in 3rd layer = total cubes
        12   +   **12**   +   **4**   =   **28**

10. What is the total volume of the figure?   **28** cubic units

Intervention Lesson I55 **199**

Name _____

Math Diagnosis and
Intervention System
Intervention Lesson I55

Counting Cubes to Find Volume (continued)

Find the volume of each figure in cubic units.

11.   **18** cubic units

12.   **16** cubic units

13.   **18** cubic units

14.   **13** cubic units

15.   **26** cubic units

16.   **18** cubic units

17. **Reasoning** Yao made a rectangular prism with 3 layers of cubes. He put 4 cubes in each layer. What is the volume of the rectangular prism?   **12** cubic units

18. **Reasoning** Box A consists of 8 cubic units. Three of Box A completely fills Box B. What is the volume of Box B?

   A

   B   **24 cubic units**

200 Intervention Lesson I55

© Pearson Education, Inc.

Teacher Notes

Ongoing Assessment

Ask: *Courtney used 16 cubes to make a rectangular prism with 4 rows of 4 cubes each. Explain why you do not have to do any computations to find the volume of the rectangular prism.* Sample answer: If Courtney used 16 cubes then the volume will be 16 cubic units.

Error Intervention

If students have trouble counting the hidden cubes,

then encourage them to use unit cubes to build each solid.

If You Have More Time

Put students in pairs. Give each student 20 unit cubes. Have one student in each pair build a solid figure. Have the partner find the volume of the solid without tearing the solid apart.

Measuring Volume

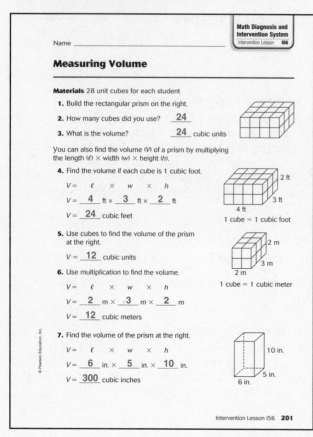

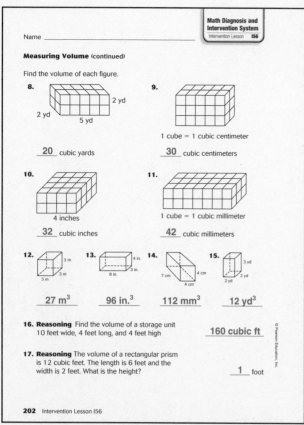

Teacher Notes

Ongoing Assessment

Ask: *Why is it important to know how to find the volume of a rectangular prism by using multiplication?* Sample answer: In the real world objects have measurements, not unit cubes to measure volume.

Error Intervention

If students have trouble with the concept of volume,

then use I55: Counting Cubes to Find Volume.

If students have trouble multiplying the numbers in the order of the formula,

then remind them of the Commutative Property of Multiplication, which allows them to multiply in any order.

If You Have More Time

Put students in pairs. Give each student 24 unit cubes. Have partners build as many rectangular prisms as they can find that have an area of 24. Have them write the multiplication expression for the volume of each. Possible prisms (in any variation):

24 × 1 × 1	6 × 2 × 2
12 × 2 × 1	4 × 3 × 2
8 × 3 × 1	
6 × 4 × 1	

Volume of Triangular Prisms and Cylinders

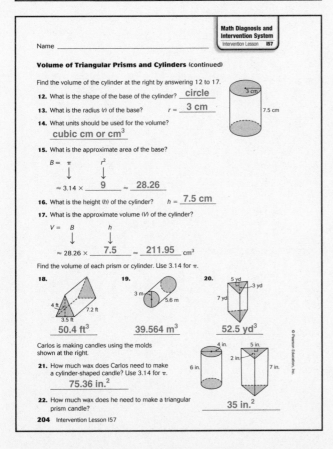

Teacher Notes

Ongoing Assessment

Ask: *How can you find the volume of any prism or cylinder?* Multiply the area of the base times the height.

Error Intervention

If students do not know how to find the area of a circle or triangle,

then use I52: Area of a Circle and I50: Area of Triangles.

If You Have More Time

Have students find the volume of real-world objects, like soft drink cans or pup tents.

Comparing Volume and Surface Area

Comparing Volume and Surface Area

Materials 24 unit cubes for each student

Kira's dad is making her a toy box in the shape of a rectangular prism. The volume of the toy box is 24 cubic feet. He wants to know how much outside area of the box he will need to paint.

The area which needs to be painted is the surface area of the box. Find the surface area of a rectangular prism with a volume of 24 cubic feet by answering 1 to 5.

1. Use 24 cubes to make a rectangular prism like the one shown at the right. If each cube represents a cubic foot, what is the volume of the prism? $24\ ft^3$

2. You can find the surface area of a figure by finding the sum of the areas of each face of the figure. Complete the first row of the table for the prism you made.

Length	Width	Height	Area of Front and Back	Area of Sides	Area of Top and Bottom	Surface Area
4	3	2	16	12	24	52
6	2	2	24	8	24	56

3. If Kira's dad makes the toy box 4 feet by 3 feet by 2 feet, how much outside area of the box will he need to paint?   52 ft²

4. Use the cubes to make a different rectangular prism with a volume of 24, a width of 2, and a height of 2. Use this prism to complete the second row of the table.

5. If Kira's dad makes the toy box 6 feet by 2 feet by 2 feet, how much outside area of the box will he need to paint?   56 ft²

The area Kira's dad needs to paint depends on the dimensions he uses.

6. **Reasoning** Why is the volume of the toy box given in cubic feet and the surface area given in square feet?
   Sample answer: Volume is a measure of how many cubes of a unit size can fit inside an object. Surface area is a measure of how many squares it would take to cover the outside of the object.

Intervention Lesson I58   **205**

Comparing Volume and Surface Area (continued)

Find the surface area and volume of each figure.

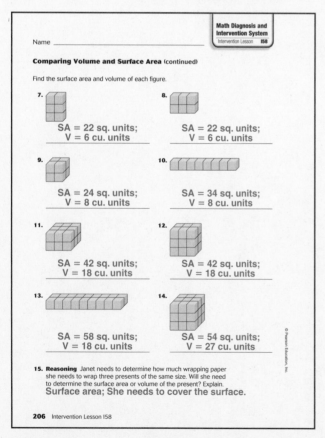

7.   SA = 22 sq. units;
     V = 6 cu. units

8.   SA = 22 sq. units;
     V = 6 cu. units

9.   SA = 24 sq. units;
     V = 8 cu. units

10. SA = 34 sq. units;
     V = 8 cu. units

11. SA = 42 sq. units;
     V = 18 cu. units

12. SA = 42 sq. units;
     V = 18 cu. units

13. SA = 58 sq. units;
     V = 18 cu. units

14. SA = 54 sq. units;
     V = 27 cu. units

15. **Reasoning** Janet needs to determine how much wrapping paper she needs to wrap three presents of the same size. Will she need to determine the surface area or volume of the present? Explain.
    Surface area; She needs to cover the surface.

Teacher Notes

Ongoing Assessment

Ask: *A cylinder has a radius of 5 meters and a height of 10 meters. What units would you use for the surface area?* square meters *For the volume?* cubic meters

Error Intervention

If students do not know how to find volume or surface area of rectangular prisms,

then use I54: Surface Area, I55: Counting Cubes to Find Volume, or I56: Measuring Volume.

If You Have More Time

Have students use unit cubes to find different rectangular prisms with a volume of 36 cubic units. Have them find which prism has the least surface area.

Recording Data from a Survey

Name _____

Math Diagnosis and Intervention System

Intervention Lesson I59

Recording Data from a Survey

Take a survey by asking, "What is your choice for a classroom mascot: a falcon, a cougar, a stingray, or a bear?" **All answers will vary.**

1. Write each student's answer in the box below.

Choice of Classroom Mascot

2. Make a tally mark for each choice given. Remember, tallies are made in groups of 5 so that they are easier to count.

Sample of 12 Tally Marks

卌 卌 ||

Choice of Classroom Mascot		
Mascot	**Tally**	**Total**
Falcon		
Cougar		
Stingray		
Bear		

3. Count the tally marks. Record the total for each mascot choice.

4. How many students answered the survey? _____

5. Which mascot was chosen the most? _____

6. Which mascot was chosen the least? _____

Intervention Lesson I59 **207**

Name _____

Recording Data from a Survey (continued)

Favorite Season of the Year					
Summer	Fall	Summer	Winter	Spring	Fall
Winter	Summer	Spring	Fall	Fall	Spring
Summer	Winter	Winter	Winter	Summer	Winter

7. Complete the tally chart for the data above.

Favorite Season of the Year		
Time of Year	**Tally**	**Total**
Spring	| | |	3
Summer	卌	5
Fall	| | | |	4
Winter	卌 |	6

8. What was the question for the survey?
What is your favorite season of the year?

9. How many people answered the survey? **18**

10. Which season was the favorite of the most people? **Winter**

11. Which season was the least favorite of the people? **Spring**

12. How many more people chose Summer over Spring? **2**

13. Reasoning Write the seasons in order from least favorite to most favorite.
Spring, Fall, Summer, Winter

14. Reasoning How many more people would have to have chosen Summer for it to be the most favorite season? **2**

208 Intervention Lesson I59

Teacher Notes

Ongoing Assessment

Ask: *What would the tally marks look like for 14?*

卌 卌 ||||

Error Intervention

If students have trouble with the concept of tally marks,

then use D72: Tallying Results.

If You Have More Time

Have students take a survey of their favorite season and make a tally chart of the data.

Reading and Making Pictographs

Name _____

Reading and Making Pictographs

The members of Tom's class voted for their favorite pizza toppings. The results are shown in the tally chart at the right. Answer 1 to 7 to help you make and use a pictograph of the data.

Favorite Pizza Toppings		
Toppings	**Tally**	**Number**
Sausage	IIII	4
Vegetables	III	3
Pepperoni	HHT HHT	10

1. In the first row of the chart below write a title that best describes the pictograph. Then list the three toppings in the first column.

Favorite Pizza Toppings	
Sausage	◯ ◯
Vegetables	◯ ◖
Pepperoni	◯ ◯ ◯ ◯ ◯

Each ◯ = 2 votes.   Each ◖ = __1__ vote.

2. Complete the pictograph key.

3. Decide how many symbols are needed for each topping. Since sausage got 4 votes, draw 2 circles next to sausage. Since vegetables got 3 votes, draw 1 circle and 1 half-circle next to vegetables.

4. How many symbols are needed for pepperoni?   __5__

5. Draw 5 circles for pepperoni. Make sure you line up the symbols.

6. Which topping got the greatest number of votes?   __pepperoni__

7. Reasoning How can you tell which topping got the greatest number of votes by looking at the pictograph?

The topping with the most number of circles got the greatest number of votes.

Intervention Lesson I60   **209**

Name _____

Reading and Making Pictographs (continued)

For Exercises 8 to 11, use the pictograph shown at the right.

Number of Fish in the Aquarium	
Silver Molly	◀🐟 ◀🐟 ◀🐟 ◀🐟
Black Neon Tetra	◀🐟 ◀🐟 ◀🐟 ◀🐟 ◀🐟
Angel Fish	◀🐟 ◀🐟

Key: Each ◀🐟 = 2 fish. Each ◀🐟 = 1 fish.

8. Which fish are there the most of in the aquarium?

__Black Neon Tetra__

9. How many Silver Molly fish are in the aquarium?   __7__

10. How many more Black Neon Tetra fish are there than Angel Fish?   __7__

11. Make a pictograph to display the data in the tally chart.

Favorite Drinks	
Fruit Juice	
Lemonade	
Milk	

Key: Each 🥤 stands for _____ votes.

Favorite Drinks		
Drinks	**Tally**	**Number**
Fruit Juice	HHT III	8
Lemonade	HHT HHT II	12
Milk	IIII	4

Sample answer: 2 votes

Use the pictograph you made in Exercise 11 to answer Exercises 12 to 15.

12. What does each 🥤 on the graph represent?   **Sample answer: 2 votes**

13. Which drink was chosen the least?   __milk__

14. How many more people chose lemonade over milk?   __8__

15. Reasoning Do any kinds of drinks on the pictograph have the same number of votes? How do you know?

No, the graph does not have the same number of symbols for any two kinds of drinks.

210   Intervention Lesson I60

Teacher Notes

Ongoing Assessment

Ask: *If sausage would have gotten 7 votes, instead of 4, how many circles would you have drawn?* 3 circles and 1 half-circle

Error Intervention

If students have trouble reading pictographs,

then use D70: Reading Picture Graphs.

If students have trouble collecting data and making pictographs,

then use D74: Data and Picture Graphs.

If You Have More Time

Have students take a survey of their favorite pizza toppings and make a pictograph of the data.

Reading and Making a Bar Graph

Reading and Making a Bar Graph

Materials colored pencils, markers, or crayons, grid paper.

Robert's class voted for their favorite country, not including the United States. The results are shown in the table.

Make and use a bar graph of the data by answering 1 to 6.

Our Favorite Countries	
Country	**Votes**
Canada	8
Great Britain	4
Japan	3
Mexico	11

1. Write a title above the graph. Label the axes: Country and Votes.

2. Complete the scale. Since the data go up to 11, make the scale by 2s.

3. Draw a bar for each country. Since Canada got 8 votes, color 4 squares above Canada, up to the 8 mark. For Japan, color one and a half squares because 3 is halfway between 2 and 4.

4. Which country got the least number of votes, that is, which has the shortest bar?

   Japan

5. Which country got the greatest number of votes, that is, which has the longest bar?

   Mexico

6. **Reasoning** Which bar is twice as long as the bar for Great Britain? What does that mean?

   Canada; Twice as many students voted for Canada as voted for Great Britain.

Our Favorite Countries bar graph — Votes (vertical axis, scale by 2s up to 12) vs. Country (horizontal axis): Canada 8, Great Britain 4, Japan 3, Mexico 11.

Reading and Making a Bar Graph (continued)

Use the grid on the right for Exercises 7 to 9.

7. Draw a graph of the data in the table.

Cities We Want to See	
City	**Votes**
Anaheim	5
Orlando	12
Chicago	2
Washington	7

8. Which city got the most votes?

   Orlando

9. Did twice as many students vote for Orlando as voted for Washington?

   no

Cities We Want to See bar graph — Votes (vertical axis) vs. City (horizontal axis): Anaheim 5, Orlando 12, Chicago 2, Washington 7.

Use the bar graph at the right to answer Exercises 10 to 12.

10. Which craft did most students say was their favorite?

    wood carving

11. How many students chose boot making as their favorite craft demonstration? ___ **8**

12. How many more students chose wood carving than chose chair-caning as their favorite crafts? ___ **12**

Favorite Crafts horizontal bar graph — Craft (vertical axis): Boot making, Chair-caning, Rug-hooking, Wood carving; Number of People (horizontal axis, marks at 4, 8, 12, 16).

Teacher Notes

Ongoing Assessment

If Great Britain had gotten 5 votes, instead of 4, how many grid squares would you color? $2\frac{1}{2}$

Error Intervention

If students do not draw a bar the correct height,

then have them use a ruler or the edge of a piece of paper to compare the height of the bar to the scale. Ask if the place the edge falls on the scale is the same as the number in the table.

If You Have More Time

Have students take a survey of the country or city they would most like to visit and graph the data on grid paper.

Making Line Plots

Making Line Plots

Name _____

Making Line Plots

A year is sometimes divided into
quarters, as show at the right.

1st quarter:	January to March
2nd quarter:	April to June
3rd quarter:	July to September
4th quarter:	October to December

1. Take a survey by asking, "Which
quarter of the year were you born?"
Write the number of the quarter
each person answers in the grid.

2. What are all of the possible
quarters that can be said?

   1st, 2nd, 3rd, 4th

Quarter of the Year You Were Born

Answer 3 to 7 to make and use a line
plot of the data.

3. Draw a line. Below the line,
list in order, all the possible
quarters that could be said. **Line plot data will vary.**

◄──┼──────┼──────┼──────┼──►
  1st   2nd   3rd   4th

Number of Birthdays by Quarter

4. Write "Number of Birthdays by Quarter" below the line plot.

5. For each quarter that was said, mark an X above that quarter
on the number line. If more than one X needs to be placed
above a quarter, stack them in a single column. **Answers will vary.**

6. Which quarter has the most number of birthdays? _____

7. How many birthdays are after the 2nd quarter? _____

Intervention Lesson I62 **213**

Name _____

Making Line Plots (continued)

The nature club leader took a survey
of the number of birdfeeders each
member had made during camp.
The results are shown in the table.

8. Make a line plot to show the data.

```
              X
              X
              X       X
      X       X       X
  X   X       X       X
  X   X   X   X   X
◄─┼───┼───┼───┼───┼─►
  3   4   5   6   7
```

**Number of Birdfeeders
Made During Camp**

Birdfeeders Made During Camp			
Member	Made	Member	Made
Ivan	4	Luther	5
Chloe	4	Marco	5
Stacey	3	Victoria	6
Victor	6	Chi	7
Tony	5	Wesley	5
Manny	6	Wendy	5

9. How many members made 4 birdfeeders? __2__

10. How many members made 2 birdfeeders? __0__

11. What was the most number of
birdfeeders made by a member? __7__

12. How many members made 5 or 6 birdfeeders? __8__

13. How many members made less than 6 birdfeeders? __8__

14. Did more members make more than
5 birdfeeders or less than 5 birdfeeders? **more than 5**

15. **Reasoning** By looking at the line plot, if one more person
attended camp, do you think that person would probably
make 4 birdfeeders or 5 birdfeeders? Explain.

   **Sample answer: The person would probably make
   5 birdfeeders, because the most number of people
   made 5 birdfeeders, and only two people made 4.**

214 Intervention Lesson I62

Teacher Notes

Ongoing Assessment

Ask: ***By looking at the line plot about the
birdfeeders, can you tell how many birdfeeders
Chloe made? Explain.*** No; a line plot does not
show the number each person made.

Error Intervention

If students have trouble reading a complete line
plot,

then have the students look at the title below the
line plot to see what the Xs represent.

If You Have More Time

Have students take a survey of the number of pets
each classmate has. Then make a line plot of the
data collected.

Interpreting Graphs

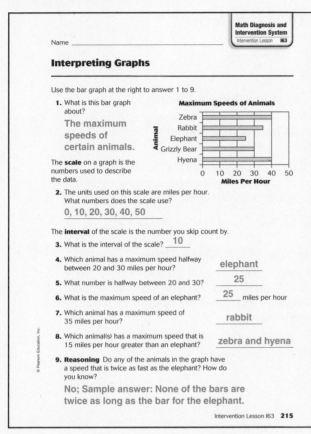

Teacher Notes

Ongoing Assessment

Ask: *How do you know that the hyena and zebra have the same maximum speed?* Both of the bars are the same length.

Error Intervention

If students have trouble reading a Bar Graph,

then use I61: Reading and Making a Bar Graph.

If You Have More Time

Have students copy the graph on Maximum Speeds of Animals, but have them include Black Mamba Snake 20 mph; Cat 30 mph; Lion 50 mph; and Cheetah 70 mph. Have them take turns asking their partners questions about their new bar graph

Reading and Making Line Graphs

Math Diagnosis and Intervention System

Intervention Lesson **I64**

Name _____

Reading and Making Line Graphs

During a blizzard, a scientist measured the amount of snowfall every 30 minutes. The measurements are shown in the table. Make and use a line graph of the data by answering 1 to 6.

Snowfall Measurements

Time	Inches
Snowfall Begins	0
30 min	1
1 h	2
1 h 30 min	4
2 h	7
2 h 30 min	9

1. Write a title above the graph. Label the axes: Time and Inches.

2. Complete the scale. Since the data go up to 9, make the scale by 2.

3. Plot a point for each time. When the snowfall began there were 0 inches on the ground, so put a point at 0 along the line above Snowfall Begins. For 30 min, put a dot halfway between the 0 and 2, because 1 is halfway between 0 and 2. Do this for each time.

4. Draw a line from each point to the next.

5. What was the total snowfall after it had snowed for 2 hours?

   7 inches

6. **Reasoning** How can you tell the total snowfall after it had snowed for 2 hours by only looking at the line graph?

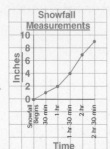

The point located above the 2 hour mark is at 7 inches.

In a line graph, when the line goes up from left to right, there is an **increase** in the data. When the line goes down, there is a **decrease**. The increase or decrease indicates the **trend.**

The trend in the snowfall graph is for the snowfall to increase over time.

Intervention Lesson I64 **217**

Teacher Notes

Ongoing Assessment

Ask: *What would the line graph look like if there was no trend in the data?* The line would be flat.

Error Intervention

If students have trouble placing points in the correct location on the line graph,

then use F30: Graphing Ordered Pairs.

If You Have More Time

Give students real-world line graphs (from newspaper, magazine, etc) and have them take turns asking questions about the graph with a partner.

Name _____

Reading and Making Line Graphs (continued)

Use the line graph to answer Exercises 7 to 10.

A cold front was expected to arrive sometime during the day.

Cold Front Arrrival

7. What is the trend in the data?

   Temperature decreased with time.

8. About what time does it appear that the cold front arrived?

   6 P.M.

9. Between what two times did the temperature decrease the most?

   6 P.M. and 7 P.M.

10. About how many degrees did it decrease? **20°F**

11. Make a line graph to display the data in the table.

Club Membership

Year	Members
2002	10
2004	15
2006	25
2008	40

Use the line graph you made in Exercise 11 for Exercises 12 and 13.

12. What was the trend?

   Membership increases over time.

13. **Reasoning** How can you tell if the number of members increased more between 2002 and 2004 or 2006 and 2008?

   The line between 2006 and 2008 goes up more sharply than the line between 2002 and 2004.

Stem-and-Leaf Plots

Name _____

Math Diagnosis and Intervention System
Intervention Lesson I65

Stem-and-Leaf Plots

The number of points earned on a history project, by each of nine students, are:

12, 27, 10, 18, 29, 12, 23, 12, 19

Answer 1 to 12, to make and use a stem-and-leaf plot of the data.

Points Earned

Stem	Leaves
1	0 2 2 2 8 9
2	3 7 9

1 | 8 = 18

Make the **stem** the first digit of each number.

1. What two stems are found in the data? _1 and 2_

2. Write the stems, 1 and 2, in order from least to greatest under the heading Stem.

3. List all the numbers that have 1 as a stem. _12, 10, 18, 12, 12, 19_

4. Write the numbers that have 1 as a stem in order from least to greatest. _10, 12, 12, 12, 18, 19_

5. List all the numbers that have 2 as a stem. _27, 29, 23_

6. Write the numbers that have 2 as a stem in order from least to greatest. _23, 27, 29_

Make the **leaf** the second digit of each number. The leaves are listed in order from least to greatest after each stem.

7. Since 10 is the least number with a stem of 1, write a 0 after the stem 1. Since 12 is next, write 2 after the 0. Write the remaining leaves after the stem 1.

8. Since 23 is the least number with a stem of 2, write a 3 after the stem 2. Put this directly below the 0. Put 7 below the first leaf of 2 for 27 and 9 below the second 2.

9. What is the mode of the points earned data? _12_

© Pearson Education, Inc.

Intervention Lesson I65 **219**

Name _____

Math Diagnosis and Intervention System
Intervention Lesson I65

Stem-and-Leaf Plots (continued)

10. What is the median of the points earned data? _18_

11. What is the range of the points earned data? _19_

12. What is the mean of the points earned data? _18_

For Exercises 13 to 17 make a stem-and-leaf plot and then answer the questions. For one-digit numbers, use a zero in the stem.

13. Organize the data below for the pounds of newspapers collected by the classes for recycling into a stem-and-leaf plot:
6, 18, 12, 13, 11, 12, 12

14. Find the mean of the data. _12_

15. Find the range of the data. _12_

Stem	Leaves
0	6
1	1 2 2 2 3 8

16. Find the median of the data. _12_

17. Find the mode(s) of the data. _12_

Use the stem-and-leaf plot on the right for Exercises 18 to 22.

Length in Miles

Stem	Leaves
2	2 4
3	5 5 8 8 9

18. What is the mode(s)? _35 and 38_

19. What is the median? _35_

20. What is the range? _17_

21. What is the mean? _33_

22. Reasoning How would the recycling stem-and-leaf plot from Exercise 13 change if the class that collected 6 pounds had collected 26 pounds?

Sample answer: There would not be a 0 stem with a 6 for the leaf, instead there would be a 2 stem with a 6 for the leaf. The 2 stem would be written below the 1 stem.

© Pearson Education, Inc.

220 Intervention Lesson I65

Teacher Notes

Ongoing Assessment

Ask: **Could you make a line plot of data like 142, 153, 147, 149, 158?** yes **What would be the stems?** 14 and 15 for 140 and 150

Error Intervention

If students omit or repeat pieces of data by mistake,

then encourage students to cross out the numbers as they are used so that they are not used twice.

If students have trouble finding mean,

then use I71: Finding the Mean.

If students have trouble finding median, mode, or range,

then use I72: Median, Mode, and Range.

If You Have More Time

Divide the class into 4 groups. Have the students in each group measure their heights, in inches or centimeters. Then, put one student from each group together to make a stem-and-leaf plot with their combined data.

Circle Graphs

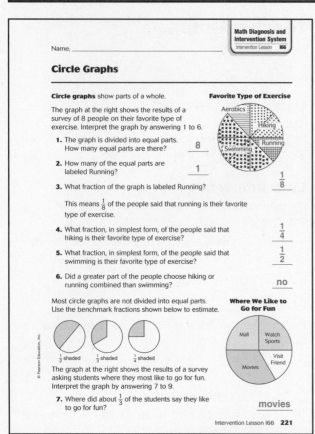

Circle Graphs

Circle graphs show parts of a whole.

The graph at the right shows the results of a survey of 8 people on their favorite type of exercise. Interpret the graph by answering 1 to 6.

Favorite Type of Exercise

Aerobics / Hiking / Running / Swimming

1. The graph is divided into equal parts. How many equal parts are there?   **8**

2. How many of the equal parts are labeled Running?   **1**

3. What fraction of the graph is labeled Running? $\frac{1}{8}$

   This means $\frac{1}{8}$ of the people said that running is their favorite type of exercise.

4. What fraction, in simplest form, of the people said that hiking is their favorite type of exercise? $\frac{1}{4}$

5. What fraction, in simplest form, of the people said that swimming is their favorite type of exercise? $\frac{1}{2}$

6. Did a greater part of the people choose hiking or running combined than swimming?   **no**

Most circle graphs are not divided into equal parts. Use the benchmark fractions shown below to estimate.

$\frac{1}{2}$ shaded $\frac{1}{3}$ shaded $\frac{1}{4}$ shaded

Where We Like to Go for Fun

Mall / Watch Sports / Visit Friend / Movies

The graph at the right shows the results of a survey asking students where they most like to go for fun. Interpret the graph by answering 7 to 9.

7. Where did about $\frac{1}{3}$ of the students say they like to go for fun?   **movies**

Intervention Lesson I66   **221**

Teacher Notes

Ongoing Assessment

Ask: *If a circle graph showing the results of a survey on favorite seasons is divided into 15 equal parts and 5 parts are labeled summer, what part of the people answered summer?* one third

Error Intervention

If students have trouble understanding fractional parts of a circle, estimating fractional parts, or finding equivalent fractions,

then use H2: Parts of a Region, H7: Using Models to Find Equivalent Fractions, H14: Equivalent Fractions, and H16: Estimating Fractional Amounts.

If You Have More Time

Provide students a circle graph from a newspaper, magazine or website. Have students interpret the circle graph by describing the fractional amounts of different parts of the graph.

Circle Graphs (continued)

8. About what fraction of the students said they like to watch sports?   about $\frac{1}{4}$

9. What two categories combined were chosen by about $\frac{1}{2}$ of the students?   **mall** and **watch sports**

Use the graph at the right for Exercises 10 to 13.

Animals in a Pet Show

guinea pigs 10 / dogs 10 / birds 5 / fish 5 / cats 10

10. How many pets are entered?   **40**

11. What fraction of the pets entering the pet show are cats? $\frac{1}{4}$

12. What fraction of the pets entered are *not* dogs nor guinea pigs? $\frac{1}{2}$

13. What fraction of pets entered have fur or feathers? $\frac{7}{8}$

Use the graph at the right for Exercises 14 to 17

Favorite Sports of 10-Year-Old Boys

soccer / baseball / football

14. About what fraction of the boys chose baseball? $\frac{1}{4}$

15. Almost half of the boys chose which sport?   **soccer**

16. Did more of the boys choose soccer or baseball and football combined?
    baseball and football combined

17. **Reasoning** Thirty boys were surveyed and 10 of them said the same sport. What fraction, in simplest form, of the boys said that sport? Which sport would it have to be, based on the graph? Explain your answers.
    $\frac{1}{3}$; football; $\frac{10}{30} = \frac{1}{3}$; Football takes up about $\frac{1}{3}$ of the graph.

18. **Reasoning** Three-tenths of a circle graph is shaded blue. How much of the circle graph is *not* shaded blue? $\frac{7}{10}$

222 Intervention Lesson I66

Making and Reading Circle Graphs

**Math Diagnosis and
Intervention System**
Intervention Lesson **I67**

Name _____

Making and Reading Circle Graphs

Materials colored pencils

A **circle graph** represents all of a set of data. Each part of the whole amount is shown by a wedge or sector of the circle.

Make a circle graph to show the data in the table by answering 1 to 13.

Favorite Type of Book	
Books	**Number of Students**
Adventure	3
Mystery	4
Biography	3
Poetry	2

1. How many students are represented by the data in the table?   **12**

2. Color 3 of the 12 sectors in the circle below red, to represent the number of students who chose Adventure books.

3. What fraction, in simplest form, of the graph is red? $\frac{1}{4}$

4. What percent of the graph is red?   **25%**

5. Write "Adventure" and the percent in the sector you colored red.

6. Color 4 sectors blue to represent the students who chose Mystery books. What fraction, in simplest form, of the graph is blue? $\frac{1}{3}$

7. Write "Mystery" and 33% in the sector you colored red.

8. Color 3 sectors yellow to represent the students who chose Biography books. What fraction, in simplest form, of the graph is yellow? $\frac{1}{4}$

9. What percent of the graph is yellow?   **25%**

10. Write "Biography" and the percent in the sector you colored yellow.

11. Color 2 sectors green to represent the students who chose Poetry books. What fraction, in simplest form, of the graph is green? $\frac{1}{6}$

12. Write "Poetry" and 17% in the sector you colored yellow.

13. Give your circle graph a title.

Favorite Type of Book

Mystery 33% Biography 25% Adventure 25% Poetry 17%

**Math Diagnosis and
Intervention System**
Intervention Lesson **I67**

Name _____

Making and Reading Circle Graphs (continued)

A survey had the results shown in the table. Use the table and the circle graph for Exercises 14 and 15.

14. Complete the table with fractions in simplest form and percent values.

Favorite Type of Music			
	Number of Responses	Fraction	Percent
Pop	10	$\frac{1}{2}$	50%
Classical	5	$\frac{1}{4}$	25%
Oldies	2	$\frac{1}{10}$	10%
Jazz	3	$\frac{3}{20}$	15%

Jazz Classical Oldies Pop

15. Color each section of the circle graph a different color and label each section with the correct category.

The graph at the right shows the results of a survey of 56 people on what they were wearing at a mall. Use the graph for Exercises 16 to 20.

Types of Clothing

Capris Pants Skirt Shorts

16. What percent of those surveyed were wearing capris?   **25%**

17. What percent of those surveyed were not wearing a skirt?   **75%**

18. About what fraction of those surveyed were wearing pants? $\frac{1}{3}$

19. How many people were wearing pants or shorts?   **28**

20. **Reasoning** About how many people were wearing shorts? Explain how to estimate.
    about 9 or 10; The sector for shorts is about $\frac{1}{6}$ or 17% of the graph and 17% of 56 is 9.52.

Teacher Notes

Ongoing Assessment

Ask: *What is the total of all the percentages in a circle graph?* 100%

Error Intervention

If students have trouble relating fractions and percents,

then use H78: Understanding Percent and H79: Relating Percents, Decimals, and Fractions.

If You Have More Time

Have students survey 12 people from the classroom by asking their favorite color. Have students make a circle graph of their findings by dividing a circle into 12 equal parts and shading each part to represent the results.

Histograms

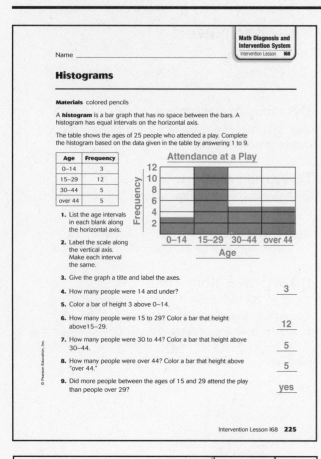

Name _____

Histograms

Materials colored pencils

A **histogram** is a bar graph that has no space between the bars. A histogram has equal intervals on the horizontal axis.

The table shows the ages of 25 people who attended a play. Complete the histogram based on the data given in the table by answering 1 to 9.

Age	Frequency
0–14	3
15–29	12
30–44	5
over 44	5

Attendance at a Play

1. List the age intervals in each blank along the horizontal axis.

2. Label the scale along the vertical axis. Make each interval the same.

3. Give the graph a title and label the axes.

4. How many people were 14 and under?   3

5. Color a bar of height 3 above 0–14.

6. How many people were 15 to 29? Color a bar that height above15–29.   12

7. How many people were 30 to 44? Color a bar that height above 30–44.   5

8. How many people were over 44? Color a bar that height above "over 44."   5

9. Did more people between the ages of 15 and 29 attend the play than people over 29?   yes

Intervention Lesson I68   **225**

Name _____

Histograms (continued)

The histogram shows the time, in minutes, that people who were surveyed spend driving to work. Use the graph for Exercises 10 to 13.

10. How many people were surveyed?
    100

11. How much time did 20% of the people surveyed spend driving to work?
    60–79 minutes

12. How much time did the most people spend driving to work?
    40–59 minutes

13. **Reasoning** Did twice as many of the people surveyed spend 40 to 59 minutes driving to work as spend 20 to 39 minutes? Explain how you can tell from the graph.
    Yes; the bar for 40–59 is twice as high as the bar for 20–39.

14. The table shows the results of a survey on the age of people visiting a restaurant. Use the data to complete the histogram.

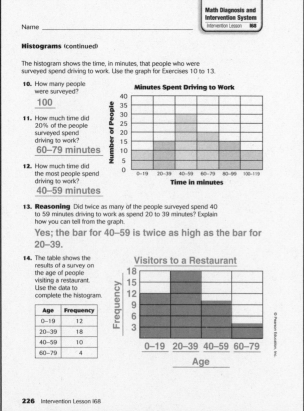

Age	Frequency
0–19	12
20–39	18
40–59	10
60–79	4

226   Intervention Lesson I68

Teacher Notes

Ongoing Assessment

Ask: *How is a histogram different from a bar graph?* The bars on a histogram do not have any space between them. The bars on a bar graph have space between them. The horizontal axis on a histogram has equal intervals with no numbers left out between intervals. A bar graph usually has categories on the horizontal axis rather than intervals.

Error Intervention

If students have trouble deciding on a scale for the vertical axis,

then have students divide the highest number in the frequency column by the number of labels they wish to have on the vertical axis; usually 3, 4, 5 or 6.

If You Have More Time

Have students ask the other students in their class the number of miles that they live from the school. Provide students with a template to draw a histogram for the data they collect. The horizontal axis is the number of miles and the vertical axis is the number of students.

Choosing Appropriate Graphs

Name _____

Choosing Appropriate Graphs

Some graphs are more appropriate to display certain types of data than other graphs.

A **line graph** shows changes over time.

A **line plot** compares data by showing clusters of information.

A **pictograph** best shows data that is multiples of a number.

A **bar graph** shows countable data and makes comparisons.

The following data lists the number of questions answered correctly on a quiz taken by 20 students.

4 7 5 9 6 4 2 8 7 6 10 5 8 6 4 3 10 8 6 6

Determine the most appropriate graph to display the data by answering 1 to 11.

1. Can a change in the quiz scores over time be determined by the data? — **no**

2. Is a line graph appropriate to display the data? — **no**

3. Are the data easily divided by a common number? — **no**

4. Is a pictograph appropriate to display the data? — **no**

5. Are there some numbers in the list that appear multiple times so that there are clusters of data? — **yes**

6. Is a line plot appropriate to display the data? — **yes**

7. Can you count the number of times each number appears in the list? — **yes**

8. Is a bar graph appropriate to display the data? — **yes**

9. What two types of graphs would be most appropriate to display the data? **line plot and bar graph**

10. How many different numbers appear in the list? — **9**

Intervention Lesson I69   **227**

Name _____

Math Diagnosis and Intervention System

Intervention Lesson **I69**

Choosing Appropriate Graphs (continued)

11. Reasoning If a bar graph is used to display the data, there would be 9 different bars. How could you avoid having so many bars in a bar graph that displays the data?

Each bar could represent a range of numbers.

Tell what type of graph would be most appropriate to represent the data and why.

12. Every hour a lifeguard checks the level of water in the swimming pool as a new pool is being filled.

line graph; shows change over time

13. The teacher wants to show what percent of the students own each type of pet.

circle graph; comparing parts to a whole

14. Marie has collected the following data. What would be the best way for her to display the data?

The number of questions answered correctly on a quiz.

4 5 8 3 4 5 6 9 4 6 9 8 7 3 2 8 7 8

A line plot would be best to show clusters of scores.

Tell what type of graph you would choose to represent the data.

15.

Life Expectancy of Animals	
Animal	Years
Bull Frog	16
Kangaroo	9
Lion	35
Sheep	15
Tiger	22

A bar graph would be the best because it would allow comparisons. A bar graph is better than a pictograph because the data do not show multiples of a number.

16. Reasoning The table shows the number of points made in a basketball game by individual players. Is a bar graph a good way to show the data? Explain.

Player	Points
Devin	8
Seth	12
Immanuel	10
Ricardo	18

Yes; it would show the baskets made by each person and would be a way to compare people.

228   Intervention Lesson I69

Teacher Notes

Ongoing Assessment

Ask: *What is the difference between a line graph and a line plot?* A line graph plots points on something similar to a coordinate axis and connects the points. It shows changes over time. A line plot shows the number of times that a category is selected in a survey. It shows clusters of information.

Error Intervention

If students need to review the different types of graphs,

then use I64: Reading and Making Line Graphs, I62: Making Line Plots, I60: Reading and Making Pictographs, and I61: Reading and Making a Bar Graph.

If You Have More Time

Have students find a graph in the newspaper, a magazine or on the internet. Have students discuss why that particular type of graph was chosen to represent the data and why it is or is not appropriate.

Double Bar Graphs

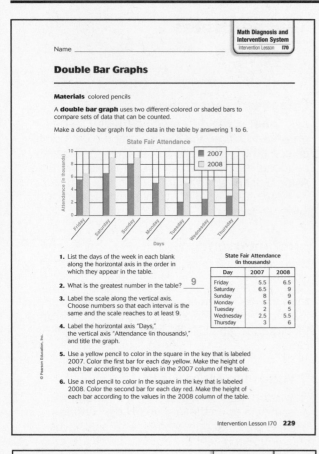

Name _____

Math Diagnosis and Intervention System
Intervention Lesson · I70

Double Bar Graphs

Materials colored pencils

A **double bar graph** uses two different-colored or shaded bars to compare sets of data that can be counted.

Make a double bar graph for the data in the table by answering 1 to 6.

1. List the days of the week in each blank along the horizontal axis in the order in which they appear in the table.

2. What is the greatest number in the table? ___9___

3. Label the scale along the vertical axis. Choose numbers so that each interval is the same and the scale reaches to at least 9.

4. Label the horizontal axis "Days," the vertical axis "Attendance (in thousands)," and title the graph.

5. Use a yellow pencil to color in the square in the key that is labeled 2007. Color the first bar for each day yellow. Make the height of each bar according to the values in the 2007 column of the table.

6. Use a red pencil to color in the square in the key that is labeled 2008. Color the second bar for each day red. Make the height of each bar according to the values in the 2008 column of the table.

State Fair Attendance (in thousands)

Day	2007	2008
Friday	5.5	6.5
Saturday	6.5	9
Sunday	8	9
Monday	5	6
Tuesday	5	2
Wednesday	2.5	5.5
Thursday	3	6

© Pearson Education, Inc.

Intervention Lesson I70   **229**

Name _____

Math Diagnosis and Intervention System
Intervention Lesson · I70

Double Bar Graphs (continued)

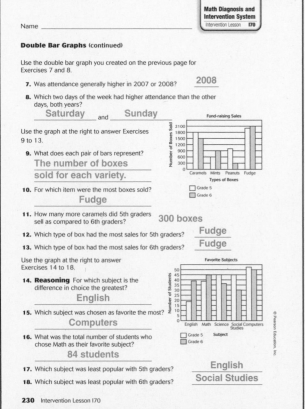

Use the double bar graph you created on the previous page for Exercises 7 and 8.

7. Was attendance generally higher in 2007 or 2008?   **2008**

8. Which two days of the week had higher attendance than the other days, both years?
   Saturday and **Sunday**

Use the graph at the right to answer Exercises 9 to 13.

9. What does each pair of bars represent?
   The number of boxes sold for each variety.

10. For which item were the most boxes sold?
    Fudge

11. How many more caramels did 5th graders sell as compared to 6th graders?   **300 boxes**

12. Which type of box had the most sales for 5th graders?   **Fudge**

13. Which type of box had the most sales for 6th graders?   **Fudge**

Use the graph at the right to answer Exercises 14 to 18.

14. **Reasoning** For which subject is the difference in choice the greatest?
    English

15. Which subject was chosen as favorite the most?
    Computers

16. What was the total number of students who chose Math as their favorite subject?
    84 students

17. Which subject was least popular with 5th graders?   **English**

18. Which subject was least popular with 6th graders?   **Social Studies**

230   Intervention Lesson I70

Teacher Notes

Ongoing Assessment

Ask: *When is a double bar graph preferred over a bar graph to display data?* When the data is divided into two categories and it is necessary to compare the two categories.

Error Intervention

If students have trouble drawing the bars on the graph,

then use I61: Reading and Making a Bar Graph.

If You Have More Time

Have students make a double bar graph similar to the one titled "Favorite Subjects" in the exercises. The entire class can collect the data and make a table for it on the board. One bar can represent boys and the other can represent girls.

© Pearson Education, Inc.

Finding the Mean

Name _____

Math Diagnosis and Intervention System
Intervention Lesson I71

Finding the Mean

Materials color tiles: 5 red, 12 blue, and 7 yellow for each student or group

The **mean,** or average, is the sum of all the numbers in a set of data divided by the total number of data.

Carlos made 5 baskets in his first basketball game of the season, 12 baskets in the second game, and 7 in the third game. What is the mean number of baskets that Carlos made during the first three games?

Find the mean by answering 1 to 3.

1. Use tiles to represent the number of baskets that Carlos made. Make one stack of 5 red tiles to represent the baskets in the first game, one stack of 12 blue tiles to represent the baskets in the second game and one stack of 7 yellow tiles to represent baskets in the third game.

2. Move tiles from one stack to another until there are three stacks of equal height.

3. How many tiles are in each stack? **8**
This number represents the average number of baskets in each game or the mean.

Find the mean without using tiles by answering 4 to 6.

4. What is the total number of baskets that Carlos made in all three games? $5 + 12 + 7 =$ __**24**__

5. If 24 tiles are divided between three stacks, how many tiles are in each stack? $24 \div 3 =$ __**8**__

6. Because there were 3 games, the total number of baskets was divided by 3. This is the mean. Is this number the same as the mean found when using the tiles? **yes**

7. Reasoning Carlos scored no points in the fourth game of the season. What effect does that have on the mean?

The mean would decrease. It would be 6 rather than 8.

© Pearson Education, Inc.

Intervention Lesson I71 **231**

Name _____

Math Diagnosis and Intervention System
Intervention Lesson I71

Finding the Mean (continued)

Find the mean for each data set.

8. $120, $280, $410, $300, $180
$258

9. 175 ft, 136 ft, 157 ft, 112 ft
145 ft

10. 23 in., 37 in., 67 in., 93 in., 25 in.
49 in.

11. 5,341 km, 6,780 km, 2,543 km
4,888 km

12. 89 weeks, 37 weeks, 27 weeks, 12 weeks, 86 weeks, 97 weeks
58 weeks

13. 3 runs, 5 runs, 8 runs, 4 runs, 10 runs, 5 runs, 4 runs, 1 run
5 runs

14. $991, $759, $610, $967, $733
$812

15. 36 lb, 53 lb, 25 lb, 14 lb
32 lb

16. 76 bulbs, 36 bulbs, 98 bulbs, 25 bulbs, 38 bulbs, 27 bulbs
50 bulbs

17. 1,664 books, 2,533 books, 1,267 books, 7,668 books
3,283 books

18. $67, $44, $32, $86, $12, $11
$42

19. 379 points, 255 points, 116 points
250 points

20. $1,561; $2,689; $1,442; $3,522; $1,756
$2,194

21. 4 h, 1 h, 0 h, 5 h, 7 h, 0 h, 5 h, 2 h
3 h

22. Dale worked 7 days and made $350. What was the average amount he made each day? **$50 each day**

23. Reasoning Mrs. Hernandez's math class made the following scores on a quiz: 5, 7, 8, 7, 9, 10, 2, 2, 3. If 2 points are added to everybody's score, how is the mean affected?

The mean is raised by 2.

© Pearson Education, Inc.

Teacher Notes

Ongoing Assessment

Ask: *Is the mean always a whole number?* No, the mean can be a decimal or fraction as well as a whole number.

Error Intervention

If students have trouble dividing,

then use G54: Dividing Two-Digit Numbers, G55: Dividing Three-Digit Numbers, and G58: Dividing Greater Numbers.

If You Have More Time

Have students find the number of years each student in the class has lived in your city or town. Have students find the mean number of years for the class.

Median, Mode, and Range

Name _____

Median, Mode, and Range

Materials 40-50 color tiles; counters or other small object
placed in a clear container

How many items are in the container? Collect your classmates'
guesses and find the median, mode, and range of the data by
answering 1 to 7.

1. Ask 9 people in your class to guess the number of items
in the container. Write the 9 guesses in the blanks below.
These numbers are the data.

Answers will vary.

___ ___ ___ ___ ___ ___ ___ ___ ___

The **median** is the middle number when the data are listed in order.

2. List the data in order from least to greatest. If there are
some data that are the same, list those multiple times.

Answers will vary. Numbers should be least to greatest.

___ ___ ___ ___ ___ ___ ___ ___ ___

3. Circle the number that is in the middle of the list.
What is the median of your data?   **Check work.**

The **mode** is the data value that occurs most often. If there is
more than one number that appears the most often, it is possible
to have more than one mode. If each number appears only
once, then there is no mode.

4. How many modes are there for your data?   **Check work.**

5. What is the mode of your data?   **Check work.**

The **range** is the difference between the greatest and least data values.

6. What is the difference between the greatest
and the least data values?   **Check work.**

7. Count the number of items in the container.
Was the median, mode, or range closest to the
actual number of items?   **Check work.**

Intervention Lesson 172   **233**

Teacher Notes

Ongoing Assessment

Ask: *What is the median when there are an even
number of values in the data set?* The median is
the mean or average of the two middle data values.

Error Intervention

If students have trouble arranging the data values,

then have them use small pieces of paper and put
a data value on each piece. Have them arrange the
papers in ascending order and then manipulate the
papers to find the middle value.

If You Have More Time

Give students some measures of central tendency
and challenge them to find a set of data that has
the measures given.

Name _____

Median, Mode, and Range (continued)

Find the median, mode and range of each data set.

8. 2, 5, 1, 8, 8, 12, 6

median ___6___

mode(s) ___8___

range ___11___

9. 25, 60, 20, 45, 25

median ___25___

mode(s) ___25___

range ___40___

10. 54, 54, 60

median ___54___

mode(s) ___54___

range ___6___

11. 4, 1, 1, 8, 8, 12, 8

median ___8___

mode(s) ___8___

range ___11___

12. 35, 23, 15, 23, 24

median ___23___

mode(s) ___23___

range ___20___

13. 15, 11, 12, 18, 14, 11, 9, 14, 13

median ___13___

mode(s) ___11, 14___

range ___9___

14. If the number 8 were removed from the data in Exercise 11,
what two numbers would be in the middle of the data?   **4 and 8**

The average, or mean, of 4 and 8 is the median. What is the
median of the data after removing the number 8?   **6**

15. Reasoning If the number 100 is added to the data in Exercise 12,
how does that affect the mean, median, mode, and range?

The mean would be quite a bit higher. The median
and mode would be the same. The range would be
much larger.

16. Brandi's scores on math exams were as follows: 96, 96, 89, 84, 25.
Find the mean, median, and mode for Brandi's quiz scores.

The mean is 78, the median is 89, and the mode
is 96.

17. Reasoning Which of the measures that you found in Exercise 16
best represents a typical exam score for Brandi? Explain.

The median is more typical. The mode is too high
and the mean is too low.

234   Intervention Lesson 172

Sampling Methods

Name _____

Sampling Methods

Materials an alphabetical roster of students in the class—one for each student, scissors, small container

A **population** is an entire group of people or things about which information is sought. A **sample** is a part of the population. Many times a sample is used to represent a population when it is too difficult to study the entire population.

What is the percent of students in your class who like yogurt? Find different ways to answer this question by answering 1 to 8.

1. What is the population you wish to study? _____ my class

2. What are three examples of a sample of this population?
   Sample answer: My friends, students who sit in one row, the boys.

Convenience sampling uses any convenient method to form the sample. Many times convenience sampling is **biased** or not representative of the entire population.

3. Ask 5 of your classmates near you if they like yogurt. How many of the 5 like yogurt? _____ **Answers will vary.**

Systematic sampling uses a pattern to identify members of the sample.

4. Using the class roster, choose a name on the list. Make a mark next to this name and every third name after it until you have chosen 5 names. If you reach the bottom of the list before 5 names are chosen, start over at the top of the list. Ask these 5 people if they like yogurt. How many of the 5 like yogurt? _____ **Answers will vary.**

Random sampling is a method in which each member of the population has an equal chance of being chosen.

5. Cut out each name on the class roster, fold the names and put them in a container. Choose 10 of the names and ask these 10 people if they like yogurt. How many of the 10 like yogurt? _____ **Answers will vary.**

© Pearson Education, Inc.

Intervention Lesson I73   **235**

Name _____

Sampling Methods (continued)

6. Fill in the table below and compare the results. **Answers will vary.**

Sample	Number who like yogurt	Number Polled	Percent who like yogurt
Convenience		5	
Systematic		5	
Random		10	

A larger sample is usually more representative of the population.

7. Which sample do you think is more representative of the population? Explain.
   The random sample is bigger so it will probably be a better representation. Also, random sampling is usually not biased.

8. Ask the entire class if they like yogurt and find the percent who say yes. Were your samples representative of the population? Which sample had results the closest to the population?
   Answers will vary.

Identify each as a population or a sample. If a sample is used, identify the type: convenience, systematic, or random.

9. A volunteer agency contacts every 20th agency in their directory to find out the number of hours volunteers work at their agency. _____ **sample; systematic**

10. When students enroll at Jefferson Middle School, they are asked to tell their method of transportation to school. The results are tallied. _____ **population**

11. Raul is running for class president. He stands outside his classroom and asks students whom they plan to vote for. _____ **sample; convenience**

© Pearson Education, Inc.

236   Intervention Lesson I73

Teacher Notes

Ongoing Assessment

Ask: *How could a random sample of your community be obtained?* Sample answer: A computer could generate a random list from the phone book or tax rolls.

Error Intervention

If students have trouble deciding which type of sample is being used,

then explain that sometimes the types of sampling can overlap.

If students have trouble remembering the different types of sampling,

then use flashcards to quiz students about the three different types.

If You Have More Time

Have students use newspapers, magazines, or the internet to find examples of sampling techniques and discuss what types they represent.

Using Statistics

Name _____

Math Diagnosis and
Intervention System
Intervention Lesson I74

Using Statistics

A **biased sample** is a sample that is not a good match for the entire population.

A student group is making a decision about the type of fundraiser they would like to hold. To help in their decision, they polled 20 students arriving at school near the sixth grade classrooms. They asked students if they would be more likely to buy petunias, flowers, or popcorn. What are the possible biases in this study and could they have been avoided?

Find the biases by answering 1 to 6. **Sample answers are given.**

1. Are there biases in the sample?
   The sample would probably include more sixth graders because of where the students were chosen from. It would also only include those who arrive early at school.

2. Who is the target population, that is, who would most likely be buying the product sold during the fund raiser?   **parents**

3. Does the sample represent the target population?   **no**

4. How could the student group get a better representation of the target population?
   They could survey parents at a school function or as they pick up students after school.

5. Are there biases in the choices offered in the survey?
   Yes, there is overlap because petunias are also flowers. The results will not be clear.

6. How could the choices be improved and biases avoided?
   Another choice could be given instead of petunias.

Name _____

Math Diagnosis and
Intervention System
Intervention Lesson I74

Using Statistics (continued)

The student group decided to ask parents the following question: "Would you buy flowers to support our student organization?" Answer 7 to 9 about this survey question.

7. Would most parents want to support a school organization?   **yes**

8. Would some parents say yes to this question, even if they would not actually buy the flowers?   **yes**

9. Is this a good question to gather the information the students need?   **no**

A government study wants to find the average family size in a community. For Exercises 10 and 11 tell whether each sample might be biased and why.

10. Survey people who are home on Monday morning
    Biased; excludes working families

11. Survey people whose children attend the elementary school
    Biased; excludes those without children or with older children

12. Byron has a jar of 500 marbles. He wants to know how many of them are blue. He takes a handful of the marbles as a sample and finds that 10 of the 50 marbles in the sample are blue and concludes that 20%, or 100 of the total jar, is blue. He later counts all the blue marbles and finds that 200 of them are blue. Was Byron's sample biased? What could have made it biased?
    Yes; the blue marbles may not have been mixed well.

13. Which question do you think is most fair? Explain.
    A. Do you want your neighborhood to be safer?
    B. Are you in favor of a Neighborhood Watch program in your area?
    C. Do you think other people should invade your privacy?
    Choice B; Choice A uses the word safer which is positive and Choice C uses the word invade which is negative.

Teacher Notes

Ongoing Assessment

Ask: *Why would an organization want a biased study?* A biased study can be used to support a false claim that they wish to make.

Error Intervention

If students have trouble answering the questions in the class activity,

then ask more specific questions to help guide their thought process.

If You Have More Time

Have students develop some crazy headlines as a class. Examples could include "People Choose 3 A.M. as Favorite Time of Day" or "Most People Dislike Ice Cream". Then have groups of students discuss how a biased study could produce results that support the headline.

How Likely?

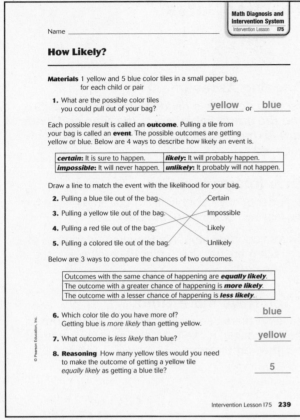

Math Diagnosis and Intervention System
Intervention Lesson I75

Name _____

How Likely?

Materials 1 yellow and 5 blue color tiles in a small paper bag, for each child or pair

1. What are the possible color tiles you could pull out of your bag?   yellow or blue

Each possible result is called an **outcome**. Pulling a tile from your bag is called an **event**. The possible outcomes are getting yellow or blue. Below are 4 ways to describe how likely an event is.

| **certain:** It is sure to happen. | **likely:** It will probably happen. |
| **impossible:** It will never happen. | **unlikely:** It probably will not happen. |

Draw a line to match the event with the likelihood for your bag.

2. Pulling a blue tile out of the bag.   Certain
3. Pulling a yellow tile out of the bag.   Impossible
4. Pulling a red tile out of the bag.   Likely
5. Pulling a colored tile out of the bag.   Unlikely

Below are 3 ways to compare the chances of two outcomes.

| Outcomes with the same chance of happening are **equally likely**. |
| The outcome with a greater chance of happening is **more likely**. |
| The outcome with a lesser chance of happening is **less likely**. |

6. Which color tile do you have more of?   blue
   Getting blue is *more likely* than getting yellow.

7. What outcome is *less likely* than blue?   yellow

8. **Reasoning** How many yellow tiles would you need to make the outcome of getting a yellow tile *equally likely* as getting a blue tile?   5

© Pearson Education, Inc.

Intervention Lesson I75   **239**

Math Diagnosis and Intervention System
Intervention Lesson I75

Name _____

How Likely? (continued)

Use the spinner for Exercises 9 to 12.
Tell whether each event is likely, unlikely, certain, or impossible.

9. checked
   unlikely

10. red   11. gray or dotted
    impossible   likely

12. gray, striped, dotted, or checked
                          certain

For Exercises 13 to 16, use the spinner above.

13. What outcome is more likely than dotted?
                          gray

14. What outcomes are equally likely?
    dotted and striped

15. What outcome is less likely than striped?
                          checked

16. What outcomes are less likely than gray?
    checked, dotted, and striped

17. **Reasoning** Draw a spinner for which the chance of spinning A, B, or C is equally likely.
    Sample is shown.

18. **Reasoning** Draw a spinner for which the chance of spinning A is more likely than spinning B or C.
    Sample is shown.

19. **Reasoning** How can you tell by looking at a spinner that one outcome is less likely than another outcome?
    Sample answer: Compare the sizes of the parts of the spinner. The outcome that covers a smaller part of the spinner than the other is the outcome that is less likely.

© Pearson Education, Inc.

240 Intervention Lesson I75

Teacher Notes

Ongoing Assessment

Ask: *What is the difference between an impossible event and an unlikely event?* Sample answer: An impossible event will never happen. There is a good chance that an unlikely event will not happen, but there also is a chance that it will happen.

Error Intervention

If students have trouble with the concept of likely or unlikely,

then use D78: Likely or Unlikely.

If students have trouble with the concept of certain or impossible,

then use D79: Certain or Impossible and D80: Certain, Probable, Impossible.

If You Have More Time

Give each pair of students a bag containing 4 yellow tiles and 1 green tile. Tell them to not look inside the bag. Have them pull a tile out of the bag, record the result in a tally chart, put the tile back in the bag, and repeat at least 10 times. Have them decide which colors are likely, unlikely, impossible, and certain based on the tally chart. Finally, let them look in the bag to check their conclusions.

Outcomes and Experiments

Outcomes and Experiments

Materials transparent spinner, for each pair or group; red, yellow, blue crayons

A **prediction** tells what may happen using information you know.

1. Color the spinner at the right.

If you spin the spinner 20 times, how many times would you **predict** spinning each color? Answer 2 to 10 to make and test your predictions.

2. How many of the 4 equal parts of the spinner is each color?

___1___ part yellow   ___1___ part blue   ___2___ parts red

So, if you spin the spinner 4 times you would predict that it would land on yellow 1 time, blue 1 time, and red 2 times.

3. Complete the spinning prediction table.

4. How many times do you predict the spinner will land on each color, if you spin the spinner 20 times?

Yellow	1	2	3	4	5
Blue	1	2	3	4	5
Red	2	4	6	8	10
Total Spins	4	8	12	16	20

yellow ___5___ times   blue ___5___ times   red ___10___ times

5. Place the transparent spinner on the spinner above so the centers match. Spin the spinner 20 times. Make a tally chart of your results.

Result	Tally	Number
Yellow		
Blue		
Red		

© Pearson Education, Inc.

Outcomes and Experiments (continued)

6. How many times did you spin each color in 20 spins? Results will vary but red should occur about twice as often as yellow or blue.

yellow _____ times   blue _____ times   red _____ times

7. **Reasoning** How do your predictions compare to your actual spin results? Sample answer: The results were close to the predictions.

8. How many times do you predict the spinner will land on each color, if you spin the spinner 40 times?

yellow ___10___ times   blue ___10___ times   red ___20___ times

9. Spin the spinner 20 more times. Add the results to the tally chart above. How many times did you spin each color in 40 spins? Results will vary but red should occur about twice as often as yellow or blue.

yellow _____ times   blue _____ times   red _____ times
The results should be closer with 40 spins.

10. **Reasoning** Are your predictions closer to your actual spin results with 20 spins or with 40 spins? _____

11. Complete the table to predict the results of pulling a shape from the bag and returning it, each number of times.

Triangle	7	14	21	28	42	84
Circle	2	4	6	8	12	24
Square	1	2	3	4	6	12
Total Picks	10	20	30	40	60	120

© Pearson Education, Inc.

12. Complete the table to predict the results of spinning the spinner, each number of times.

Yellow	3	6	9	12	24	48
Blue	2	4	6	8	16	32
Total Spins	5	10	15	20	40	80

Teacher Notes

Ongoing Assessment
Ask: *If a spinner is divided into 3 equal parts, and the prediction of spins is 1 blue and 2 red, how is the spinner colored?* One part blue and 2 parts red.

Error Intervention
If students have trouble filling out predictions for the last two columns of the exercises,

then encourage students to write the number of picks that are missing under the total spins in each column.

If You Have More Time
Have partners use 6 color tiles, with variations of their choosing, make a prediction table, and then test their predictions.

© Pearson Education, Inc.

Line Plots and Probability

Teacher Notes

Name _____

**Math Diagnosis and
Intervention System**
Intervention Lesson I77

Line Plots and Probability

Some answers will vary depending on survey.
Materials 2 cubes, each numbered 1, 1, 2, 2, 3, 3 per pair

1. Toss the two number cubes. Find the sum of the two cubes. Record the sum in a box in the grid. Do this until all 30 boxes are filled.

Sum of Numbers

2. Find, then list all the possible outcomes for the sum of the two number cubes.

$1 + 1 =$ **2** $1 + 2 =$ **3**

$1 + 3 =$ **4** $2 + 2 =$ **4**

$2 + 3 =$ **5** $3 + 3 =$ **6**

2, 3, 4, 5, 6

Answer 3 to 7 to make and use a line plot of the results.

3. Draw a line. Below the line, list the possible outcomes in order from least to greatest.

4. Write a title below the line plot.

Answers will vary, but 4 should have the most X's and 2 and 6 should have the least

2   3   4   5   6

Sum of Numbers

5. For each sum that was rolled, mark an X above that sum on the number line. If more than one X needs to be placed above a sum, stack them in a single column.

6. Which outcome has the most number of Xs? **4**

7. Reasoning Predict the next sum most likely to be rolled and least likely to be rolled. Explain.

The sum 4 is most likely because it was tossed the most number of times. The sum 2 or 6 is least likely because it was tossed the least number of times.

© Pearson Education, Inc.

Name _____

**Math Diagnosis and
Intervention System**
Intervention Lesson I77

Line Plots and Probability (continued)

Larry recorded the total January precipitation (to the nearest inch) for the past 30 years in the chart at the right. Use the data for Exercises 8 to 14.

**January
Inches of Precipitation**

4	6	3	4	5	4
7	7	5	3	4	5
3	4	5	5	6	7
3	1	4	2	6	5
5	5	5	1	2	1

8. Make a line plot to show the data.

9. How many times did January have 4 inches of precipitation? **6**

10. How many times did January have 5 inches of precipitation? **9**

11. Which number of inches occurred 4 times in the 30 years? **3**

12. Which numbers of inches occurred the same number of times?

1 inch, 6 inches, and 7 inches

13. Reasoning Why was 0 not included on your line plot?

There were not any times that there were 0 inches of precipitation.

14. Reasoning How many inches of precipitation do you predict Larry's area will have next January? Explain.

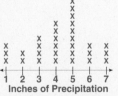

1   2   3   4   5   6   7

Inches of Precipitation

Sample answer: I predict there will be 5 inches of precipitation because 5 inches of precipitation occurred more often than the other amounts.

© Pearson Education, Inc.

Ongoing Assessment

Ask: ***How can you use a line plot to predict which outcome(s) is least likely?*** The outcome with either no Xs or the least number of Xs is least likely.

Error Intervention

If students have trouble making or reading line plots,

then use D85: Making Line Plots.

If You Have More Time

Have students repeat the activity with the number cubes, however change the labels of one of the cubes to 3, 3, 4, 4, 5, 5. Have the students draw a line plot for the results and predict the next roll.

Making Bar Graphs to Show Outcomes

Making Bar Graphs to Show Outcomes

Materials 3 index cards (cut in half vertically), bag

1. Write each letter in the word "MUMMY" on an index card. Use the extra index card to make a tally chart for the possible outcomes: M, U, and Y.

2. Place the letters in a bag. Shake them and without looking pick a letter. Tally the letter. Replace the letter, shake, pick, and tally. Do this 20 times.

Answer 3 to 8 to make and use a bar graph of the results.

3. Write the title: Letters Picked from Bag above the graph and label the axes: Outcome and Number of Times.

4. Complete the scale. Make the scale by 2s.

5. Draw a bar for each letter. For every 2 tally marks for the letter M, color in one square above the letter M. After coloring a square for every 2 tallies, if you have a tally left over, color half of a square. Do this for U and Y.

6. Which two letters were picked about the same number of times?

   U and Y

7. Which bar is the longest? **M**

   The lengths of the bars will vary, the bar for M should be the tallest.

   Since the bar above M is the longest, M is the outcome that occurred most often.

8. **Reasoning** Predict the next letter picked. Explain how you made your prediction.

   M; it is the outcome that occurred most often.

Letters Picked from Bag

16
14
12
10
8
6
4
2
0

Number of Times

M | u | y

Outcome

© Pearson Education, Inc.

Intervention Lesson I78 **245**

Making Bar Graphs to Show Outcomes (continued)

Kendra spun a spinner 20 times. She recorded the number of times each color was spun. Use the data for Exercises 9 to 13.

Spinner Results

Outcome	Tally	Number
Purple	ЖНТ ЖНТ I	11
Green	IIII	4
Orange	IIII	4
Yellow	I	1

9. Make a bar graph in the grid on the right to show the data.

10. Which color occurred most often? least often?

    purple; yellow

11. **Reasoning** What can you tell from the orange and green bars?

    Sample answer: The were spun the same number of times.

12. **Reasoning** Which color do you predict would be spun next?

    purple

13. **Reasoning** Draw what you think the spinner looked like that Kendra used.

    Sample spinner is shown.

Spinner Results

12
10
8
6
4
2
0

Number of Times

Purple Green Orange Yellow

Outcome

Orange
Purple | Green
Yellow

246 Intervention Lesson I78

Teacher Notes

Ongoing Assessment

Ask: *How can you tell which color on a spinner covers the most area by looking at a line plot?* The color that has the longest bar probably has the largest area on the spinner.

Error Intervention

If students have trouble make or reading bar graphs,

then use D84: Reading and Making a Bar Graph, D71: Reading Bar Graphs, and D75: Making Bar Graphs.

If You Have More Time

Have students repeat the activity, but with the word "COMPUTER". Pick one letter from the bag 40 times. After the students have drawn their bar graph, ask: *Will it be easy to predict what letter would be drawn next?* Sample answer: No, all the letters were drawn about the same amount of times. It could be any of the letters. Then ask: *Why do you think all the letters were drawn about the same number of times?* There are only 1 of each letter. So they are all equally likely to be drawn.

© Pearson Education, Inc.

Probability as a Fraction

Name _____

Math Diagnosis and Intervention System
Intervention Lesson I79

Probability as a Fraction

Probability is the likelihood that an event will happen.

Find the probability of getting an even number when spinning the spinner at the right, by answering 1 to 6.

1. List the possible outcomes.

   1, 2, 3, 4, 5, 6, 7, 8, 9, 10

2. How many possible outcomes are there?   10

3. What are the favorable outcomes, the even numbers?   2, 4, 6, 8, 10

You can describe the probability (*P*) of an event by writing a fraction with the number of favorable outcomes over the number of possible outcomes.

4. How many favorable outcomes are there?   5

5. Probability $= \dfrac{\text{number of favorable outcomes}}{\text{number of possible outcomes}}$

   $P = \dfrac{\text{number of even numbers}}{\text{total numbers}}$

   $P = \dfrac{5}{10}$ or $\dfrac{1}{2}$

6. What is the probability of spinning an even number? $\dfrac{1}{2}$

Probability can be described in 4 ways.

Certain events are sure to happen and have a probability of 1.

Impossible events never happen and have a probability of 0.

Likely events probably will happen and have a probability between $\frac{1}{2}$ and 1.

Unlikely events probably will not happen and have a probability between 0 and $\frac{1}{2}$.

© Pearson Education, Inc.

Intervention Lesson I79   **247**

Name _____

Math Diagnosis and Intervention System
Intervention Lesson I79

Probability as a Fraction (continued)

For Exercises 7 and 8 use the spinner at the right.

7. How likely is it that a 12 will be spun?   impossible

8. What is the probability that a 12 will be spun?   0

For Exercises 9 to 13, use the spinner at the right. Write the probability of spinning each.

9. circle $\dfrac{2}{8}$ or $\dfrac{1}{4}$

10. octagon   0

11. not a triangle $\dfrac{5}{8}$

12. star, circle, or triangle $\dfrac{7}{8}$

13. Reasoning To have a probability of 1, what would the spinner have to land on?

   Sample answers: any shape; star, circle, triangle, or square

For Exercises 14 to 19, write the probability and tell whether it is likely, unlikely, impossible, or certain that a triangle will be picked.

14. $\dfrac{3}{9}$ or $\dfrac{1}{3}$; unlikely

15. $\dfrac{8}{14}$ or $\dfrac{4}{7}$; likely

16.   1; certain

17.   0; impossible

18. $\dfrac{6}{12}$ or $\dfrac{1}{2}$; likely

19. $\dfrac{5}{9}$; likely

© Pearson Education, Inc.

248   Intervention Lesson I79

Teacher Notes

Ongoing Assessment

Ask: *If you wrote each letter of the word "SCISSORS" on a piece of paper and placed them in a bag, what is the probability that you would randomly pull out the letter S? Explain.* $\frac{1}{2}$, because 4 out of the 8 letters in the word "scissors" are S.

Error Intervention

If students have trouble with certain, impossible, likely, and unlikely,

then use I75: How Likely?

If You Have More Time

Have students use the shape spinner in the exercises to write 3 probability questions for each likelihood: certain, impossible, likely, and unlikely. Have students trade questions with a partner to solve.

Outcomes and Tree Diagrams

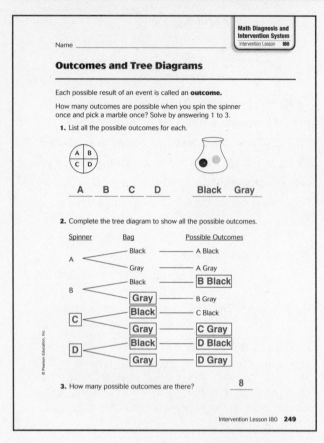

Teacher Notes

Ongoing Assessment

Ask: **Why can't "A Gray" and "Gray A" both be a possible outcome in the Activity?** They are the same thing, just done in a different order.

Error Intervention

If students are not sure they have listed all the possible outcomes in their tree diagram,

then have them check by using multiplication.

If You Have More Time

Have one partner draw a spinner, and the other draw a bag of items to be drawn. Have the partners work together to make a tree diagram for all the possible combinations of spinning the spinner once and picking from the bag once.

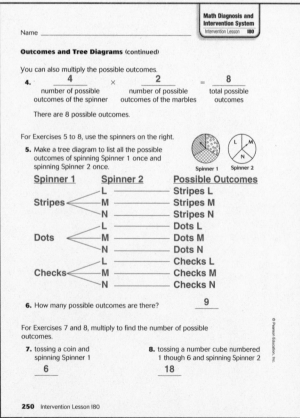

Finding Combinations

Name _____

Finding Combinations

Materials nickel, dime, and penny, equilateral triangle, pentagon, and square power polygon for each student

You can pick one coin and one shape. Find how many different combinations you can choose by answering 1 to 5.

1. Put the nickel next to each shape and list each combination below.

nickel and **triangle**   nickel and **pentagon**   nickel and **square**

2. Do the same with the dime and penny.

dime and **triangle**   dime and **pentagon**   dime and **square**

penny and **triangle**   penny and **pentagon**   penny and **square**

3. How many different combinations can you choose from? __9__

You can also make a table to find all the combinations.

4. Draw the coin in the bottom part of each box in its row, and the shape in the top part each box in its column.

	Triangle	Pentagon	Square
Nickel	△ 5¢	⬠ 5¢	☐ 5¢
Dime	△ 10¢	⬠ 10¢	☐ 10¢
Penny	△ 1¢	⬠ 1¢	☐ 1¢

5. How many combinations can you choose from? __9__

Name _____

Finding Combinations (continued)

For Exercises 6 and 7, complete the table to find all the combinations.

6. Choose one shoe and one hat.

	Cowboy Hat	Cap	Visor	Top Hat
Boot	Cowboy Hat Boot	Cap Boot	Visor Boot	Top Hat Boot
Sneaker	Cowboy Hat Sneaker	Cap Sneaker	Visor Sneaker	Top Hat Sneaker
Sandal	Cowboy Hat Sandal	Cap Sandal	Visor Sandal	Top Hat Sandal

7. How many different combinations are listed in the table? __12__

For Exercises 8 to 12, use objects, pictures, or a table to find the number of possible combinations.

8. Choose one vehicle (car, truck, van, or motorcycle) and one color (silver, white, black, or red)

_____16 combinations_____

9. Choose one movie (science fiction, comedy, or cartoon) and one time of day (afternoon or evening)

_____6 combinations_____

10. Choose one painting (Picasso, or Monet) and one frame (wood, or metal)

_____4 combinations_____

11. Choose one meat (ham, turkey, chicken, bologna, or salami) and one bread (white or wheat)

_____10 combinations_____

12. Reasoning If a third kind of bread was offered in Exercise 11, how many combinations would there be?

_____15 combinations_____

Teacher Notes

Ongoing Assessment

Ask: **If you want to make a table to show the combinations of 3 pizza crusts and 5 toppings, how many rows and columns do you need?**
3 rows and 5 columns or 5 rows and 3 columns

Error Intervention

If students have trouble solving the combinations that do not use a table,

then encourage the students to draw a table.

If You Have More Time

Have students list their 3 favorite places to eat and 4 favorite movies. Have them find all the possible combinations of places to eat and movies they could see for an afternoon of fun.

Predictions and Probability

Name _____

Predictions and Probability

Maureen counted the colors of cars that were in one section of the school's parking lot. The table at the right shows the data that she recorded. If there are 200 cars in the entire parking lot, predict the total number of green cars.

A **prediction** is a statement about a future or unknown event. Use the data in the table and answer 1 to 5 to make a prediction about the number of green cars in the entire lot.

Car Colors	
red	ЖЖ ЖЖ II
blue	ЖЖ ЖЖ ЖЖ II
black	ЖЖ II
green	ЖЖ ЖЖ
gold	IIII

1. How many green cars did Maureen count? **10**
   This value represents the number of favorable outcomes.

2. How many total cars did Maureen count? **50**
   This value represents the number of possible outcomes.

3. Complete to find the probability that a car in the parking lot is green.

   $\dfrac{\text{number of favorable outcomes}}{\text{total number of outcomes}} = \dfrac{10}{\boxed{50}} = \dfrac{1}{\boxed{5}}$

   So, 1 out of every 5 cars in the parking lot is green. Use this probability to predict how many cars are green if there is a total of 200 cars.

4. Find $200 \times \frac{1}{5}$. **40**

5. If the parking lot has 200 cars, predict the number of cars that are green. **40 cars**

The table shows the number of cell phones that sold in one week. If 250 total phones are sold, predict the number of phones that are Model X. Answer 6 to 10.

Model	Number Sold
X	12
y	20
Z	8

6. How many Model X phones were sold in one week? **12**

7. How many total phones were sold in one week? **40**

8. Find the probability that a customer will buy a Model X phone. **$\dfrac{3}{10}$**

   So, 3 out of 10 customers will buy a Model X phone.

9. Find $250 \times \frac{3}{10}$. **75**

10. If 250 phones are sold, predict the number of Model X phones. **75 phones**

Name _____

Predictions and Probability (continued)

A bag has beads of 3 colors: orange, purple, and pink. Beads are drawn from the bag and replaced. The results are recorded in the table shown.

Orange	ЖЖ ЖЖ II
Purple	ЖЖ ЖЖ III
Pink	ЖЖ ЖЖ ЖЖ ЖЖ ЖЖ

Use the table to answer Exercises 11 to 15.

11. How many bead were drawn? **50**

12. What is the probability that the next bead drawn will be orange? **$\dfrac{12}{50}$ or $\dfrac{6}{25}$**

13. What is the probability that the next bead drawn will be pink? **$\dfrac{25}{50}$ or $\dfrac{1}{2}$**

14. If there are 300 beads in the bag, predict the number that are pink. **150**

15. If there are 150 beads in the bag, predict the number that are purple. **39**

Veronica conducted a survey in which she asked 35 people to choose their favorite food category: 10 chose Mexican, 15 chose Italian, and 10 chose Chinese.

Use the survey results to answer Exercises 16 to 21.

16. How many people were surveyed? **35**

17. What is the probability that the next person surveyed will choose Mexican as their favorite food category? **$\dfrac{10}{35}$ or $\dfrac{2}{7}$**

18. What is the probability that the next person surveyed will choose Italian as their favorite food category? **$\dfrac{15}{35}$ or $\dfrac{3}{7}$**

19. Predict how many people out of 70 would choose Chinese as their favorite food category. **20**

20. Predict how many people out of 140 would choose Italian as their favorite food category. **60**

21. **Reasoning** Predict how many people out of 7 would choose Mexican as their favorite food category. **2**

Teacher Notes

Ongoing Assessment

Ask: *What is the probability that a car is yellow?* 0 *How many cars out of 100 in the parking lot would you predict to be yellow?* 0

Error Intervention

If students have trouble finding equivalent fractions,

then use H14: Equivalent Fractions and H17: Simplest Form.

If students need more practice in finding probabilities,

then use I79: Probability as a Fraction.

If You Have More Time

Place some dried beans in a container. Use different kinds of beans such as black beans, pinto beans, and lentils. Have students randomly choose a bean and record the results in a table on the board or overhead. Repeat 50 times. Then have students predict the number of each type of bean in the container given a number of total beans in the container.

Counting Methods

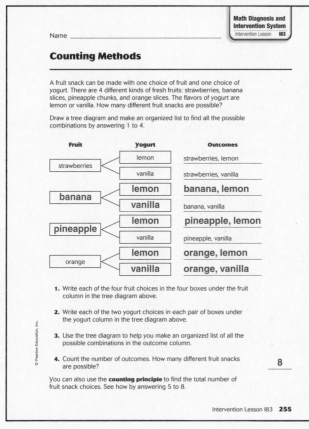

Name _____

Counting Methods

A fruit snack can be made with one choice of fruit and one choice of yogurt. There are 4 different kinds of fresh fruits: strawberries, banana slices, pineapple chunks, and orange slices. The flavors of yogurt are lemon or vanilla. How many different fruit snacks are possible?

Draw a tree diagram and make an organized list to find all the possible combinations by answering 1 to 4.

Fruit	Yogurt	Outcomes
strawberries	lemon	strawberries, lemon
	vanilla	strawberries, vanilla
banana	lemon	banana, lemon
	vanilla	banana, vanilla
pineapple	lemon	pineapple, lemon
	vanilla	pineapple, vanilla
orange	lemon	orange, lemon
	vanilla	orange, vanilla

1. Write each of the four fruit choices in the four boxes under the fruit column in the tree diagram above.

2. Write each of the two yogurt choices in each pair of boxes under the yogurt column in the tree diagram above.

3. Use the tree diagram to help you make an organized list of all the possible combinations in the outcome column.

4. Count the number of outcomes. How many different fruit snacks are possible? **8**

You can also use the **counting principle** to find the total number of fruit snack choices. See how by answering 5 to 8.

Intervention Lesson I83   **255**

Name _____

Counting Methods (continued)

5. How many different choices for fruit are possible? **4**

6. How many different choices of yogurt are possible? **2**

7. What is the product of 4 × 2? **8**

8. How many different fruit snacks are possible? **8**

9. **Reasoning** If an additional choice of 3 toppings is offered on the fruit snack, how many different fruit snacks would be possible? $4 \times 2 \times \boxed{3} = $ **24**

10. A store sells long-sleeved and short-sleeved T-shirts. The T-shirts come in the colors white, black, yellow, and gray. Draw a tree diagram or table to show the possible combinations of shirts. How many possible combinations are there? **8**

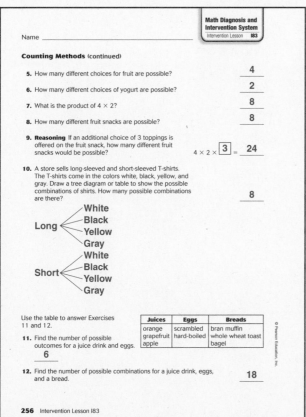

Long — White, Black, Yellow, Gray
Short — White, Black, Yellow, Gray

Use the table to answer Exercises 11 and 12.

Juices	Eggs	Breads
orange	scrambled	bran muffin
grapefruit	hard-boiled	whole wheat toast
apple		bagel

11. Find the number of possible outcomes for a juice drink and eggs. **6**

12. Find the number of possible combinations for a juice drink, eggs, and a bread. **18**

Teacher Notes

Ongoing Assessment

Ask: *How many fruit snacks would be possible if the tree diagram started with the two kinds of yogurt and then each of the two choices had 4 types of fruit branching from them?* It would still be eight.

Error Intervention

If students need more practice with tree diagrams,

then use I80: Outcomes and Tree Diagrams.

If You Have More Time

Have students make up a real-life situation to match a given number of possible outcomes. For example, have students find situations with 24 outcomes. Discuss as a class the different ways that this is possible.

Permutations and Combinations

Name _____

Permutations and Combinations

Salvador wants to take two of the following five classes next year: Spanish, Music, Gym, Art, or Band. Find the number of class arrangements Salvador can choose by answering 1 to 5.

1. Complete the table to find all the possible arrangements of classes. Note: SM stands for Spanish-Music.

	Spanish	Music	Gym	Art	Band
Spanish		SM	SG	SA	SB
Music	MS		MG	MA	MB
Gym	GS	GM		GA	GB
Art	AS	AM	AG		AB
Band	BS	BM	BG	BA	

2. How many different arrangements are listed in the grid?   **20**

When the order of items in an arrangement is important, each possible arrangement is called a **permutation**. In the table, there are 20 different arrangements of classes.

3. Is the order in which Salvador takes the classes important?   **no**

The selection of items in which the order of items does *not* matter is called a **combination**.

4. Each pair of classes is listed in the table twice, because each pair of classes can be arranged 2 ways. Since order does not matter, and SM and MS are the same, divide the number of permutations, 20, by 2 to find the total number of combinations. 20 ÷ 2 = **10**

5. How many class arrangement choices does Salvador have?   **10**

Salvador wants to take one of the five classes in the table above during 1st period and another class during 4th period. Use the table and answer 6 to 11 to find the number of ways Salvador can arrange his schedule.

6. Is the order in which Salvador takes the classes important?   **yes**

7. Since the order is important, are the arrangements a permutation or a combination?   **permutation**

Name _____

Permutations and Combinations (continued)

8. How many classes does Salvador have to choose from for his 1st period class?   **5**

9. How many classes are remaining for Salvador to choose from for his 4th period elective?   **4**

10. The number of arrangements is 5 × 4. How many arrangements are possible?   **20**

11. How many different ways can Salvador arrange his class schedule?   **20**

12. Reasoning The number of permutations found for Salvador's electives was twice as many as the number of combinations. How can the combinations listed be used to find the number of permutations?

Each combination can be listed again in the opposite order to get a list of permutations. Therefore there are twice as many.

Decide whether order matters in each situation. Write Yes or No.

13. Choosing a line up of 10 band members to march in the front row from 25 band members   **Yes**

14. Choosing 3 room monitors from 18 students in the class   **No**

15. A combination to a school locker   **Yes**

Find the number of possible arrangements. State whether it is a permutation or combination.

16. Holly is choosing 2 books to read from a shelf of 6 books.   **15**   **combination**

17. A club is choosing a president and vice-president, from 10 club members.   **90**   **permutation**

18. Tito is arranging 3 toys on a shelf from a box of 10 toys.   **720**   **permutation**

Teacher Notes

Ongoing Assessment

Ask: *Why is Music and Music not listed as one of the possible choices for Salvador's classes?* Because he cannot take two music classes, or two of any other of the same class. The two classes he chooses have to be different.

Error Intervention

If students have trouble understanding how to multiply to find permutations,

then have students list the possible outcomes in a table.

If You Have More Time

Place students in various sizes of small groups. Have each group list the possible outcomes for choosing 3 students from their group as captain, co-captain, and secretary. Discuss the results as a class. Point out how the size of each group affected the number of possible outcomes.

Representing Probability

Worksheet page 1

Name _____

Math Diagnosis and
Intervention System
Intervention Lesson **I85**

Representing Probability

The **probability** of an event describes the likelihood that an event will occur. The probability of an event can be any number from 0 to 1. You can represent probability as a faction, decimal, or percent.

Falisha spins the spinner shown. Find the probability that the spinner will land on 1. Answer 1 to 6 to represent the probability as a fraction, decimal, and percent.

1. How many sections of the spinner have a 1? $\dfrac{2}{8}$

2. How many total sections are on the spinner?

3. Complete to write the probability as a fraction in simplest form.

$P = \dfrac{\text{number of favorable outcomes}}{\text{total number of outcomes}} = \dfrac{2}{8} = \dfrac{1}{4}$

4. To write $\frac{1}{4}$ as a decimal, divide 1 by 4. $1 \div 4 = 0.25$

5. To write 0.25 as a percent, move the decimal point two places to the right and add the % sign.   25%

6. So, the probability that the spinner will land on 1 is:
$\frac{1}{4} = 0.\underline{25} = \underline{25}\%$.

Find the probability that Falisha will spin a number less than 4. Answer 7 to 12 to write the probability as a fraction, decimal, and percent.

7. How many sections on the spinner have a number less than 4? $\dfrac{5}{8}$

8. How many total sections are on the spinner?

9. Complete to write the probability as a fraction in simplest form.

$P = \dfrac{\text{number of favorable outcomes}}{\text{total number of outcomes}} = \dfrac{5}{8}$

10. To write $\frac{5}{8}$ as a decimal, divide 5 by 8.   0.625

11. To write 0.625 as a percent, move the decimal point two places to the right and add the % sign.   62.5%

12. So, the probability that that spinner will land on a number less than 4 is: $\frac{5}{8} = 0.\underline{625} = \underline{62.5}\%$.

© Pearson Education, Inc.

Intervention Lesson I85   **259**

Worksheet page 2

Name _____

Math Diagnosis and
Intervention System
Intervention Lesson **I85**

Representing Probability (continued)

A **complement** of an event is the probability that the event does **not** happen. To find the probability of a complement, subtract the probability of the event from 1.

Find the *complement* of Falisha spinning the spinner and it landing on a number less than 4 by answering 13 and 14.

13. Previously, you found that the probability of the spinner landing on a number less than 4 was 0.625.

What is $1 - 0.625$?   0.375

14. So, what is the probability of the spinner NOT landing on a number less than 4?   0.375

A marble is chosen from the jars without looking. Find each probability as a fraction, a decimal, and a percent.

Jar 1   Jar 2

15. P(black from Jar 1) $\dfrac{2}{5}$; 0.4; 40%

16. P(black from Jar 2) $\dfrac{3}{8}$; 0.375; 37.5%

17. P(gray from Jar 1) $\dfrac{1}{5}$; 0.2; 20%

18. P(not gray from Jar 2) $\dfrac{3}{4}$; 0.75; 75%

19. P(not white from Jar 1) $\dfrac{3}{5}$; 0.6; 60%

20. P(gray or white from Jar 1) $\dfrac{3}{5}$; 0.6; 60%

21. **Reasoning** Are you more likely to get a black marble from Jar 1 or Jar 2? Explain.

P(black from Jar 1) $= \dfrac{4}{10} = 40\%$;

P(black from Jar 2) $= \dfrac{3}{8} = 37.5\%$;

Jar 1 has the higher probability.

© Pearson Education, Inc.

260   Intervention Lesson I85

Teacher Notes

Ongoing Assessment

Ask: *What is the probability that Falisha will spin a number less than 10?* $\frac{8}{8}$ or 1 or 100%

Error Intervention

If students have trouble converting between fractions, decimals, and percents,

then use H31: Decimals to Fractions, H32: Fractions to Decimals, and H79: Relating Percents, Decimals, and Fractions.

If You Have More Time

Give students a description of a jar of marbles using probabilities. For example, the probability of choosing red is $\frac{3}{10}$, the probability of choosing yellow is $\frac{1}{10}$, and the probability of choosing green is $\frac{2}{5}$. Have students draw a possible jar of marbles that has the given probabilities. Discuss as a class the different possibilities for a jar of marbles with the same given probabilities.

Experimental Probability and Predictions

Name _____

Math Diagnosis and Intervention System
Intervention Lesson **I86**

Experimental Probability and Predictions

Materials 8 yellow, 7 red, and 5 blue color tiles in a small paper bag, for each student or pair

Do not look in the bag of tiles Use it to help answer 1 to 12.

1. Do the following experiment. Pull out one tile from the bag without looking, and record the color in the tally chart. Place the tile back into the bag. Repeat this process 40 times. **Answers will vary.**

Tile Experiment		
Color	Tally	Number
Yellow		
Red		
Blue		

Experimental probability is based on the results of an experiment.

2. How many times did you get a yellow tile? **Answers will vary.**

3. How many trials were there, that is how many times did pull a tile? **40**

4. Complete to find the experimental probability that the next tile pulled from the bag will be yellow.

$$P = \frac{\text{Number of Yellow Tiles Pulled}}{\text{Total Number of Trials}} = \frac{\boxed{}}{40}$$

Answers will vary. Check that probabilities are consistent with results in the table.

5. Complete to find the experimental probability that the next tile pulled from the bag will be red.

$$P = \frac{\text{Number of Red Tiles Pulled}}{\text{Total of Number of Trials}} = \frac{\boxed{}}{40}$$

6. Complete to find the experimental probability that the next tile pulled from the bag will be blue.

$$P = \frac{\text{Number of Blue Tiles Pulled}}{\text{Total of Number of Trials}} = \frac{\boxed{}}{40}$$

7. Find the sum of the experimental probability of randomly selecting a yellow tile, a red tile, or a blue tile.

_____ + _____ + _____ = **1**

The probability of an event can be any number from 0 to 1. So the sum of each event occurring in an experiment should equal 1.

8. Does the sum of the probabilities equal 1? **yes**

© Pearson Education, Inc.

Intervention Lesson I86   **261**

Name _____

Math Diagnosis and Intervention System
Intervention Lesson **I86**

Experimental Probability and Predictions (continued)

You can use the experimental probability of an event to make predictions.

9. There are 20 tiles in the bag. Use the results of your experiment to predict how many tiles of each color are in the bag. **Answers will vary, but should reflect results in the tally chart.**

_____ yellow, _____ red, and _____ blue

10. Look in the bag. Were your predictions close to the actual number of each color of tiles in the bag? **yes**

11. Predict how many tiles would be yellow, if a tile was pulled from the bag 200 times. **Answers will vary.**

Multiply the experimental probability from item 4 by 200. _____

12. Predict how many tiles would be red, if a tile was pulled from the bag 200 times. _____

The table at the right shows the number of times Jeffrey's school bus has been early, on time, and late to pick him up over the past 10 days. Use the table to answer Exercises 13 to 17.

Jeffrey's Bus		
Early	On Time	Late
2	5	3

13. What is the experimental probability that the bus will be early the next time Jeffrey rides it? $\frac{1}{5}$ **or 20%**

14. How many times can Jeffrey expect the bus to be early over the next 20 school days? **4 times**

15. What is the experimental probability that the bus will be late the next time Jeffrey rides it? $\frac{3}{10}$ **or 30%**

16. How many times can Jeffrey expect the bus to be late over the next 20 school days? **6 times**

17. What is the sum of the experimental probabilities of the bus being early, the bus being on time, and the bus being late? **1**

18. A manufacturer sampled 100 screws and found that 5% were defective. Predict how many screws, out of 500, you would expect to be defective. **25**

19. **Reasoning** A craft store recorded the colors of yarn they sold. After 50 packages were sold, they found there was a 20% chance that a shopper buying yarn would buy a red color. How many of the 50 packages sold were red? **10**

© Pearson Education, Inc.

262 Intervention Lesson I86

Teacher Notes

Ongoing Assessment

Ask: *If the tiles were drawn 50 times rather than 40, would you expect the experimental probability to be more, less, or similar to the experimental probability for 40 trials?* It would be similar *Why?* The ratio should be about the same.

Error Intervention

If students have trouble finding probabilities,

then use I79: Probability as a Fraction and I85: Representing Probability.

If You Have More Time

Have students record the type of shoe being worn by people at their school. Categories could include sandal, tennis shoe, boot, etc. Samples of the population could be taken in the lunch room, in the hallway, or in the classroom. Have students find the experimental probability that the next student who enters the school will be wearing a particular type of shoe. Have students predict how many students in the school are wearing a particular type of shoe given the number of students at the school.

© Pearson Education, Inc.

Adding Probabilities

Worksheet 1

Name _____

Math Diagnosis and Intervention System
Intervention Lesson I87

Adding Probabilities

Materials index card, scissors, and a small bag for each student or group

Cut an index card into 12 pieces and label each with a number 1 to 12. Place the card pieces into a bag. Draw one card at random from the bag. Answer 1 to 9 to determine the probability that the number drawn is a prime number or a 6.

Prime | **6**

1. Write the prime numbers from 1 to 12 in the circle at the right labeled Prime. Write the number 6 in the circle labeled 6.

   2, 3, 5, 7, 11 | 6

   Are any of the numbers in both circles? **no**

Mutually exclusive events are events that cannot happen at the same time.

2. Can you randomly draw a card that is both a prime number and the number 6? **no**

3. So, are the events "drawing a prime number or a 6" mutually exclusive? **yes**

If events are mutually exclusive you can add their probabilities to find the probability of either event happening.

4. How many favorable outcomes are there for randomly drawing a prime number? **6**

5. What is the probability of drawing a prime number? $\dfrac{5}{12}$

6. How many favorable outcomes are there for randomly drawing a 6? **1**

7. What is the probability of drawing a 6? $\dfrac{1}{2}$

8. Find the sum of the two probabilities.

   $P(\text{prime number}) + P(6) = P(\text{prime or 6})$

   $\dfrac{5}{12} + \dfrac{1}{12} = \dfrac{6}{12} = \dfrac{1}{2}$

9. So, what is the probability of choosing a prime number or a 6? $\dfrac{1}{2}$

Intervention Lesson I87 **263**

Worksheet 2

Name _____

Math Diagnosis and Intervention System
Intervention Lesson I87

Adding Probabilities (continued)

You have a bag containing tiles with numbers labeled 1 to 20. Tell whether the events are mutually exclusive. Write Yes or No.

10. $P(\text{odd or 13})$ **no**

11. $P(\text{odd or 14})$ **yes**

12. $P(\text{even or odd})$ **yes**

13. $P(\text{even or prime})$ **no**

14. $P(2 \text{ or less than 12})$ **no**

15. $P(14 \text{ or greater than 18})$ **yes**

16. $P(\text{multiple of 3 or multiple of 5})$ **no**

17. $P(\text{divisible by 2 or 7})$ **yes**

You toss two number cubes each labeled with the numbers 1–6. Tell whether the events are mutually exclusive. Then, find the probability.

18. $P(3 \text{ or } 4)$

   Mutually exclusive; $\dfrac{1}{3}$

19. $P(1 \text{ or number less than 3})$

   Not mutually exclusive; $\dfrac{1}{3}$

20. $P(\text{even or 3})$

   Mutually exclusive; $\dfrac{2}{3}$

21. $P(\text{number less than 3 or number greater than 3})$

   Mutually exclusive; $\dfrac{5}{6}$

22. **Reasoning** The probability that it will rain today is 25%. The probability that it will rain tomorrow is 75%. Mark concludes that the probability it will rain in the next 2 days is 100%. Is he right? Why or why not.

   He's wrong; the events are not mutually exclusive; it could rain both or neither days.

264 Intervention Lesson I87

Teacher Notes

Ongoing Assessment

Ask: *There are 12 cards in a bag, 3 have a number greater than 9, and 4 have a number less than 5. What is the probability of getting a card with a number greater than 9 or less than 4, when drawing one card from the bag?* $\dfrac{7}{12}$

Error Intervention

If students have trouble adding fractions,

then use H38: Adding and Subtracting Fractions with Like Denominators and H40: Adding Fractions with Unlike Denominators.

If You Have More Time

Have students list five events that are mutually exclusive and five events that are not mutually exclusive using the letters of their names.

Independent Events

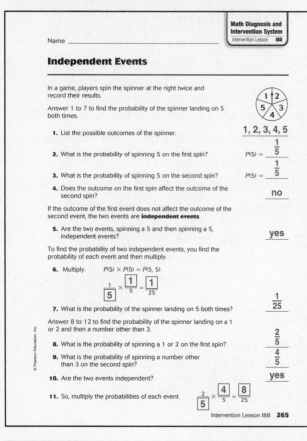

Name _____

Math Diagnosis and Intervention System
Intervention Lesson   **I88**

Independent Events

In a game, players spin the spinner at the right twice and record their results.

Answer 1 to 7 to find the probability of the spinner landing on 5 both times.

1. List the possible outcomes of the spinner.   1, 2, 3, 4, 5

2. What is the probability of spinning 5 on the first spin? $P(5) = \dfrac{1}{5}$

3. What is the probability of spinning 5 on the second spin? $P(5) = \dfrac{1}{5}$

4. Does the outcome on the first spin affect the outcome of the second spin?   no

If the outcome of the first event does not affect the outcome of the second event, the two events are **independent events**.

5. Are the two events, spinning a 5 and then spinning a 5, independent events?   yes

To find the probability of two independent events, you find the probability of each event and then multiply.

6. Multiply. $P(5) \times P(5) = P(5, 5)$

$\dfrac{1}{5} \times \dfrac{1}{5} = \dfrac{1}{25}$

7. What is the probability of the spinner landing on 5 both times? $\dfrac{1}{25}$

Answer 8 to 12 to find the probability of the spinner landing on a 1 or 2 and then a number other than 3.

8. What is the probability of spinning a 1 or 2 on the first spin? $\dfrac{2}{5}$

9. What is the probability of spinning a number other than 3 on the second spin? $\dfrac{4}{5}$

10. Are the two events independent?   yes

11. So, multiply the probabilities of each event. $\dfrac{2}{5} \times \dfrac{4}{5} = \dfrac{8}{25}$

Intervention Lesson I88   **265**

Name _____

Math Diagnosis and Intervention System
Intervention Lesson   **I88**

Independent Events (continued)

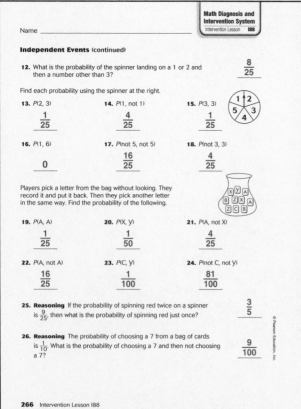

12. What is the probability of the spinner landing on a 1 or 2 and then a number other than 3? $\dfrac{8}{25}$

Find each probability using the spinner at the right.

13. $P(2, 3)$ $\dfrac{1}{25}$

14. $P(1, \text{not } 1)$ $\dfrac{4}{25}$

15. $P(3, 3)$ $\dfrac{1}{25}$

16. $P(1, 6)$ 0

17. $P(\text{not } 5, \text{not } 5)$ $\dfrac{16}{25}$

18. $P(\text{not } 3, 3)$ $\dfrac{4}{25}$

Players pick a letter from the bag without looking. They record it and put it back. Then they pick another letter in the same way. Find the probability of the following.

19. $P(A, A)$ $\dfrac{1}{25}$

20. $P(X, y)$ $\dfrac{1}{50}$

21. $P(A, \text{not } X)$ $\dfrac{4}{25}$

22. $P(A, \text{not } A)$ $\dfrac{16}{25}$

23. $P(C, y)$ $\dfrac{1}{100}$

24. $P(\text{not } C, \text{not } y)$ $\dfrac{81}{100}$

25. **Reasoning** If the probability of spinning red twice on a spinner is $\dfrac{9}{25}$, then what is the probability of spinning red just once? $\dfrac{3}{5}$

26. **Reasoning** The probability of choosing a 7 from a bag of cards is $\dfrac{1}{10}$. What is the probability of choosing a 7 and then not choosing a 7? $\dfrac{9}{100}$

Teacher Notes

Ongoing Assessment

Ask: *Is the probability of spinning a 5 on the second spin more likely or less likely if a 5 is spun on the first spin?* Neither, the likelihood is the same regardless of the results of the first spin. That is why the events are independent.

Error Intervention

If students have trouble multiplying fractions,

then use H46: Multiplying Two Fractions.

If students have trouble understanding why the fractions are multiplied to find the probability of two events,

then have students make a table or a tree diagram to find all the possible outcomes for the two events and then find the probability of the event from the list of outcomes.

If You Have More Time

Have students find the probability of 3 spins on the spinner from the activity. This will involve multiplying 3 fractions together.

© Pearson Education, Inc.

Dependent Events

Name _____

Math Diagnosis and Intervention System
Intervention Lesson I89

Dependent Events

Materials index card, scissors, and small bag for each student or group

Cut an index card into 8 pieces. Write the following numbers, one on each card: 1, 3, 2, 2, 4, 4, 5 and 5. Place the card pieces into the bag.

If you draw one card without looking, record its value, replace the card, and then select another card and record its value, what is the probability that you draw a 5 both times? Answer 1 to 5 to find the probability.

1. How many favorable outcomes are there for getting a 5 on the first draw?

2

2. What is the probability of getting a 5 from the bag on the first draw?

$\frac{2}{8}$ or $\frac{1}{4}$

If the outcome of the first event does not affect the outcome of the second event, the two events are **independent events**.

3. Are the events of getting a 5 on the first draw and getting a 5 on the second draw independent?

yes

4. What is the probability of getting a 5 from the bag on the second draw?

$\frac{2}{8}$ or $\frac{1}{4}$

To find the probability of two independent events, you find the probability of each event and then multiply.

$P(5) \times P(5) = P(5, 5)$

5. Multiply to find the probability of drawing a 5, replacing the card, and then drawing a 5 again.

$\frac{1}{4} \times \boxed{\frac{1}{4}} = \boxed{\frac{1}{16}}$

If you draw one card without looking, do NOT replace the card, and then select another card, what is the probability that you draw a 5 both times? Answer 6 to 12 to find the probability.

6. What is the probability of getting a 5 from the bag on the first draw?

$\frac{2}{8}$ or $\frac{1}{4}$

7. Assume the card you got on the first draw was a 5. Take a card with 5 on it out of the bag. How many cards are left in the bag?

7

8. How many of the cards that are left in the bag have a 5?

1

9. What is the probability of getting a 5 from the bag on the second draw if you get a 5 on the first draw and do not replace it?

$\frac{1}{7}$

© Pearson Education, Inc.

Intervention Lesson I89   **267**

Name _____

Math Diagnosis and Intervention System
Intervention Lesson I89

Dependent Events (continued)

10. Does the outcome of the first event affect the outcome of the second event?

yes

If the outcome of the first event affects the outcome of the second event, the two events are **dependent events**.

11. Are the events of getting a 5 on the first draw and getting a 5 on the second draw when the first card is not replaced dependent?

yes

To find the probability of two dependent events, you find the probability of each event and then multiply.

$P(5) \times P(5) = P(5, 5)$

12. Multiply to find the probability of drawing a 5 and then a 5 again if the card is NOT replaced.

$\frac{1}{4} \times \boxed{\frac{1}{7}} = \boxed{\frac{1}{28}}$

Players pick a letter from the bag without looking. They record it and put it back. Then they pick another letter in the same way. Find the probability of the following.

13. $P(A, A)$

$\frac{1}{25}$

14. $P(X, Y)$

$\frac{1}{50}$

15. $P(A, \text{not } X)$

$\frac{4}{25}$

Players pick a letter from the bag without looking. They record it and do *not* put it back. Then they pick another letter in the same way. Find the probability of the following.

16. $P(A, A)$

$\frac{1}{45}$

17. $P(X, Y)$

$\frac{1}{45}$

18. $P(A, \text{not } X)$

$\frac{7}{45}$

19. **Reasoning** The probability of choosing a 7 from a bag of cards is $\frac{3}{10}$. What is the probability of choosing a 7 and then a 7 again if the card is not replaced? Explain.

$\frac{1}{15}$; Sample answer: The probability of choosing a 7 in the second draw is $\frac{2}{9}$. So the probability for two draws is $\frac{3}{10} \times \frac{2}{9} = \frac{1}{15}$.

© Pearson Education, Inc.

© Pearson Education, Inc.

268 Intervention Lesson I89

Teacher Notes

Ongoing Assessment
Ask: *If a 2 is drawn from the number cards and not replaced, what is the probability that a 4 will be drawn the second time?* $\frac{2}{7}$

Error Intervention
If students have trouble multiplying fractions, **then** use H46: Multiplying Two Fractions.

If You Have More Time
Have students repeat the activity without replacement for other given probabilities such as $P(2, 3)$, $P(1, \text{not } 1)$ and $P(1 \text{ or } 2, \text{not } 3)$. Student pairs can also take turns asking a probability of two events without replacement and finding the probability.

Solid Figures

Materials power solids arranged in stations around the room

Find each solid to complete the tables below.

	Solid	Number of Faces	Number of Edges	Number of Vertices	Shapes of Faces
1.	Pyramid	5	8	5	1 square 4 triangles
2.	Rectangular Prism				
3.	Cube				

Objects that roll do not have faces, edges, or vertices.

	Solid	Number of Flat Surfaces	Shape of Flat Surfaces
4.	Cone	1	1 circle

Solid Figures (continued)

	Solid	Number of Flat Surfaces	Shape of Flat Surfaces
5.	Cylinder		
6.	Sphere		

Name the solid figure that each object looks like.

7.

8.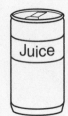

9.

_____   _____   _____

Use the solids in the table above to answer Exercises 10–12.

10. Which solid figure has 2 flat surfaces that are circles?

_____

11. Which of the 6 solid figures has 6 rectangular faces?

_____

12. Which 3 figures have no vertices?

_____

13. Reasoning How are the sphere and cone alike?

Breaking Apart Solids

Materials power solids arranged in stations around the room,
index card one for each child

Find each shape. Discuss with your partner what the solid figure
would look like if it were cut horizontally. Draw a line to match
the cut solid with the correct description. Use your index card to
help visualize the cut. One description is used twice.

1.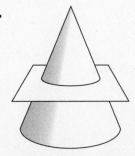

two small
rectangular prisms

2.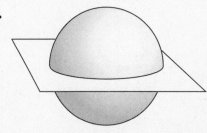

two parts that each
have 1 flat surface

3.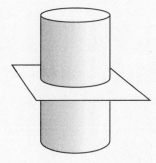

a small cone and 1
other solid figure

4.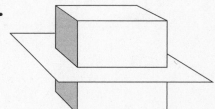

two small cylinders

5.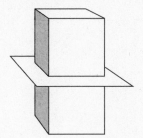

a small pyramid
and 1 other figure

6.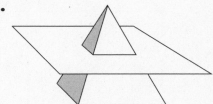

Breaking Apart Solids (continued)

Write the letters of the two smaller solids that make up the larger
solids in Exercises 7–10.

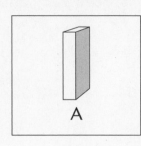 A

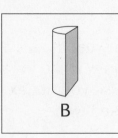 B

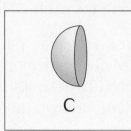 C

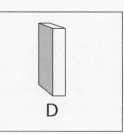 D

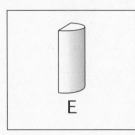 E

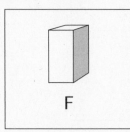 F

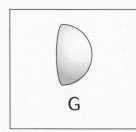 G

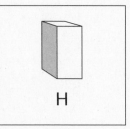 H

7.

_____

8.

_____

9.

_____

10.

_____

11. Reasoning Which two solids, when cut in half, can form two
smaller versions of the solid itself?

Name _____

Lines and Line Segments

Materials crayons, markers, or colored pencils

A point is an exact place. It is shown by a very small dot.

1. Color in the circle to show a point.   ○

A *line* is an endless number of points going on forever in two directions. There is no beginning and no end.

2. Color over the points to make a solid line.
Color in the two arrows to show the line
goes on forever in both directions.

A *line segment* is a part of a line. It has a beginning and an end.

3. Color over the points to make a solid line segment.
Color in the points that are shown larger, to show
the line segment's beginning and end. These points
are called *endpoints*.

Box A	Box B
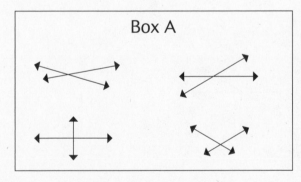	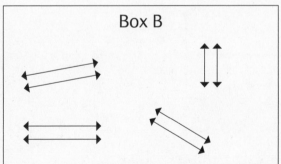

4. Reasoning How are the pairs of lines in Box A different
from those in Box B?

_____

Intersecting lines cross in a point. *Parallel lines* never cross.

5. What type of lines are shown in Box A?   _____

6. What type of lines are shown in Box B?   _____

Lines and Line Segments (continued)

7. Circle each figure with the color named below.

points—red   lines—blue   line segments—green

pairs of intersecting lines—orange   pairs of parallel lines—purple

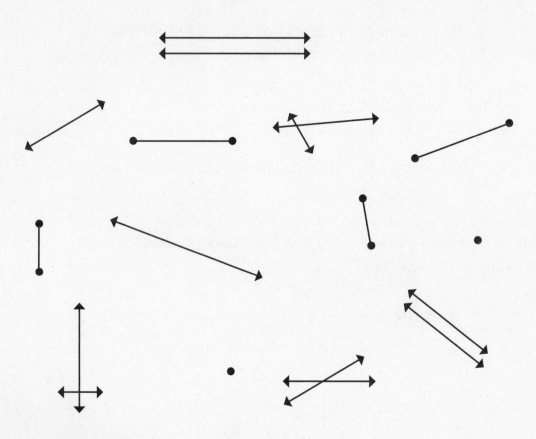

Draw an example of each.

8. parallel lines   **9.** line segment   **10.** line

11. Reasoning Draw an example of intersecting line segments.

Name _____

Acute, Right, and Obtuse Angles

Materials 1 inch square piece of paper for each student,
crayons or markers

A *ray* is part of a line. The endpoint is the beginning
of the ray, and the arrow shows it goes on forever.

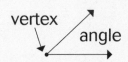

ray

An *angle* is made by two rays that have the same
endpoint. That endpoint is called the *vertex*.

vertex

angle

1. Color each ray of the angle at the
right, a different color.

Place a side of your square on one ray, and the corner on the
vertex for each angle in 2 to 4.

2. Reasoning *Right angles* are shown below. What do you
notice about the openings of right angles?

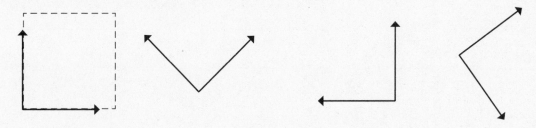

3. Reasoning *Obtuse angles* are shown below. What do you notice about
the openings of obtuse angles?

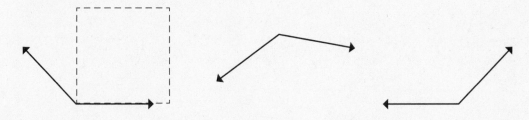

Acute, Right, and Obtuse Angles (continued)

4. **Reasoning** *Acute angles* are shown below. What do you notice about the openings of acute angles?

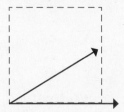

Write *ray*, *vertex*, *right angle*, *acute angle*, or *obtuse angle* to name each.

5.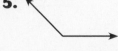

6.

7.

_____ _____ _____

8.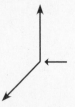

9.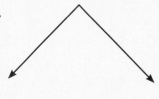

10.

_____ _____ _____

What kind of angle do the hands of each clock show?

11.

12.

13.

_____ _____ _____

Polygons

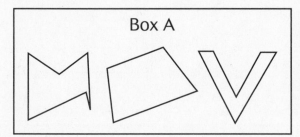

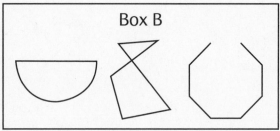

1. The figures in Box A are polygons. The figures in Box B are not.
How are the figures in Box A different from those in Box B?

To be a polygon:

- All sides must be made of straight line segments.
- Line segments must only intersect at a vertex.
- The figure must be closed.

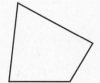

Polygons are named by the number of sides each has.
Complete the table.

	Shape	**Number of Sides**	**Number of Vertices**	**Name**
2.				Triangle
3.				Quadrilateral
4.				Pentagon
5.				Hexagon
6.				Octagon

© Pearson Education, Inc.

Polygons (continued)

Tell if each figure is a polygon. Write *yes* or *no*.

7.

_____

8.

_____

9.

_____

Name each polygon. Then tell the number of sides and the number of vertices each polygon has.

10.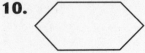

_____

11.

_____

12.

_____

13.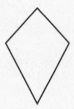

_____

14.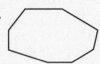

_____

15.

_____

16. Reasoning What is the least number of sides a polygon can have?

_____

17. Reasoning A regular polygon is a polygon with all sides the same length. Circle the figure on the right that is a regular polygon.

 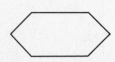

Classifying Triangles Using Sides and Angles

Materials 2 yards of yarn, scissors, 6 sheets of construction paper, markers for each student and glue

Create a book about triangles by following 1 to 7.

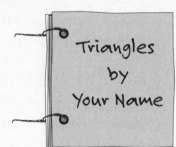

1. Put the pieces of construction paper together and fold them in half to form a book. Punch two holes in the side and use yarn to tie the book together. Write "Triangles" and your name on the cover.

Each two-page spread will be about one type of triangle. For each two page spread:

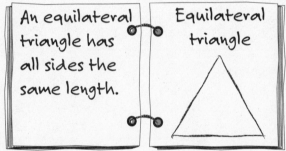

- Write the definition on the left page.
- Write the name of the triangle near the top of the right page.
- Create a triangle with yarn pieces and glue the yarn pieces under the name of the triangle to illustrate the triangle.

2. Pages 1 and 2 should be about an **equilateral triangle.** This triangle has 3 sides of equal length. So, your 3 yarn pieces should be cut to the same length.

3. Pages 3 and 4 should be about an **isosceles triangle.** This triangles has at least two sides the same length. Cut 2 pieces of yarn the same length and glue them on the page at an angle. Cut and glue a third piece to complete the triangle.

4. Pages 5 and 6 should be about a **scalene triangle.** This triangle has no sides the same length. So your 3 yarn pieces can be cut to different lengths.

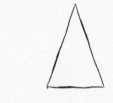

5. Pages 7 and 8 should be about a **right triangle.** This triangle has exactly one right angle. Two of your yarn pieces should be placed so that they form a right angle. Cut and glue a third piece to complete the triangle.

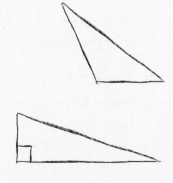

Classifying Triangles Using Sides and Angles (continued)

6. Pages 9 and 10 should be about an **obtuse triangle.** This triangle has exactly one obtuse angle. Two pieces of yarn should be placed so that it forms an obtuse angle. Cut and glue down a third yarn piece to complete the triangle.

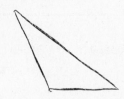

7. Pages 11 and 12 should be about an **acute triangle.** This triangle has three acute angles. Your 3 yarn pieces should be placed so that no right or obtuse angles are formed.

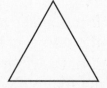

Tell if each triangle is equilateral, isosceles, or scalene.

8.

9.

10.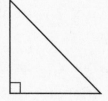

_____   _____   _____

Tell if each triangle is right, acute, or obtuse.

11.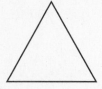

12.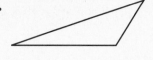

13.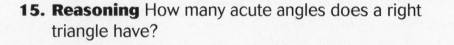

_____   _____   _____

14 How many acute angles does an acute triangle have? _____

15. Reasoning How many acute angles does a right triangle have?   _____

16. Describe this triangle by its sides and by its angles. (Hint: Give it two names.)

_____   _____

Quadrilaterals

Materials Have quadrilateral power shapes available for
students who want to use them.

For 1 to 5 study each quadrilateral with your partner. Identify
the types of angles. Compare the lengths of the sides. Then
draw a line to match the quadrilateral with the best description.
Descriptions can be used only once.

1. Trapezoid

| Four right angles and all four sides the same length |

2. Parallelogram

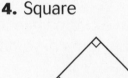

| All sides are the same length |

3. Rectangle

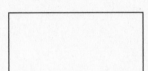

| Exactly one pair of parallel sides |

4. Square

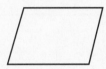

| Two pairs of parallel sides |

5. Rhombus

| Four right angles and opposite sides the same length |

6. Reasoning What quadrilateral has four right angles
and opposite sides the same length, and can also
be called a rectangle? _____

7. Reasoning What quadrilaterals have two pairs of
parallel sides, and can also be called parallelograms?

_____

Quadrilaterals (continued)

For Exercises 8–13, circle squares red, rectangles blue,
parallelograms green, rhombuses orange and trapezoids purple.
Some quadrilaterals may be circled more than once.

8.   9.    10.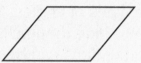

11. 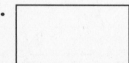   12.   13.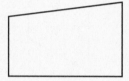

14. I have two pairs of parallel sides, and all of my sides are
    equal, but I have no right angles. What quadrilateral am I? _____

15. I have two pairs of parallel sides and 4 right angles, but
    all 4 of my sides are not equal. What quadrilateral am I? _____

16. Name all of the quadrilaterals in the
    picture at the right.

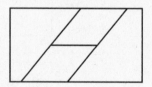

17. **Reasoning** Why is the quadrilateral on the
    right a parallelogram, but not a rectangle?

Congruent Figures and Motions

Materials construction paper, markers, and scissors

Follow 1–10.

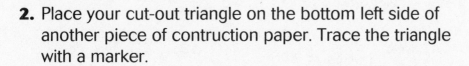

1. Cut a scalene triangle out of construction paper.

2. Place your cut-out triangle on the bottom left side of
another piece of contruction paper. Trace the triangle
with a marker.

Slide

3. Slide your cut-out triangle to the upper right of the
same paper and trace the triangle again.

4. Look at the two triangles that you just traced. Are the
two triangles the same size and shape?

_____

When a figure is moved up, down, left, or right, the motion is
called a **slide**, or **translation**.

Figures that are the exact same size and shape are called
congruent figures.

5. On a new sheet of paper, draw a straight dashed line as
shown at the right. Place your cut-out triangle on the left
side of the dashed line. Trace the triangle with a marker.

Flip

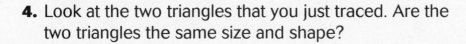

6. Pick up your triangle and flip it over the dashed line, like
you were turning a page in a book. Trace the triangle again.

7. Look at the two triangles that you just traced. Are the
two triangles congruent?

_____

When a figure is picked up and flipped over, the motion is called
a **flip**, or **reflection**.

8. On a new sheet of paper, draw a point in the middle of
the paper. Place a vertex of your cut-out triangle on
the point. Trace the triangle with a marker.

Turn

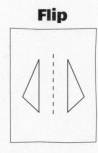

9. Keep the vertex of your triangle on the point and move
the triangle around the point like the hands on a clock.
Trace the triangle again.

Name _____

Congruent Figures and Motions (continued)

10. Look at the two triangles you just traced. Are the two triangles congruent?

_____

When a figure is turned around a point, the motion is a **turn**, or **rotation**.

Write slide, flip, or turn for each diagram.

11.

_____

12.

_____

13.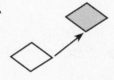

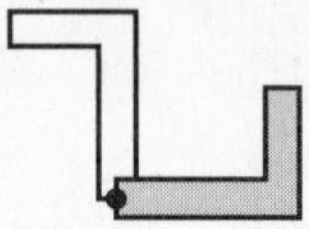

_____

14.

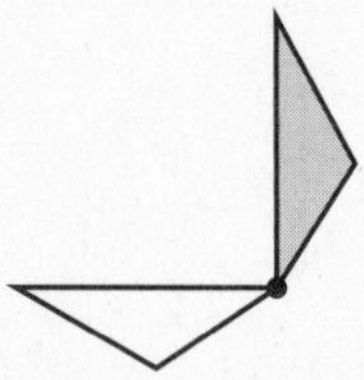

_____

15.

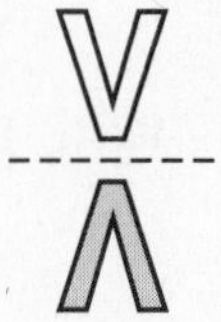

_____

16.

_____

For Exercises 17 and 18, use the figures to the right.

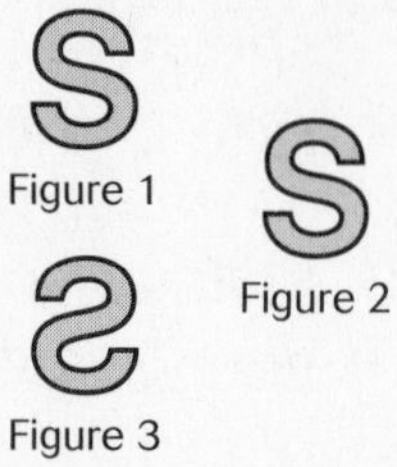

17. Are Figures 1 and 2 related by a slide, a flip, or a turn? _____

18. Are Figures 1 and 3 related by a slide, a flip, or a turn? _____

Figure 1

Figure 2

Figure 3

19. Reasoning Are the polygons at the right congruent? If so, what motion could be used to show it?

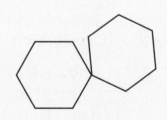

Name _____

Line Symmetry

Materials one sheet of 3″ x 3″ paper, two sheets of 2″ x 4″
paper, for each student

1. How many ways can you fold a rectangular sheet of paper
so that the two parts match exactly?

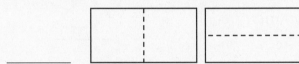

_____

A **line of symmetry** is a line on which a figure can be folded so
the two parts match exactly.

2. Fold the square sheet of paper as many ways
as you can so the two sides match. One way
is shown at the right. How many lines of
symmetry does a square have?   _____

3. Cut a rectangular sheet of paper in half as
shown at the right. Cut out one of the
triangles formed.

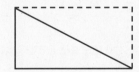

4. Fold the right triangle as many ways as you
can so two sides match. How many lines of
symmetry does the right triangle have?   _____

If a figure has at least one line of symmetry, it is **symmetric**.

5. Circle the figures that are symmetric.

To draw a symmetric figure, flip the given half over the line of symmetry.

Line Symmetry (continued)

Complete the figure below to make a symmetric figure by answering 6 to 8.

6. Find a vertex that is not on the line of symmetry. Count the number of spaces from the line of symmetry to the vertex.

7. Count the same number of spaces on the other side of the line of symmetry and mark a point.

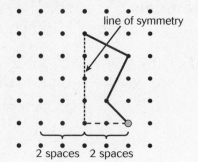

8. Use line segments to connect the new vertices. Do this until the figure is complete.

Decide whether or not each figure is symmetric. Write Yes or No

9.

10.

11.

_____   _____   _____

Complete each figure so the dotted line segment is the line of symmetry.

12.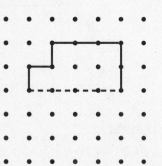

13.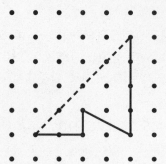

Draw all lines of symmetry for each figure.

14.

15.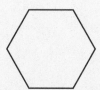

Solids and Nets

Materials tape, scissors, copy of nets
for all prisms, square and
rectangular pyramids from
Teaching Tool Masters

Cut out and tape each net to help
complete the tables. Each group
should make 7 solids.

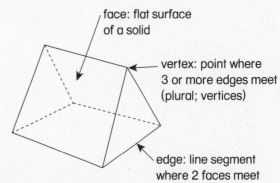

face: flat surface
of a solid

vertex: point where
3 or more edges meet
(plural; vertices)

edge: line segment
where 2 faces meet

	Solid	Faces	Edges	Vertices	Shapes of Faces
1.	Pyramid	5	8	5	1 square 4 triangles
2.	Rectangular Pyramid				
3.	Cube				
4.	Rectangular Prism				
5.	Triangular Prism				

Solids and Nets (continued)

What solid will each net form?

6.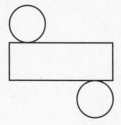

_____

7.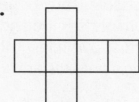

_____

8.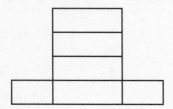

_____

9.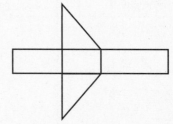

_____

10.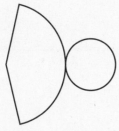

_____

11.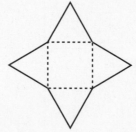

_____

12. Reasoning Is the figure a net for a cube? Explain.

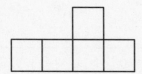

Views of Solid Figures

Materials 6 blocks or small cubes from place-value blocks for
each pair or group, crayons or markers

Stack blocks to model the solid shown at the
right. Assume that there are only 6 cubes in
the solid so that none are hidden.

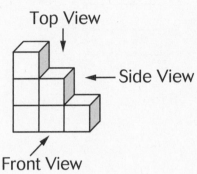

Top View

Side View

Front View

The top view of the solid is the image seen
when looking straight down at the figure.

Draw the top view of the solid at the right by
answering 1 and 2.

1. How many cubes can you see when you look straight
down at the solid?

_____

2. Color in squares on the grid to indicate
the blocks seen from the top view.

The front view is the image seen when
looking straight at the cubes.

Draw the front view of the solid above
by answering 3 and 4.

3. How many cubes can you see when you look straight
at the solid?

_____

4. Color in squares on the grid to indicate
the blocks seen from the front view.

The side view is the image seen when
looking at the side of the cubes.

Draw the side view of the solid above
by answering 5 and 6.

5. How many cubes can you see when
you look at the solid from the side?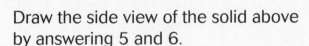

6. Color in squares on the grid to indicate
the blocks seen from the side view.

Views of Solid Figures (continued)

Draw the front, right, and top views of each solid figure. There
are no hidden cubes.

7.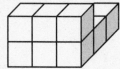

Front   Side   Top

8.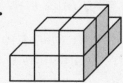

Front   Side   Top

9.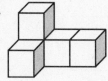

Top

Front

Side

10.

Top

Front

Side

11.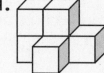

Top

Front

Side

12. Reasoning If a cube is added to the top of the solid in
Exercise 11, what views would change? What view would
not change?

Geometric Ideas

Materials crayons, markers, or colored pencils

A **plane** is an endless flat surface, such as this paper if it extended forever.

1. Name another real-world object
which could represent a plane.   _____

Use the diagram at the right to answer 2 to 8.

A **point** is an exact location in space.

2. Draw a circle around point *D* in orange.

A **line** is a straight path of points that
goes on forever in two directions.

3. Trace over line *AD* in blue.

Line *AD* is written $\overleftrightarrow{AD}$.

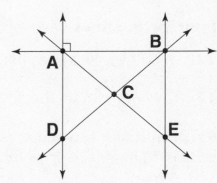

A **line segment** is a part of a line with two endpoints.

4. Trace over line segment *CD* in red. Be sure to stop at point *C*
and point *D*.

Line segment *CD* is written $\overline{CD}$.

A **ray** is a part of a line with one endpoint.

5. Trace over ray *AB* in green. Ray *AB* is written $\overrightarrow{AB}$.

6. What point is the endpoint in ray *AB*?   _____

An **angle** is formed by two rays with the same endpoint.

7. Trace over angle *ACB* in brown. Angle *ACB* is
written ∠*ACB*.

The common endpoint of the rays is called the **vertex**
of the angle.

8. Which point is the vertex of ∠*ACB*?   _____

Geometric Ideas (continued)

Parallel lines never cross and stay the same distance apart. The symbol || means *is parallel to*.

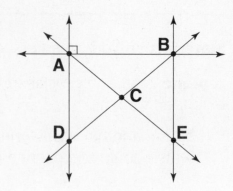

9. Trace over two lines that appear to be parallel, in purple.

10. Write the names of the parallel lines using the line symbol over the letters.

_____ || _____

Intersecting lines have a point in common.

11. Trace over two lines that intersect, in yellow.

12. At what point do the lines intersect?   _____

Perpendicular lines intersect and form a right angle. The symbol ⊥ means *is perpendicular to*.

13. Trace over two lines that are perpendicular, in orange.

14. Write the names of the perpendicular lines using the line symbol over the letters.   _____ ⊥ _____

Draw each of the following.

15. ray *HJ*   **16.** line segment *KL*   **17.** line *RS*

18. $\overleftrightarrow{TV}$ is parallel to $\overleftrightarrow{WX}$.   **19.** $\overline{EF}$ is perpendicular to $\overline{JK}$.   **20.** $\overrightarrow{YZ}$ intersects $\overleftrightarrow{AB}$.

Congruent Figures

Materials tracing paper and scissors

Two figures that have exactly the same size and shape are congruent.

1. Place a piece of paper over Figure *A*
and trace the shape. Is the figure
you drew congruent to Figure *A*? _____

Figure A

Cut out the figure you traced and use it to
answer 2 to 10.

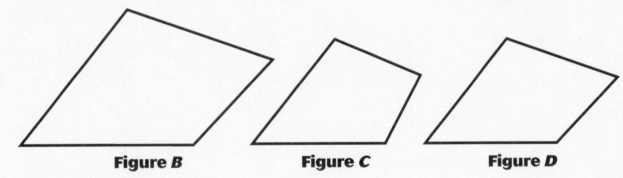

Figure B   **Figure C**   **Figure D**

2. Place the cutout on top of Figure *B*.
Is Figure *B* the same size as Figure *A*?   _____

3. Is Figure *B* congruent to Figure *A*?   _____

4. Place the cutout on top of Figure *C*.
Is Figure *C* the same shape as Figure *A*?   _____

5. Is Figure *C* congruent to Figure *A*?   _____

6. Place the cutout on top of Figure *D*.
Is Figure *D* the same size as Figure *A*?   _____

7. Is Figure *D* the same shape as Figure *A*?   _____

8. Is Figure *D* congruent to Figure *A*?   _____

9. Circle the figure that is congruent to the figure at the right.

Congruent Figures (continued)

Tell if the two figures are congruent. Write Yes or No.

10.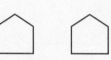

_____

11.

_____

12.

_____

13.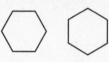

_____

14.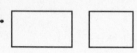

_____

15.

_____

16.

_____

17.

_____

18.

_____

19. Divide the isosceles triangle shown at the right into 2 congruent right triangles.

20. Divide the hexagon shown at the right into 6 congruent equilateral triangles.

21. Divide the rectangle shown at the right into 2 pairs of congruent triangles.

22. Reasoning Are the triangles at the right congruent? Why or why not?

Circles

Materials crayons, markers, or colored pencils

Use the figure at the right to answer 1 to 10.

A **circle** is the set of all points in a plane that are the same distance from a point called the **center.**

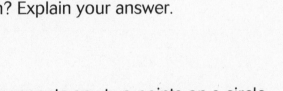

1. Color the point that is the center of the circle red.

A **radius** is any line that connects the center of the circle to a point on the circle.

2. Color a radius of the circle blue.

3. Reasoning Will every radius that is drawn on the circle have same length? Explain your answer.

A **chord** is a line segment that connects any two points on a circle. A chord may or may not go through the center of the circle.

4. Color a chord on the circle that does not include the center of the circle, green.

5. Reasoning Will every chord that is drawn on the circle have the same length? Explain your answer.

A **diameter** is a chord that goes through the center of the circle.

6. Color a diameter of the circle orange.

7. Reasoning Will every diameter that is drawn on the circle have the same length? Explain your answer.

Circles (continued)

The length of the diameter of a circle is two times the length of the radius.

8. Use a centimeter ruler to measure the length of the radius.
What is the length of the radius? _____ cm

9. Use a centimeter ruler to measure the length of the diameter.
What is the length of the diameter? _____ cm

10. Is the diameter two times the length of the radius? _____

Identify the part of each circle indicated by the arrow.

11.

12.

13.

_____ _____ _____

14.

15.

16.

_____ _____ _____

Find the radius or diameter of each circle.

17.

6 in.

radius:

_____

18.

5 ft

diameter:

_____

19.

18 cm

radius:

_____

20. The radius of a circle is 11 centimeters.
What is the diameter of the circle? _____

Rotational Symmetry

Materials paper and scissors

If a figure can be turned less than
a full turn about a point and fit
back on itself, then the figure
has **rotational symmetry.**

All turns in this activity are assumed
to be clockwise. Find the types of
rotational symmetry for the figure
shown at the right by answering
1 to 11.

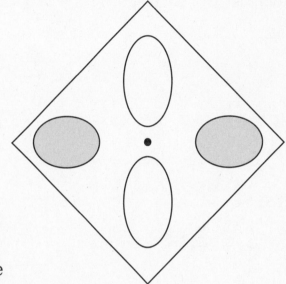

1. Place a piece of paper over the figure
   shown and trace it. Cut out the figure.

2. Place the cutout on top of the original figure, put your
   pencil on the dots to hold them in place, and rotate
   90 degrees clockwise or to the right around the point.

3. Does the cutout fit on top of the original figure?   _____

4. Does the figure have 90° rotational symmetry?   _____

5. Rotate the figure an additional 90 degrees clockwise
   around the point for a total of 180 degrees.

6. Does the cutout fit on top of the original figure?   _____

7. Does the figure have 180° rotational symmetry?   _____

8. Rotate the shape an additional 90 degrees clockwise
   around the point for a total of 270 degrees.

9. Does the cutout fit on top of the original figure?   _____

10. Does the figure have 270° rotational symmetry?   _____

11. What types of rotational symmetry does the figure have?   _____

Rotational Symmetry (continued)

Write 90°, 180°, 270°, or none to describe the rotational symmetry of each figure.

12.

_____

13.

_____

14.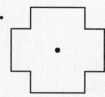

_____

15.

_____

16.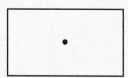

_____

17.

_____

18.

_____

19.

_____

20.

_____

21.

_____

22.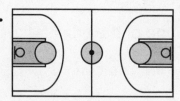

_____

23.

_____

24. Reasoning Draw a figure with 90°, 180°, and 270° rotational symmetry.

Transformations

Materials paper, scissors, and markers.

Transformations do not change the size or shape of a figure. There are three types of transformations: translation, reflection, and rotation.

Use a piece of paper to trace the house figure shown on the grid. Then, cut it out. Answer 1 to 8.

A **translation** is a slide.

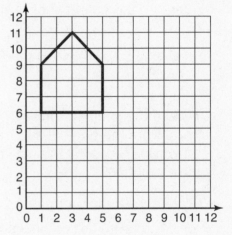

1. Place the cutout shape over the shape on the grid. What are the coordinates of each of the 5 vertices of the pentagon?

   _____

2. Slide the cutout shape 5 units to the right and trace around it. What are the coordinates of each of the 5 vertices after the translation?

   _____

3. Now slide the cutout shape 6 units down so that it is 5 units to the right and 6 units down from the original position and trace around it. What are the coordinates of each vertex after the translation?

   _____

A **reflection** is a flip or a mirror image.

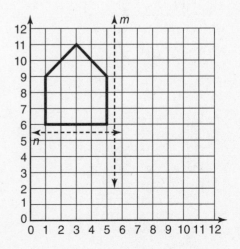

4. Place the cutout shape over the shape shown on the grid. Flip the house over line *m* and trace around it. The left side of the shape in the new position should be the same distance from the line as the right side was in the original position.

5. Place the cutout shape back in the original position. Flip the house over line *n* and trace around it.

Transformations (continued)

A **rotation** is a turn that moves a figure about a point. Each quarter turn
is the same as a 90 degree rotation.

6. Place the cutout shape over the shape on the
grid. Make a mark on the cutout at the same
place as the dot. Turn the shape around the
point clockwise so that the roof on the house
is now pointing to the right or at 3 o'clock. The
mark on the cutout should still be touching the
point. Trace around the figure. This is a $\frac{1}{4}$ turn.
How many degrees did the figure rotate?

_____

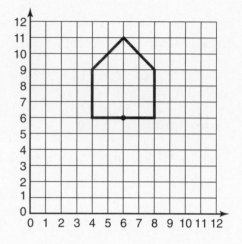

7. Rotate the shape a total of 180 degrees, or $\frac{1}{2}$
turn, from the original and trace around it.
In what direction is the roof of the house
now pointing?

_____

8. Rotate the shape a total of 270 degrees,
or $\frac{3}{4}$ turn, from the original and trace around
it. In what direction is the roof pointing?

_____

Tell whether the figures in each pair are related by a translation,
a reflection, or a rotation.

9.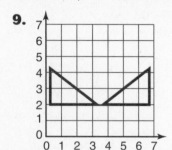

_____

10.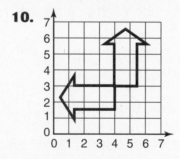

_____

11.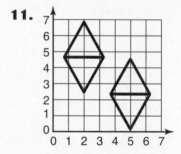

_____

12.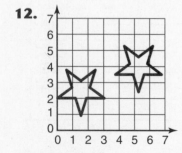

_____

13.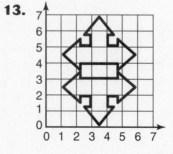

_____

14.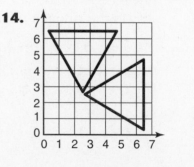

_____

Math Diagnosis and
Intervention System
Intervention Lesson   I17

Measuring and Classifying Angles

Materials protractor, straightedge, and crayons, markers, or
          colored pencils

A protractor can be used to measure and draw angles. Angles are
measured in degrees.

Use a protractor to measure the angle shown by
answering 1 to 2.

1. Place the protractor's center on the angle's
vertex and place the 0° mark on one side
of the angle.

2. Read the measure where the other side
of the angle crosses the protractor.
What is the measure of the angle?   _____

Use a protractor to draw an angle with a measure of 60°
by answering 3 to 5.

3. Draw $\overrightarrow{AB}$ by connecting the points shown
with the endpoint of the ray at point *A*.

4. Place the protractor's center on point *A*.
Place the protractor so the the 0° mark is
lined up with $\overrightarrow{AB}$.

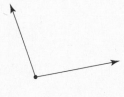

5. Place a point at 60°. Label it *C* and draw $\overrightarrow{AC}$.

Use a protractor to measure the angles shown,
if necessary, to answer 6 to 9.

6. Acute angles have a measure between 0° and
90°. Trace over the acute angles with blue.

7. Right angles have a measure of 90°. Trace
over the right angles with red.

8. Obtuse angles have a measure between 90°
and 180°. Trace over the obtuse angles with
green.

9. Straight angles have a measure of 180°. Trace
over the straight angles with orange.

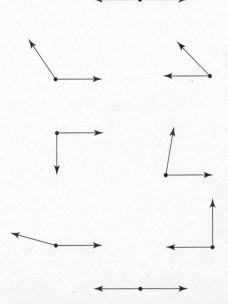

Name _____

Measuring and Classifying Angles (continued)

Classify each angle as acute, right, obtuse, or straight. Then measure
the angle.

10.

_____

_____

11.

_____

_____

12.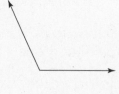

_____

_____

13.

_____

_____

14.

_____

_____

15.

_____

_____

Use a protractor to draw an angle with each measure.

16. 120°   **17.** 35°   **18.** 70°

19. Reasoning If two acute angles are placed next to each other to
form one angle, will the result always be an obtuse angle? Explain.
Provide a drawing in your explanation.

Angle Pairs

Adjacent angles are a pair of angles with a common vertex and a common side but no common interior points.

1. The picture at the right shows adjacent angles. Trace over the common side in the picture.

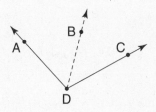

2. Name the two adjacent angles that share the side you traced.

   _____ and _____

Complementary angles are two angles whose measures add up to 90 degrees. **Supplementary angles** are two angles whose measures add up to 180 degrees.

3. One of the right angles in the diagram is formed by two smaller angles. These two angles are complementary. Name the complementary angles.

   _____ and _____

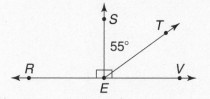

4. What is the measure of ∠SET?   _____

5. What is the measure of ∠TEV?   _____

6. Name an angle in the picture whose measure is 180°.   _____

7. Angle REV is divided into two angles, ∠RET and another one. Draw an arc on ∠RET. Name the other angle that makes up ∠REV. These two angles are supplementary.   _____

8. What angle is supplementary to ∠RES?   _____

When two lines intersect, angles are formed. Angles that are opposite one another with no common side are called **vertical angles.** Vertical angles have the same measure.

Angle Pairs (continued)

9. Draw an arc on ∠WOX. Name an angle
in the picture that does not have a
common side with ∠WOX.

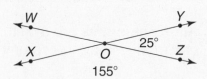

_____

10. What type of angles are ∠WOX and ∠YOZ?
Write the measure of ∠WOX on the picture. _____

11. What type of angles are ∠WOY and ∠YOZ?
Write the measure of ∠WOY on the picture. _____

12. What types of angles are ∠WOY and ∠XOZ? _____

Find the measure of each angle labeled with a letter.

13.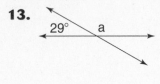

14. 165°
b

15.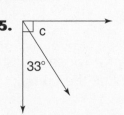

16.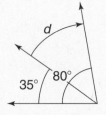

_____   _____   _____   _____

Find the measure of an angle that is complementary to an angle with
each measure.

17. 84°   **18.** 4°   **19.** 16°   **20.** 72°

_____   _____   _____   _____

Find the measure of each angle by using the picture at the right.

21. ∠NOT   **22.** ∠PON

_____   _____

23. ∠POQ   **24.** ∠ROS

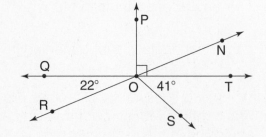

_____   _____

25. Reasoning What word can be used to describe two
intersecting lines whose vertical angles are 90°? _____

Name _____

Missing Angles in Triangles and Quadrilaterals

Materials index card and scissors

Find the relationship among angles in a triangle by answering 1 to 9.

1. Draw a triangle on an index card and cut it out.

2. Label each angle in the triangle with A, B, and C.

3. Cut out each corner of your triangle so that angles A, B, and C are separated from the triangle.

4. Start with angle A. Place the vertex on the point shown above and one side of the angle on the dashed line. Trace around the angle.

5. Next place angle B's vertex on the point and one side of the angle so that it is sharing a side with angle A. Trace around the angle.

6. Next place angle C's vertex on the point and one side of the angle so that it is sharing a side with angle B. Trace around the angle.

7. Reasoning What do you notice about the angles of a triangle?

8. Compare your results with that of other students. Do the angles of the triangle have the same relationship?   _____

9. What is the sum of the measures of the three angles in any triangle?   _____

Find the relationship among angles in a quadrilateral by answering 10 to 16.

10. Draw a quadrilateral, that does not have any right angles, on an index card and cut it out.

11. Label each of the angles in the quadrilateral with A, B, C, and D.

Name _____

Missing Angles in Triangles and Quadrilaterals (continued)

12. Cut out each corner of your
quadrilateral so that angles *A*, *B*, *C*,
and *D* are separated from the
quadrilateral.

13. Place the vertex of each angle on the
point shown. Position the angles so
that they are adjacent and share a
common side.

14. Reasoning What do you notice about the angles of a
quadrilateral?

15. Compare your results with that of other students. Do the
angles of their quadrilateral have the same relationship?   _____

16. What is the sum of the measures of the four angles in
a quadrilateral?   _____

Find the missing angle measures.

17.

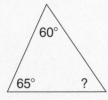

18.

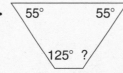

19.

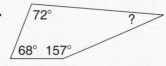

_____   _____   _____

20.

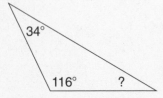

21.

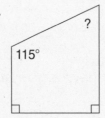

22.

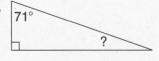

_____   _____   _____

Constructions

Materials compass and straightedge

Construct a segment congruent to $\overline{XY}$ by answering 1 to 3.

1. Use a compass to measure the length of $\overline{XY}$,
   by placing one point on X and the other on Y.

2. Draw a horizontal ray with endpoint W. Place the
   compass point on point W. Use the compass
   measure of $\overline{XY}$ to draw an arc intersecting the ray
   drawn. Label this intersection J.

3. Are $\overline{XY}$ and $\overline{WJ}$ congruent? _____

Construct an angle congruent to $\angle A$ by answering 4 to 6.

4. Place the compass point on A, and draw an arc
   intersecting both sides of $\angle A$. Draw a ray with
   endpoint S. With the compass point on S, use
   the same compass setting from $\angle A$ to draw an
   arc intersecting the ray at point T.

5. Use a compass to measure the length of the arc
   intersecting both sides of $\angle A$. Place the compass
   point on T. Use the same measure from $\angle A$ to draw
   an arc that intersects the first arc. Label the point of
   intersection R and draw the $\overrightarrow{SR}$.

6. Are $\angle A$ and $\angle RST$ congruent? _____

Construct a line perpendicular to $\overleftrightarrow{AB}$ by answering 7 to 9.

7. Open the compass to more than half the distance
   between A and B. Place the compass point at A
   and draw arcs above and below the line.

8. Without changing the compass setting, place the
   point at B. Draw arcs that intersect the arcs made
   from point A. Label the point of intersection
   above the line as C and below the line as D. Draw
   line CD.

9. Are $\overleftrightarrow{AB}$ and $\overleftrightarrow{CD}$ perpendicular? _____

Constructions (continued)

Construct a line that is parallel to $\overleftrightarrow{AB}$ on the previous page, by answering 10 to 12.

10. Draw point E on $\overleftrightarrow{CD}$ above point C.

11. Use points E and D to construct a line perpendicular to $\overleftrightarrow{CD}$. (Hint: See 7 and 8.) Label this line FG.

12. Are $\overleftrightarrow{AB}$ and $\overleftrightarrow{FG}$ parallel?   _____

Construct a triangle congruent to triangle LMN by answering 13 to 16.

13. Construct $\angle R$ congruent to $\angle L$.

14. On one side of $\angle R$, construct $\overline{RS}$ so that it is congruent to $\overline{LM}$. On the other side of $\angle R$, construct $\overline{RT}$ so that it is congruent to $\overline{LN}$.

15. Draw segment ST.

16. Are $\triangle LMN$ and $\triangle RST$ congruent?   _____

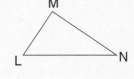

Construct a rectangle by answering 17 to 21.

17. Construct a line that is perpendicular to $\overleftrightarrow{PQ}$. Label the point of intersection G.

18. Use points P and G to construct another line perpendicular to $\overleftrightarrow{PG}$. Label the point of intersection H.

19. Choose a point on the first line and label it K. Construct segment HJ on the second line so that it is congruent to $\overline{GK}$.

20. Draw segment JK.

21. Reasoning How do you know that $GHJK$ is a rectangle?

Measuring Length to $\frac{1}{2}$ and $\frac{1}{4}$ Inch

Materials inch ruler for each student, crayons or markers.

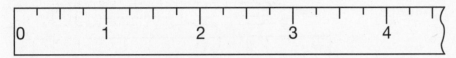

The distance between 0 and 1 on the ruler is one inch. So is the space between 1 and 2, 2 and 3, and so on.

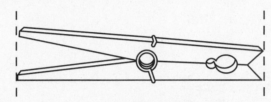

1. Line up the left edge of the clothespin with the 0 mark on the ruler. Is the clothespin's length closer to the 2 inch mark or the 3 inch mark? _____

2. What is the clothespin's length to the nearest inch? _____

3. How many spaces are between 0 and 1 on the ruler above? _____

4. So each space is what part of an inch? _____

5. Color the marks in the ruler above that are $\frac{1}{4}$ inch and $\frac{3}{4}$ inch from zero red. Then color the rest of the $\frac{1}{4}$ inch marks red including $1\frac{1}{4}$, $1\frac{3}{4}$, $2\frac{1}{4}$, $2\frac{3}{4}$, and so on. Color the mark that is $\frac{2}{4}$ or $\frac{1}{2}$ inch from zero blue. Then color the rest of the $\frac{1}{2}$ inch marks blue, including $1\frac{1}{2}$, $2\frac{1}{2}$, and so on.

6. What is the length of the clothespin to the nearest $\frac{1}{2}$ inch? _____

Measure the length of the cricket to the nearest inch, $\frac{1}{2}$ inch and $\frac{1}{4}$ inch.

7. nearest inch _____ inch

8. nearest $\frac{1}{2}$ inch _____ inches

9. nearest $\frac{1}{4}$ inch _____ inches

Measuring Length to $\frac{1}{2}$ and $\frac{1}{4}$ Inch (continued)

Measure each object to the nearest inch, $\frac{1}{2}$ inch, and $\frac{1}{4}$ inch.

10. Nearest inch: _____ inches

11. Nearest $\frac{1}{2}$ inch: _____ inches

Nearest $\frac{1}{4}$ inch: _____ inches

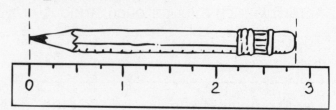

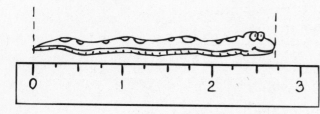

12. Nearest inch: _____ inches

13. Nearest $\frac{1}{2}$ inch: _____ inches

Nearest $\frac{1}{4}$ inch: _____ inches

14. Nearest inch: _____ inch

15. Nearest $\frac{1}{2}$ inch: _____ inches

Nearest $\frac{1}{4}$ inch: _____ inches

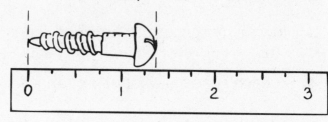

16. Reasoning Which gives the closest measurement, measuring
to the nearest inch, $\frac{1}{2}$ inch, or $\frac{1}{4}$ inch? Explain.

Using Customary Units of Length

A small paperclip is about 1 *inch* long.

A football is about 1 *foot* long.

A baseball bat is about 1 *yard* long.

Most people can walk a *mile* in about 15 minutes.

What is the best unit to measure each?

1. The length of your pencil   _____

2. The length of the Mississippi River   _____

3. The height of a desk   _____

4. The length of your school   _____

Answer 5 to 7 and use the table to find how many inches are in 4 feet.

5. 1 foot = _____ inches

6. To find how many inches are in 4 feet, multiply 4 × 12 inches.

   4 × 12 inches = _____ inches

7. How many inches are in 4 feet? _____

Customary Units of Length	
1 foot (ft) = 12 inches
1 yard (yd) = 3 feet
1 yard = 36 inches
1 mile (mi) = 5,280 feet
1 mile = 1,760 yards

Answer 8 to 10 and use the table to find how many feet are in 5 yards, 2 feet.

8. 1 yard = _____ feet

9. How many feet are in 5 yards?   5 × 3 feet = _____ feet

10. How many feet are in 3 yards, 2 feet?   15 feet + 2 feet = _____ feet

Using Customary Units of Length (continued)

Which unit would you use to measure each item?
Write *inch*, *foot*, *yard*, or *mile*.

11. The length of a gerbil

_____

12. The length of a football field

_____

13. The height of a door

_____

14. The distance to the sun

_____

Circle the better estimate.

15. The distance you travel on
an airplane

560 yards   or   560 miles

16. The height of a full grown
adult giraffe

6 feet   or   6 yards

17. The length of a bar of soap

3 inches   or   7 inches

18. The length of your bed

7 feet   or   7 yards

Find each missing number.

19. 2 yards = _____ feet

20. 3 feet = _____ inches

21. 4 yards = _____ inches

22. 3 yards, 2 feet = _____ feet

23. 1 foot, 9 inches = _____ inches

24. 2 yards, 2 feet = _____ inches

25. Reasoning What unit would you use to measure the length
of an earthworm? Explain why your choice is the best unit.

Name _____

Using Metric Units of Length

Materials centimeter ruler for each student

Your finger is about 1 centimeter wide.

1. Use the width of your finger to estimate the length of the pencil.

   Estimate: _____ of my finger widths = about _____ centimeters

2. Line up the 0 mark on the ruler with the left edge of the pencil.

3. What is the length of the pencil
   to the nearest centimeter?   _____

A dime is about 1 *millimeter* thick.

A new crayon is almost
1 *decimeter* long.

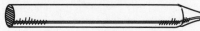

A door knob is about 1 *meter*
above the floor.

Most people can walk a
kilometer in about 10 minutes.

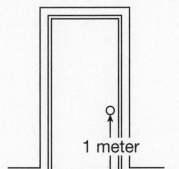

1 meter

What is the best unit to measure each?

4. the length of your finger   _____

5. the distance across your state   _____

6. the length of a lady bug   _____

Using Metric Units of Length (continued)

Answer 7 to 9 and use the table to find how many centimeters
are in 4 meters, 76 centimeters.

7. 1 meter = _____ centimeters

8. How many centimeters are
in 4 meters?

4 × 100 cm = _____ cm

9. How many centimeters are in
4 meters, 76 centimeters?

400 cm + 76 cm = _____ cm

Metric Units of Length		
1 centimeter (cm)	=	10 millimeters
1 decimeter (dm)	=	10 centimeters
1 meter (m)	=	100 centimeters
1 kilometer (km)	=	1,000 meters

Estimate the length of the spoon. Then measure to the
nearest centimeter.

10.

_____

What unit would you use to measure each item?
Write *millimeter*, *centimeter*, *decimeter*, *meter*, or *kilometer*.

11. An adult's height

_____

12. Distance traveled on vacation

_____

Choose the best estimate.

13. Length of a car

5 decimeters or 5 meters

14. Length of a calculator

12 centimeters or 12 decimeters

Find each missing number.

15. 3 meters 18 centimeters = _____ centimeters

16. 6 meters 3 centimeters = _____ centimeters

Using Customary Units of Capacity

Materials 6 stations each equipped with the following: cup, pint, quart, and gallon measuring containers labeled with their units; one of 6 different sized containers to be measured labeled A, B, C, D, E, and F; enough rice to fill the container at least one and a half times; a piece of paper taped into a funnel for containers with small openings

The **capacity** of a container is the amount the container can hold.

Go to each station. Find the row in the table which matches the letter on the container. Complete the table by doing the following.

Customary Units of Capacity	
1 pint (pt) = 2 cups (c)	
1 quart (qt) = 2 pints	
1 gallon (gal) = 4 quarts	

- Decide what unit to use to measure the lettered container.

- Estimate the capacity of the container.

- Then measure the capacity of the container by filling the cup, pint, quart, or gallon container with rice and pouring it into the container until that container is full.

	Container	Best Unit	Estimate	Capacity
1.	A			
2.	B			
3.	C			
4.	D			
5.	E			
6.	F			

Using Customary Units of Capacity (continued)

What unit would you use to measure the capacity of each item?
Write *cup, pint, quart,* or *gallon*.

7. A pond

8. A watering can

9. A juice box

_____   _____   _____

10. A kitchen sink

11. A coffee mug

12. A pitcher of water

_____   _____   _____

13.

1 pt or 1 gal

14.

1 c or 1 qt

15.
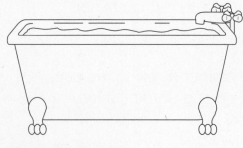

25 c or 25 gal

16.

2 c or 2 qt

17. Reasoning Martin bought a pint of grape juice. Franco
bought a gallon of orange juice. Seth bought a quart of
apple juice. List the type of juice in order from least to
greatest capacities.

_____

18. Reasoning Romona is making spaghetti. Explain why the
better estimate for the amount of water boiling in the pot is
2 quarts and not 2 cups.

Using Metric Units of Capacity

A water bottle holds about 1 liter.   A medicine dropper holds about
1 milliliter.

←1 milliliter

Garrison wants to find out how much
a small bottle of perfume holds.
Decide whether he should measure
the amount in liters or
milliliters by answering 1 and 2.

Metric Units of Capacity	
1 liter (L) = 1,000 milliliters (mL)	

1. Would the perfume bottle hold more
than a medicine dropper?   _____

2. Would the perfume bottle hold more
than a water bottle?   _____

Since the perfume bottle holds less than 1 liter, it should be
measured in milliliters.

Decide whether 2 milliliters or 2 liters is a better estimate
for the amount of soup the bowl holds by answering 3 to 5.

3. Would 2 medicine droppers fill the bowl?   _____

4. Would 2 water bottles fill the bowl?   _____

5. Which is better estimate?   _____

6. Reasoning Explain why the better estimate for the
amount of water a bucket holds is 8 liters and not
8 milliliters.

Using Metric Units of Capacity (continued)

Choose a unit to measure the capacity of each item. Write *liters* or *milliliters*.

7. A can of soda   **8.** A swimming pool   **9.** A kitchen sink

_____   _____   _____

10. A birdbath   **11.** A measuring spoon   **12.** A soup bowl

_____   _____   _____

Circle the best estimate.

13.

4 L or 400 mL

14.

6 L or 650 mL

15.
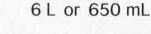

7 L or 700 mL

16.
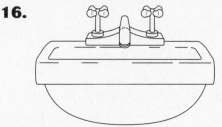

6 L or 60 mL

17.
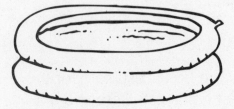

4 liters   1 liter   40 liters

Name _____

Using Customary Units of Weight

The **weight** of an object is the measure of how heavy the object is.

A key weighs
about 1 ounce.

A football weighs
about 1 pound.

A bull weighs
about 1 ton.

Lucy wants to find out how much her cat weighs. Decide whether she should use ounces, pounds, or tons by answering 1 to 3.

Customary Units of Weight
1 pound (lb) = 16 ounces (oz)
1 ton (T) = 2,000 pounds

1. Would the cat be
heavier than a key?   _____

2. Would the cat be heavier than a football?   _____

3. Would the cat be heavier than a bull?   _____

Since the cat would weigh more than a key, and more than a football, but less than a bull, it should be measured in pounds.

When measuring the weight of light objects, use ounces. When measuring the weight of heavier objects, use pounds. When measuring the weight of very heavy objects, like a bull, use tons.

Decide whether 4 pounds or 4 ounces is a better estimate for the weight of a carrot by answering 4 to 6.

4. Would a carrot feel as heavy as 4 footballs? _____

5. Would a carrot feel as heavy as 4 keys?   _____

6. Which is a better estimate for the weight of a carrot,
4 ounces or 4 pounds?

_____

Using Customary Units of Weight (continued)

Choose a unit to measure the weight of each item. Write *ounces*,
pounds, or *tons*.

7. Eyeglasses

_____

8. An adult whale

_____

9. A dog

_____

10. A tomato

_____

11. An eraser

_____

12. A school bus

_____

13. A ship

_____

14. A guitar

_____

15. A desk

_____

16. A mouse

_____

17. A motor scooter

_____

18. A feather

_____

Circle the best estimate for the weight of each item.

19. The space shuttle

45 lb   or   45 T

20. A bowling ball

10 oz   or   10 lb

21. A slice of bread

1 oz   or   1 lb

22. A turkey

15 oz   or   15 lb

23. A chicken

7 oz   or   7 lb

24. A hippopotamus

5 lb   or   5 T

25. Reasoning Explain why the better estimate for the weight of
a pencil is 1 ounce and not 1 pound.

26. Reasoning If you had a bag of apples that weighed a pound
and a bag of marshmallows that weighed a pound, which
bag would have more items in it? Explain.

Using Metric Units of Mass

The amount of matter in an object is its **mass**.

A cantaloupe has
a mass of about
1 kilogram.

1 kilogram

A grape has
a mass of about
1 gram.

1 gram

Chi wants to find the mass of a bag of
potatoes. Decide whether he should
use grams or kilograms by answering
1 and 2.

Metric Units of Mass
1 kilogram (kg) = 1,000 grams (g)

1. Would the bag be heavier than
a grape?   _____

2. Would the bag be heavier than
a cantaloupe?   _____

Since the bag of potatoes has a mass greater than a grape, and
greater than a cantaloupe, it should be measured in kilograms.

When measuring the mass of lighter objects, use grams. When
measuring the mass of heavier objects, use kilograms.

Decide whether 300 kilograms or 300 grams is a better
estimate for the mass of a bag of pretzels by answering 3 to 5.

3. Would a bag of pretzels feel as heavy as
300 cantaloupes?   _____

4. Would a bag of pretzels feel as heavy as
300 grapes?   _____

5. Which is the better estimate for the mass of
a bag of pretzels, 300 kilograms or 300 grams? _____

Name _____

Using Metric Units of Mass (continued)

Choose a unit to measure the mass of each item. Write *grams*
or *kilograms*.

6. car _____   **7.** pencil _____

8. calculator _____   **9.** dog _____

10. key _____   **11.** hairbrush _____

12. flowerpot _____   **13.** flower _____

Choose the better estimate.

14.

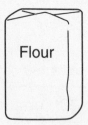

200 g   or   2 kg

15.

40 g   or   4 kg

16.

250 g   or   250 kg

17.

5 g   or   5 kg

18. Reasoning Why would you measure the mass of a goldfish
in grams and not kilograms?

19. Reasoning Explain why the better estimate for the mass of
a baby is 4 kilograms and not 4 grams.

Time to the Quarter Hour

Use the clocks at the right to answer 1 to 6.

hours minutes

1. What two numbers is the hour hand between?

_____ and _____

2. Since the hour hand has not reached the 1, it is after 12:00. Write 12 for the hours in the digital clock.

3. What number is the minute hand on?   _____

4. Each number on the clock represents 5 minutes after the hour. Count by 5s. How many minutes is it after 12?   _____

5. Write 15 for the minutes in the digital clock.

The clock shows 12:15 or twelve fifteen.

6. Write 12:15 in two other ways.

15 minutes past _____;   quarter past _____

Use the clock at the right to answer 7 to 11.

7. What two numbers is the hour hand between?

_____ and _____

8. What is the hour? _____

9. What number is the minute hand on?   _____

10. Count by 5s. How many minutes is it after the hour?   _____

11. Write the time in three ways.

_____ : _____;   _____ minutes past _____;   _____ past _____

Name _____

Time to the Quarter Hour (continued)

For Exercises 12 to 15, use the clock at the right.

12. What time is shown on the clock?   _____ : _____

13. What hour is it about to be?   _____

14. Count by 5s. How many minutes is it before 2 o'clock?   _____

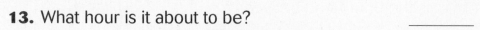

15. Write the time in two other ways.

15 minutes to _____;   quarter to _____

Write the hour and then the minutes after the hour. Then circle the two correct times.

16.

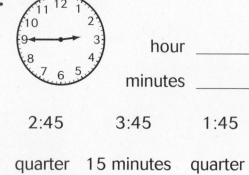

hour _____

minutes _____

2:45   3:45   1:45

quarter   15 minutes   quarter
to 2   to 3   past 2

17.

hour _____

minutes _____

4:15   6:15   5:15

quarter   quarter   15 minutes
past 6   past 5   to 5

18.

hour _____

minutes _____

7:30   8:30   9:30

half   quarter   30 minutes
past 8   past 8   past 9

19.

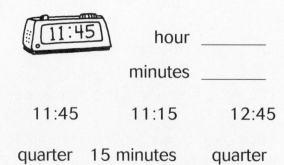

hour _____

minutes _____

11:45   11:15   12:45

quarter   15 minutes   quarter
to 11   to 11   to 12

Telling Time

Find the time on the clock by answering 1 to 8.

1. What two numbers is the hour hand between?

_____ and _____

hours minutes

2. Since the hour hand has not reached the 6, it is after 5:00. Write 5 for the hours in the digital clock.

3. It takes the minute hand 5 minutes to move from one number to the next. To find the minutes, first count by 5s from the 12 to the 7. Then count by 1s for each small mark after the 7.

4. How many minutes is it after 5? _____
Write the minutes in the digital clock above.

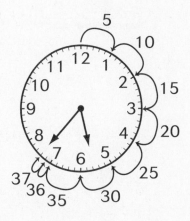

5. Write the time in three different ways.

_____ : _____;

_____ thirty-seven;

_____ minutes past 5

6. To find how many minutes before the next hour, count the other way. Count by 5s from the 12 to the 8, then count by 1s for each small mark after the 8.

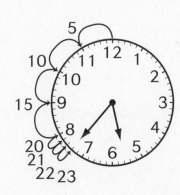

7. How many minutes is it before 6? _____

8. Write the time another way.

_____ minutes to 6

9. Write the time shown on the clock at the right in two different ways.

2 : 24

_____ twenty-_____;   _____ minutes past 2

Telling Time (continued)

Write the time shown on each clock in two ways.

10.

_____

_____

11.

_____

_____

12.

_____

_____

13.

_____

_____

14.

_____

_____

15.

_____

_____

16. Reasoning When finding the number of minutes on the clock
at the right, why do you first count by 5s and then by ones?

Units of Time

Benny spent 3 weeks at his cousin's house. Find how many days Benny spent at his cousin's by using the table and answering 1 to 3.

1. 1 week = _____ days

2. To find how many days are in 3 weeks, multiply 3 × 7 days.

   3 × 7 days = _____ days

3. How many days did Benny spend at his cousin's? _____ days

Relating Units of Time		
1 week	=	7 days
1 day	=	24 hours
1 hour	=	60 minutes

The talent show lasted 2 hours and 17 minutes. Find how many minutes the talent show lasted by using the table and answering 4 to 6.

4. 1 hour = _____ minutes

5. First, find the number of minutes in 2 hours. Then add the 17 minutes.

   2 × 60 minutes = _____ minutes

   120 minutes + 17 minutes = _____ minutes

6. How many minutes did the talent show last? _____ minutes

Cindy left her radio on for 4 days, 5 hours. Find how many hours Cindy's radio stayed on by using the table and answering 7 to 9.

7. 1 day = _____ hours

8. First find the number of hours in 4 days. Then add the 5 hours.

   4 × 24 hours = _____ hours

   96 hours + 5 hours = _____ hours

9. How many hours did Cindy's radio stay on? _____ hours

Name _____

Units of Time (continued)

Find the missing numbers.

10. 6 hours = _____ minutes   **11.** 8 days = _____ hours

12. 9 weeks = _____ days   **13.** 5 hours = _____ minutes

14. 5 days, 3 hours = _____ hours   **15.** 1 hour, 2 minutes = _____ minutes

16. 6 weeks, 6 days = _____ days   **17.** 3 days, 16 hours = _____ hours

18. The first space flight when humans orbited the earth lasted
1 hour, 48 minutes.
How many minutes did the flight last?   _____

19. The first space flight when humans orbited the moon
lasted 6 days, 3 hours. How many hours did the
mission last?   _____

20. It normally takes a duck egg 4 weeks, 2 days to
hatch. How many days is 4 weeks, 2 days?   _____

21. It normally takes a pigeon egg 2 weeks, 4 days to
hatch. How many days is 2 weeks, 4 days?   _____

22. Reasoning A chicken egg normally hatches in 21 days.
A turkey egg normally hatches in 3 weeks, 5 days. How
many more days does it normally take a turkey egg to
hatch than a chicken egg? Explain how you solved.

23. Eddie ran a marathon in 4 hours and 7 minutes. His goal
was to finish the race in less than 250 minutes. Did Eddie
achieve his goal? Explain your reasoning.

Elapsed Time

The party starts at 2:00 P.M. and ends at 4:45 P.M. How long is the party?

Start   **End**

1. How many hours from 2:00 P.M. to 4:00 P.M.?   _____ hours

2. How many minutes from 4:00 P.M. to 4:45 P.M.?   _____ minutes

3. How long did the party last?   _____ hours, _____ minutes

School starts at 8:20 A.M. and ends at 3:30 P.M. How long does school last?

Start   **End**

4. How many hours from 8:20 A.M. to 3:20 P.M.?   _____ hours

5. How many minutes from 3:20 P.M. to 3:30 P.M.?   _____ minutes

6. How long does school last?   _____ hours, _____ minutes

Reasoning The flight lasted 3 hours 20 minutes. If the plane took off at 4:10 P.M., what time did it land?

7. What time is 3 hours after 4:10 P.M.?   _____ P.M.

8. What time is 20 minutes after 7:10 P.M.?   _____ P.M.

9. What time did the plane land?   _____ P.M.

Elapsed Time (continued)

Find the elapsed time.

10. Start Time: 1:00 P.M.
End Time: 8:00 P.M.

_____

11. Start Time: 7:00 A.M.
End Time: 10:35 A.M.

_____

12. Start Time: 11:35 A.M.
End Time: 3:50 P.M.

_____

13. Start Time: 6:10 P.M.
End Time: 12:25 A.M.

_____

14. Start Time: 2:00 P.M.
End Time: 6:05 P.M.

_____

15. Start Time: 9:20 A.M.
End Time: 2:40 P.M.

_____

16. Start Time: 4:35 P.M.
End Time: 5:15 P.M.

_____

17. Start Time: 8:15 A.M.
End Time: 2:55 A.M.

_____

18. Reasoning The baseball game started at
3:00 P.M. It lasted 2 hours and 45 minutes.
What time did the baseball game end?   _____

19. Reasoning Erin got home from the
soccer match at 5:20 P.M. She went to
bed 3 hours and 45 minutes later.
What time did she go to bed?   _____

20. Reasoning The rainstorm began at
1:15 P.M. Marco's class came in from
recess 25 minutes earlier. What time
did the class come in from recess?   _____

21. Reasoning What is 30 minutes before
12:25 P.M.?   _____

Name _____

Temperature

Temperature is the measure of how hot or how cold something is.

Temperature can be measured in **degrees Fahrenheit** (°F) or **degrees Celsius** (°C).

1. Look at the thermometer at the right. Does the right side show °F or °C? _____

2. What is the temperature in °C? _____

Find the temperature in °F by answering 3 to 7.

3. Which side shows °F? _____

4. Look at the left side of the thermometer. How many spaces are between 30° and 40°? _____

5. What is 40° − 30°? _____

6. Each space on the left side of the thermometer equals how many degrees? 10° ÷ 5 = _____

7. Start at 60°F. Then count up by 2s to where the dark bar stops.

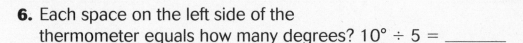

60, 62, _____, _____, _____

The top of the dark bar is at 68, so the temperature is 68°F.

8. Reasoning Would you build a snowman in 34°F or 64°F weather? Use the table to decide and explain your reasoning.

	°F	°C
Water boils	212	100
Normal body temperature	98.6	37
Room temperature	68	20
Water Freezes	32	0

Temperature (continued)

Choose the better temperature for each activity.

9. bicycle riding   **10.** camping   **11.** ice skating   **12.** wearing shorts

   30°F or 70°F   0°C or 30°C   32°F or 72°F   35°C or 100°C

Choose the better estimate for the temperature.

13. hot pizza   **14.** ice cream   **15.** bathwater   **16.** cold drink

   80°F or 160°F   0°C or 30°C   45°F or 95°F   0°C or 10°C

Write each temperature in °F and °C.

17.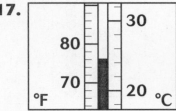

_____°F   _____°C

18.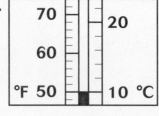

_____°F   _____°C

19.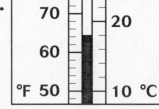

_____°F   _____°C

20.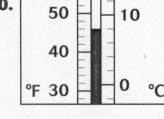

_____°F   _____°C

21.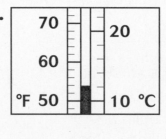

_____°F   _____°C

22.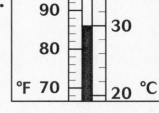

_____°F   _____°C

23. One cold morning, the temperature was 35°F. The
temperature rose to 53°F later in the day. How many
degrees had the temperature increased?   _____

24. Reasoning This morning the temperature was 65°F.
Then it rose 3°. Then the temperature dropped 10°.
What was the final temperature?   _____

Name _____

Converting Customary Units of Length

Mayla bought 6 yards of ribbon. How many feet of ribbon did she buy?

Answer 1 to 4 to change 6 yards to feet.

To change larger units to smaller units, multiply. To change smaller units to larger units, divide.

Customary Units of Length
1 foot (ft) = 12 inches (in.)
1 yard (yd) = 36 (in.)
1 yard (yd) = 3 feet (ft)
1 mile (mi) = 5,280 feet (ft)
1 mile (mi) = 1,760 yards (yd)

1. 1 yard = _____ feet

2. Do you need to multiply or divide to change from yards to feet?   _____

3. What is 6 × 3 feet? _____ feet

4. How many feet of ribbon did Mayla buy? _____

Deidra bought 60 inches of ribbon. How many feet of ribbon did she buy? Change 60 inches to feet by answering 5 to 8.

5. 1 foot = _____ inches

6. Do you need to multiply or divide to change from feet to inches?   _____

7. What is 60 ÷ 12? _____

8. How many feet of ribbon did Deidra buy? _____

Troy ran 4 miles. How many yards did he run? Change 4 miles to yards by answering 9 to 11.

9. 1 mile = _____ yards

10. Do you need to multiply or divide to change from miles to yards?   _____

11. 4 miles = _____ yards

12. How many yards did Troy run? _____

Name _____

Converting Customary Units of Length (continued)

Find each missing number.

13. 1 yd = _____ ft   **14.** 72 in. = _____ ft   **15.** 3 mi = _____ ft

16. 5,280 ft = _____ mi   **17.** 5 mi = _____ yd   **18.** 4 yd = _____ ft

19. 48 in. = _____ ft   **20.** 1 yd = _____ in.   **21.** 6 mi = _____ ft

22. 5 yd = _____ ft   **23.** 3 mi = _____ yd   **24.** 2 ft = _____ in.

25. 21 ft = _____ yd   **26.** 3 yd = _____ in.   **27.** 4 yd = _____ in.

For Exercises 28 to 32 use the information in the table.

28. How many inches did Speedy crawl?

_____ inches

29. How many inches did Pokey crawl?

_____ inches

30. How many inches did Pickles crawl?

_____ inches

Turtle Crawl Results

Turtle	Distance
Snapper	38 inches
Speedy	3 feet
Pokey	2 yards
Pickles	4 feet

31. Reasoning Which turtle crawled the greatest distance? _____

32. Reasoning Which turtle crawled the least distance? _____

33. Reasoning Explain how you could use addition to find how many yards are in 72 inches.

Converting Customary Units of Capacity

The bread recipe calls for
2 cups of milk. How many
fluid ounces (fl oz) is that?
Change 2 cups to fluid ounces
by answering 1 to 3.

To change larger units to
smaller units, multiply.
To change smaller units
to larger units, divide.

Customary Units of Capacity
1 tablespoon (tbsp) = 3 teaspoons (tsp)
1 cup (c) = 8 fluid ounces (fl oz)
1 pint (pt) = 2 cups (c)
1 quart (qt) = 2 pints (pt)
1 gallon (gal) = 4 quarts (qt)

1. 1 cup = _____ fluid ounces

2. Do you need to multiply or divide to change from cups to
fluid ounces? _____

3. What is 2 × 8 fluid ounces? _____ fluid ounces

4. How many fluid ounces of milk is 2 cups? _____

Change 18 teaspoons to tablespoons by answering 5 to 8.

5. 1 tablespoon = _____ teaspoons

6. Do you need to multiply or divide to change from teaspoons
to tablespoons? _____

7. What is 18 ÷ 3? _____

8. 18 teaspoons = _____ tablespoons

Javier made 5 quarts of punch. How many pints did he make?
Change 5 quarts to pints by answering 9 to 12.

9. 1 quart = _____ pints

10. Do you need to multiply or divide to change from quarts
to pints? _____

11. 5 quarts = _____ pints

12. How many pints of punch did Javier make? _____

Converting Customary Units of Capacity (continued)

Find each missing number.

13. 40 fl oz = _____ c   **14.** 3 gal = _____ qt   **15.** 15 tsp = _____ tbsp

16. 4 qt = _____ pt   **17.** 12 pt = _____ qt   **18.** 8 c = _____ fl oz

19. 3 tbsp = _____ tsp   **20.** 18 c = _____ pt   **21.** 14 gal = _____ qt

22. 24 fl oz = _____ c   **23.** 16 qt = _____ pt   **24.** 32 qt = _____ gal

25. 3 pt = _____ c   **26.** 8 qt = _____ gal   **27.** 4 c = _____ pt

Lee has the supplies listed in the table to use in his science fair project. Use the table for Exercises 28 to 32.

28. How many cups of orange juice does Lee have?   _____ cups

29. How many cups of milk does Lee have?   _____ cups

30. How many cups of water does Lee have?   _____ cups

Science Project Supplies

Liquid	Amount
Orange Juice	32 fl oz
Milk	1 pt
Vinegar	3 c
Water	3 pt

31. Reasoning Which liquid does Lee have the most of?   _____

32. Reasoning Which liquid does Lee have the least of?   _____

33. Reasoning Lee also needs 4 tablespoons of baking soda, but he can only find a teaspoon to measure with. How many teaspoons of baking soda does he need?   _____

34. Reasoning Explain how to convert 6 pints to quarts.

Converting Customary Units of Weight

An average size ostrich egg weighs 3 pounds. How many ounces does an average size ostrich egg weigh?

Change 3 pounds to ounces by answering 1 to 4.

To change larger units to smaller units, multiply. To change smaller units to larger units, divide.

Customary Units of Weight
1 pound (lb) = 16 ounces (oz)
1 ton (T) = 2,000 pounds (lb)

1. 1 pound = _____ ounces

2. Do you need to multiply or divide to change from pounds to ounces? _____

3. What is 3 × 16 ounces? _____ ounces

4. How many ounces does an average size ostrich egg weigh? _____

An African elephant can weigh up to 22,000 pounds. How many tons can an African elephant weigh? Change 22,000 pounds to tons by answering 5 to 8.

5. 1 ton = _____ pounds

6. Do you need to multiply or divide to change from pounds to tons? _____

7. What is 22,000 ÷ 2,000? Hint: Think 22 ÷ 2. _____

8. How many tons can an African elephant weigh? _____

An Asian elephant can grow to a little more than 5 tons. How many pounds can the Asian elephant weigh? Change 5 tons to pounds by answering 9 to 12.

9. 1 ton = _____ pounds

10. Do you need to multiply or divide to change from tons to pounds? _____

Converting Customary Units of Weight (continued)

11. 5 tons = _____ pounds

12. How many pounds can an Asian elephant weigh? _____

Find each missing number.

13. 8 lb = _____ oz   **14.** 12 T = _____ lb   **15.** 48 oz = _____ lb

16. 24,000 lb = _____ T   **17.** 80 oz = _____ lb   **18.** 22 T = _____ lb

19. 64 oz = _____ lb   **20.** 4,000 lb = _____ T   **21.** 22 lb = _____ oz

22. 14,000 lb = _____ T   **23.** 160 oz = _____ lb   **24.** 10 T = _____ lb

25. 4 T = _____ lb   **26.** 32 oz = _____ lb   **27.** 16,000 lb = _____ T

For Exercises 28 to 32, use the information in the table.

28. How many pounds of
carrots were shipped? _____ pounds

29. How many pounds of
peas were shipped? _____ pounds

30. Reasoning Which vegetable shipment
was the heaviest?

_____

Vegetable Shipments

Vegetable	Amount
Carrots	4 T
Celery	12,000 lb
Peas	2 T
Potatoes	16,000 lb

31. Reasoning Which vegetable shipment was the lightest?   _____

32. Reasoning Five tons of corn were shipped. Explain how
to find how many more pounds of potatoes than corn
were shipped.

Converting Metric Units

The table shows how metric units are related. Every unit is 10 times greater than the next smaller unit. Abbreviations are shown for the most commonly used units.

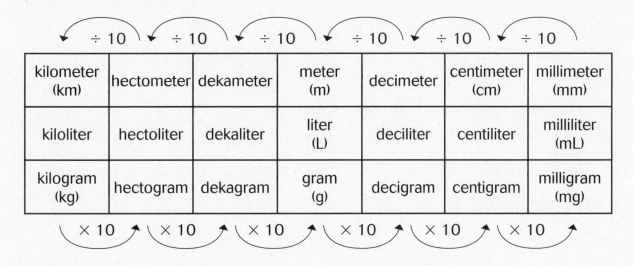

To change from one metric unit to another, move the decimal point to the right or to the left to multiply or divide by 10, 100, or 1,000.

The length of a sheet of paper is 27.9 centimeters. Convert 27.9 cm to millimeters by answering 1 to 3.

1. To move from centimeters to millimeters in the table, do you move right or left? _____

2. How many jumps are there between centimeters and millimeters in the table? _____

Move the decimal one place to the right to convert from centimeters to millimeters. This is the same as multiplying by 10.

3. What is the length of the paper in millimeters? _____mm

Convert 27.9 cm to meters by answering 4 to 6.

4. To move from centimeters to meters in the table, do you move right or left? _____

Converting Metric Units (continued)

5. How many jumps are there between centimeters and
meters in the table?   _____

Move the decimal two places to the left to convert from
centimeters to meters. This is the same as dividing by 100.

6. What is the length of the paper in meters?   _____ m

Tell the direction and number of jumps in the table for each conversion.
Then convert.

7. 742 cm to meters   **8.** 12.4 kg to g   **9.** 0.62 L to mL

_____ jumps _____   _____ jumps _____   _____ jumps _____

_____ m   _____ g   _____ mL

Write the missing numbers.

10. 150 mg = _____ g   **11.** 2,600 m = _____ km   **12.** 0.4 L = _____ mL

13. 300 mL = _____ L   **14.** 4 kg = _____ mg   **15.** 2.6 m = _____ mm

16. 2,670 mg = _____ g **17.** 34 cm = _____ mm   **18.** 16 L = _____ mL

For Exercises 19 to 21 use the table at the right.

19. What is the height of the
Petronas Towers in centimeters?

_____

20. What is the height of the CN Tower
in meters?

_____

Building	Height
John Hancock Center	344 m
Petronas Towers	452 m
Sears Tower	44,200 cm
CN Tower	553,000 mm

21. What is the height of the John
Hancock Center in km?

_____

22. Reasoning Which is shorter, 15 centimeters or 140 millimeters? Explain.

Converting Between Measurement Systems

The table shows the relationships between customary and metric unts. Only the equivalent for inches and centimeters is exact. All other equivalents are approximate. The symbol ≈ means "approximately equal to."

A standard CD has a diameter of 4.75 inches. How many centimeters is the diameter of the CD?

Convert 4.75 inches to centimeters by answering 1 to 4.

Customary and Metric Unit Equivalent
Length
1 in. = 2.54 cm
1 m ≈ 39.97 in.
1 mi ≈ 1.61 km
Weight and Mass
1 oz ≈ 28.35 g
1 kg ≈ 2.2 lb
1 metric ton (t) ≈ 1.102 tons (T)
Capacity
1 L ≈ 1.06 qt
1 gal ≈ 3.79 L

1. How many centimeters equal one inch?   _____

To change larger units to smaller units multiply. To change smaller units to larger units, divide.

2. Do you need to multiply or divide to change from inches to centimeters?   _____

3. What is 4.75 × 2.54 to the nearest tenth?   _____

4. How many centimeters is the diameter of the CD?   _____cm

The average golden retriever weighs 65 pounds. What is the approximate mass in kilograms of an average golden retriever?

Convert 65 pounds to kilograms by answering 5 to 8.

5. According to the table, how many pounds equal about one kilogram?   _____

6. Do you need to multiply or divide to change from pounds to kilograms?   _____

7. What is 65 ÷ 2.2 rounded to the nearest tenth?   _____

8. What is the approximate mass in kilograms of an average golden retriever?   _____kg

Converting Between Measurement Systems (continued)

Complete. Round to the nearest tenth, if necessary.

9. 3.8 m ≈ ■ in.   **10.** 50 g ≈ ■ oz   **11.** 3 L ≈ ■ gal

_____   _____   _____

12. 44 in. ≈ ■ cm   **13.** 2.5 t ≈ ■ T   **14.** $3\frac{1}{2}$ kg ≈ ■ lb

_____   _____   _____

15. $5\frac{1}{4}$ qt ≈ ■ L   **16.** 100 km ≈ ■ mi   **17.** 10 cm ≈ ■ in.

_____   _____   _____

18. 2 cm ≈ ■ in.   **19.** 2.4 t ≈ ■ T   **20.** $8\frac{2}{3}$ m ≈ ■ yd

_____   _____   _____

21. $3\frac{1}{2}$ yd ≈ ■ m   **22.** 500 lb ≈ ■ kg   **23.** 11 in. ≈ ■ m

_____   _____   _____

24. Rewrite the materials list at the right using meters for
fabric, inches for thread, and kilograms for stuffing.
Write your conversions to the nearest tenth below:

fabric: _____m   thread: _____in.   stuffing: _____kg.

Materials List
$1\frac{1}{2}$ yd fabric
65 cm thread
$1\frac{3}{4}$ lb stuffing

25. Reasoning A necklace measures $16\frac{1}{2}$ inches.

About how many centimeters is this to the nearest tenth?   _____

Name _____

Units of Measure and Precision

Materials inch and centimeter rulers, rectangle measuring

$3\frac{5}{16}$ inches by $\frac{7}{8}$ inches for each student, pair, or group

The smaller the units on the scale of a measuring device, the more precise the measurement.

Explore precision by answering 1 to 12.

1. What are the dimensions of the cut out rectangle to the nearest inch? _____

2. Draw a rectangle with the dimensions found in item 1.

3. What are the dimensions of the cut out rectangle to the nearest eighth inch? _____

4. Draw a rectangle with the dimensions found in item 3.

5. Which of the rectangles you drew is closest in size to the cut out rectangle? _____

6. Which unit is more precise, inch or eighth inch? _____

7. What are the dimensions of the cut out rectangle to the nearest centimeter? _____

8. Draw a rectangle with the dimensions found in item 7.

9. What are the dimensions of the cut out rectangle to the nearest millimeter? _____

10. Draw a rectangle with the dimensions found in item 9.

Units of Measure and Precision (continued)

11. Which of the last two rectangles you drew is closest
in size to the cut out rectangle?   _____

12. Which unit is more precise, centimeter or millimeter?   _____

13. Reasoning Which unit is more precise,
eighth inch or millimeter?   _____

Find the length of the crayon to each unit.

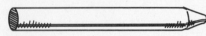

14. whole inch _____   **15.** quarter inch _____   **16.** eighth inch _____

17. sixteenth inch _____   **18.** centimeter _____   **19.** millimeter _____

20. Which measure of the crayon is the most precise?   _____

Measure each line segment to the nearest $\frac{1}{8}$ inch and nearest centimeter.

21. _____   **22.** _____

Measure each line segment to the nearest $\frac{1}{16}$ inch and nearest millimeter.

23. _____   **24.** _____

Circle the more precise measure in each.

25. 4 km or 2 mi   **26.** 2 gal or 8 L   **27.** 3 in. or 4 cm

More Units of Time

Natalia, one of the finalists at a dance marathon, danced 1,740 minutes. Tony, the other finalist, danced 28 hours and 20 minutes. Which finalist danced the longest?

Solve by answering 1 to 6.

To change a smaller unit to a larger unit, divide. To change a larger unit to a smaller unit, multiply.

Units of Time
1 minute = 60 seconds
1 hour = 60 minutes
1 day = 24 hours
1 week = 7 days
1 month = about 4 weeks
1 year = 52 weeks
1 year = 12 months
1 year = 365 days
1 leap year = 366 days
1 decade = 10 years
1 century = 100 years
1 millennium = 1,000 years

1. How many minutes are in an hour? _____

2. Do you need to multiply or divide to change from minutes to hours? _____

3. What is 1,740 ÷ 60? _____

4. How many hours equal 1,740 minutes? _____

5. Compare. Write >, <, or =.

   1,740 min ◯ 28 h 20 min

6. Which finalist danced the longest? _____

Fred is two years and ten days older than Ron. Alfonzo is 745 days older than Ron. Who is older, Fred or Alfonzo?

Solve by answering 7 to 12.

7. How many days are in a year? _____

8. Do you need to multiply or divide to change years to days? _____

9. What is (2 × 365) + 10? _____

10. How many days are two years and ten days? _____

More Units of Time (continued)

11. Compare. Write $>$, $<$, or $=$.   2 years 10 days $\bigcirc$ 745 days

12. Who is older, Fred or Alfonzo?   _____

13. Reasoning Find the missing numbers.

75 minutes = _____ hour, _____ minutes

Compare. Write $>$, $<$, or $=$.

14. 2 minutes $\bigcirc$ 126 seconds   **15.** 4 weeks $\bigcirc$ 28 days

16. 2 weeks and 3 days $\bigcirc$ 16 days   **17.** 50 weeks $\bigcirc$ 350 days

18. 50 hours $\bigcirc$ 2 days   **19.** 208 minutes $\bigcirc$ 4 hours

20. 2 decades $\bigcirc$ 34 years   **21.** 28 months $\bigcirc$ 2 years

22. 23 weeks $\bigcirc$ 161 days   **23.** 6 hours $\bigcirc$ 150 minutes

Find each missing number.

24. 420 seconds = _____ minutes   **25.** 156 weeks = _____ years

26. 105 days = _____ weeks   **27.** 3 hours = _____ seconds

28. Reasoning Jerome slept 8 hours and 35 minutes on
Tuesday night while Manuel slept 525 minutes. Who
slept longer? Explain how you solved.

More Elapsed Time

Elapsed time is the amount of time that passes between the beginning and the end of an event.

Simone's school starts at 8:40 A.M. and ends at 3:45 P.M. How much time does Simone spend at school?

Find the elapsed time that Simone is at school by answering 1 to 7.

1. How much time passes
from 8:40 to 9:00?   _____

2. How much time passes
from 9:00 to 12:00?   _____

3. How much time passes
from 12:00 to 3:00?   _____

4. How much time passes
from 3:00 to 3:45?   _____

5. What is 20 minutes + 3 hours +
3 hours + 45 minutes?   _____

6. What is 65 minutes in hours and minutes?   _____

7. How much time does Simone spend at school?   _____

After school Simone spends 20 minutes walking home and she has 30 minutes before she must leave for soccer practice. What time must she leave for soccer practice?

Find the end time by answering 8 to 10.

8. School ends at 3:45 P.M. If Simone spends 20 minutes
walking home, what time does she arrive at home?   _____

Name _____

More Elapsed Time (continued)

9. Simone must leave for practice 30 minutes later.
What time is it 30 minutes after 4:05? _____

10. What time must Simone leave for soccer practice? _____

11. Start: 3:05 A.M.   **12.** Start: 10:45 A.M.   **13.** Start: 4:58 P.M.
Finish: 5:37 A.M.   Finish: 3:07 P.M.   Finish: 6:56 P.M.

_____   _____   _____

Write the time each clock will show in 38 minutes.

14.    **15.**

_____   _____

Write the time each clock will show in 3 hours and 35 minutes

16.    **17.**

_____   _____

Find each start or finish time.

18. Start: 2:24 P.M.   **19.** Start: _____

Elapsed time: Elapsed time:
3 hours and 32 minutes   55 minutes

Finish: _____   Finish: 11:30 A.M.

20. A theater started a movie promptly at 6:30 P.M. If the
movie finished at 8:22 P.M., how long was the movie? _____

Elapsed Time in Other Units

Salvador went to bed at 10:40 P.M. and woke up at a quarter to 8 the next morning. How many hours did Salvador sleep?

One way to find the elapsed time is with a number line.

Find the elapsed time by answering 1 to 6.

Elapsed Time

| 10:00 P.M. | 12:00 A.M. | | | | | | | | | 8:00 A.M. |

1. Label each of the tick marks on the number line.

2. Plot and label a point on the number line that represents 10:40 P.M.

3. What time is a quarter to 8 in the morning? _____

4. Make jumps of length one hour on the number line, until you get close to 7:45, without going past it. How many jumps did you make? _____

5. Draw a small jump to 7:45 A.M.
   How much time is represented by all the jumps? ____ h _____ min

6. How many hours did Salvador sleep? ____ h _____ min

Another way to find elapsed time is to subtract.
End Time − Start Time = Elapsed Time

Find the elapsed time another way by answering 7 to 14.

$$\begin{array}{r} 11\text{ h }\boxed{}\text{ min} \\ \cancel{12\text{ h }00\text{ min}} \\ -\ 10\text{ h }40\text{ min} \\ \hline \boxed{} \end{array}$$

7. Subtract to find the elapsed time before midnight.
   12 hours is the same as 11 hours and how many minutes?

   12 h = 11 h _____ min
   Rename 12 hours 00 minutes at the right.

8. Subtract the minutes and record at the right. 60 min − 40 min = _____ min

9. Subtract the hours and record at the right. 11 h − 10 h = _____ h

10. How long did Salvador sleep before midnight? ____ h _____ min

11. How long did Salvador sleep after midnight? ____ h _____ min

Elapsed Time in Other Units (continued)

12. Add the elapsed time before midnight to the elapsed time after midnight to find the total elapsed time. Record at the right.

20 min + 45 min = _____ min   1 h + 7 h = _____ h

1 h 20 min
+ 7 h 45 min
_____

13. Rename 8 hours 65 minutes.

65 minutes = ____ h _____ min   8 hours 65 minutes = ____ h _____ min

14. How many hours did Salvador sleep?   ____ h _____ min

Find each elapsed time.

15. 9:15 A.M. to 4:05 P.M.

_____

16. Quarter to 8 in the evening to 2:30 A.M.

_____

17. 1:26 P.M. to 5:56 A.M.

_____

18. Quarter after 12 noon to 9:30 P.M.

_____

Find each start or end time.

19. Start: 10:24 P.M.

Elapsed time: 3 h and 41 min

Finish: _____

20. Start: _____

Elapsed time: 12 h 55 min

Finish: 4:30 A.M.

Add or subtract.

21.   6 h 20 min
       − 3 h 40 min
       _____

22.   3 h 38 min
       + 6 h 47 min
       _____

23.   2 h 39 min
       +   56 min
       _____

24.   5 h 10 min
       − 2 h 55 min
       _____

25.   5 h 24 min
       + 3 h 41 min
       _____

26.   1 h 35 min
       −   56 min
       _____

27. Reasoning An airplane takes off at 11:50 P.M. and lands at 8:12 A.M. How long was the plane in the air?   _____

Temperature Changes

Degrees Fahrenheit are customary units used to measure temperature. **Degrees Celsius** are metric units used to measure temperature.

The weatherman reports that a cold front is coming. She predicted outside temperatures as shown on the thermometers.

Find the temperature change by answering 1 to 6.

1. Label each of the marks between 40 and 50 on the thermometer that shows the temperature at 8:00 A.M.

2. What is the predicted temperature at 8:00 A.M.? _____°F

3. Label each of the marks between 20 and 30 on the thermometer that shows the temperature at 11:00 A.M.

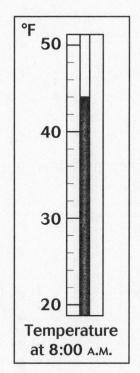

Temperature at 8:00 A.M.

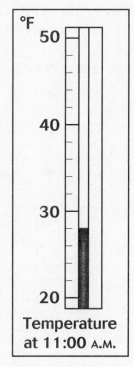

Temperature at 11:00 A.M.

4. What is the predicted temperature at 11:00 A.M. according to the thermometer? _____°F

5. Is the temperature predicted to increase or decrease between 8:00 and 11:00? _____

6. By how much is it predicted the temperature will decrease? _____°F

7. **Reasoning** How could you find the temperature change from 8:00 A.M. to 11:00 A.M., using addition or subtraction?

The temperature in a room was 18°C. After a heater was turned on, the temperature increased by 7 degrees Celsius. Find the temperature after the heater was turned on by answering 8 to 10.

Temperature Changes (continued)

8. Shade the thermometer at the right to show the beginning temperature in the room

9. Shade 7 degrees above the beginning temperature.

10. What is the temperature after
the heater is turned on?   _____°C

11. Reasoning How could you find the temperature after
the heater was turned on, using addition or subtraction?

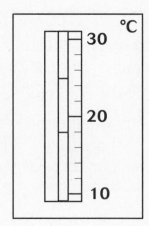

Tell whether each temperature change is an increase or decrease. Find the change.

12.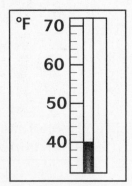

_____

13.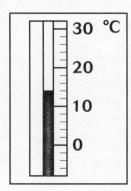

_____

Tell what the temperature would be after the change described.

14.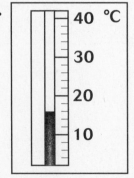

Increase of 12°C

_____

15.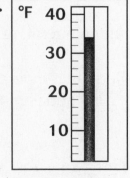

Decrease of 22°F

_____

16.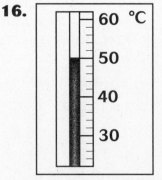

Decrease of 18°C

_____

Perimeter

Materials crayons or markers, centimeter ruler for each student.

Find the perimeter of the figure at the right by answering 1 to 3. **Perimeter** is the distance around a figure. Each space between lines equals 1 unit.

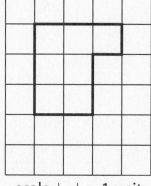

scale: |−| = 1 unit

1 unit   2 units

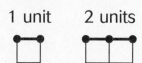

1. Trace the figure with a crayon or marker. Count the number of spaces as you trace.

2 How many spaces did you trace? _____

3. What is the perimeter of the figure? _____ units

You can also find the perimeter by adding the lengths of the sides.

Find the perimeter of the figure to the right by answering 4 to 6.

4. How many sides does this figure have? _____

5. Trace over the sides as you count and record the length of each side.

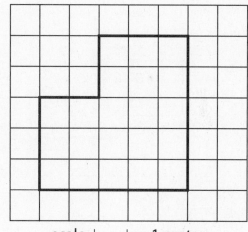

scale: |−−| = 1 meter

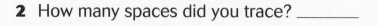

_____ + _____ + _____ + _____ + _____ + _____ = _____

6. What is the perimeter of the figure? _____ meters

Find the perimeter of the rectangle by answering 7 to 8.

Opposite sides of a rectangle have equal lengths.

7. Record the length of the sides. Find the sum.

10 + 3 + _____ + _____ = _____

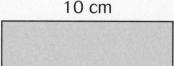

10 cm

3 cm

8. What is the perimeter of the rectangle? _____ cm

Perimeter (continued)

9. **Reasoning** Use a ruler to measure each side of the figure in inches. What is the perimeter of the figure?

_____

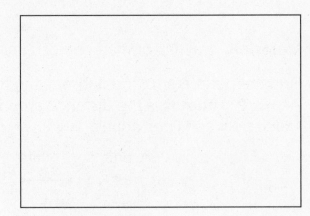

Find the perimeter of each figure.

10.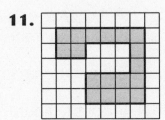

_____

11.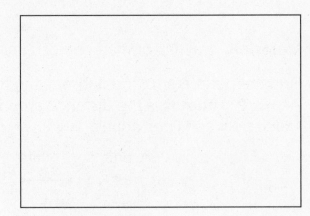

_____

12.

3 in.   5 in.

4 in.

_____

13.

5 cm

1 cm   [   ]   1 cm

5 cm

_____

14.

9 cm

9 cm

_____

15.

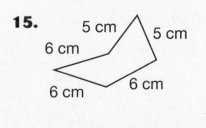

5 cm   5 cm
6 cm
6 cm   6 cm

_____

16. **Reasoning** If the length of one side of a square is 3 inches, what is the perimeter of the square? Explain your answer.

Name _____

Finding Area on a Grid

Materials crayons or markers

Area is the number of square units needed to cover the region inside a figure.

Find the area of the rectangle by answering 1 and 2.

1. Color each grid square inside the rectangle. Count as you color. How many grid squares did you color? _____

2. What is the area of the rectangle?

_____ square units

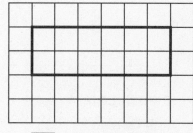

☐ = 1 square unit

Find the area of the polygon by answering 3 and 4.

3. Color each grid square inside the polygon. Count as you color. How many grid squares did you color? _____

4. What is the area of the polygon? _____ square feet

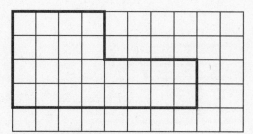

☐ = 1 square foot

Estimate the area of the triangle by answering 5 to 8.

5. Color the whole squares blue. How many squares did you color? _____

6. Combine partial square to make whole squares. Color the partial squares red. The partial squares make up about how many whole squares? _____

7. Add. 6 + 3 = _____

8. What is the estimated area of the triangle?

_____ square inches

☐ = 1 square inch

Finding Area on a Grid (continued)

Find each area. Write your answer in square units.

9.

10.

11.

_____

_____

_____

Find each area. Write your answer in square units.

12.

13.

14.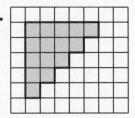

_____

_____

_____

Judy baked several different shapes of crackers and wants
to know which is largest. Each cracker was placed on a grid.
Estimate the area of each cracker in Exercises 15 to 17.

15. Triangle

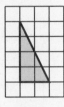

16. Hexagon

17. Quadrilateral

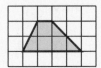

_____

_____

_____

18. Which cracker in Exercises 15–17 has the greatest area?

More Perimeter

Jonah's pool is a rectangle. The pool is 15 feet long and 10 feet wide. What is the perimeter of the pool?

Find the perimeter of the pool by answering 1 to 3.

1. Write in the missing measurements on the pool shown at the right.

2. Add the lengths of the sides.

10 ft + _____ ft + 15 ft + _____ ft = _____ ft

3. What is the perimeter of the pool? _____ ft

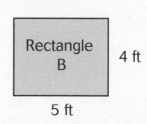

15 ft

10 ft   _____ ft

_____ ft

Find a formula for the perimeter of a rectangle by answering 4 to 10.

Rectangle A   3 in.

8 in.

Rectangle B   4 ft

5 ft

4. Write the side lengths of the rectangle.

8 + 3 + _____ + 3 = _____ in.

5. Rearrange the numbers.

8 + 8 + 3 + _____ = _____ in.

6. Rewrite the number sentence.

2(8) + 2 (_____) = _____ in.

16 + _____ = _____ in.

7. Write the side lengths of the rectangle.

5 + 4 + _____ + _____ = _____ ft

8. Rearrange the numbers.

5 + 5 + _____ + _____ = _____ ft

9. Rewrite the number sentence.

2(5) + 2(_____) = _____ ft

8 + _____ = _____ ft

10. Complete the table.

Rectangle	Length	Width	Perimeter
A	8		2(_____) + 2(3)
B			2(5) + 2(4)
Any	ℓ	w	$2\ell + 2$ _____

More Perimeter (continued)

The formula for the perimeter of a rectangle is $P = 2\ell + 2w$

11. Reasoning Use the formula to find the perimeter of Jonah's pool.

$$P = \quad 2\ell \quad + \quad 2w$$

$$P = 2(\underline{\quad}) + 2(\underline{\quad}) = \underline{\quad} + \underline{\quad} = \underline{\quad} \text{ ft}$$

12. Is the perimeter the same as you found on the previous page? _____

A square is a type of rectangle where all of the side lengths are equal.

Find a formula for the perimeter of the square by answering 13 to 15.

13. Add to find the perimeter of the square shown at the right.

_____ + _____ + _____ + _____ = _____

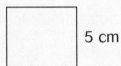

5 cm

14. What could you multiply to find
the perimeter of the square? _____

15. If s equals the length of a side of a
square, how could you find the perimeter? $P = $ _____

Find the perimeter of the rectangle with the given dimensions.

16. $\ell = 9$ mm, $w = 12$ mm

17. $\ell = 13$ in., $w = 14$ in.

_____

_____

18. $\ell = 2$ ft, $w = 15$ ft

19. $\ell = 17$ cm, $w = 25$ cm

_____

_____

Find the perimeter of the square with the given side.

20. $s = 2$ yd   **21.** $s = 10$ in.   **22.** $s = 31$ km   **23.** $s = 11$ m

_____   _____   _____   _____

24. Reasoning Could you use the formula for the perimeter of
a rectangle to find the perimeter of a square? Explain your
reasoning.

Area of Rectangles and Squares

Maria's flower garden is in the shape of rectangle that measures 6 feet long and 4 feet wide. What is the area of the garden?

Find a formula for area of a rectangle by answering 1 to 6.

1. The rectangle at the right is a model of the garden. How many squares are in the model? _____

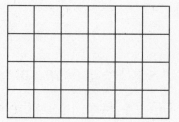

2. What is the area of the garden? _____ square feet

3. What is the length of the garden? _____ feet

4. What is the width of the garden? _____ feet

5. What could you multiply to find the area of the garden? _____

6. Find the area of each rectangle by counting squares. Write the area in the table below. Complete the table.

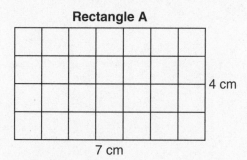

Rectangle A
4 cm
7 cm

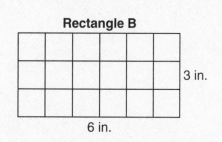

Rectangle B
3 in.
6 in.

Rectangle	Area	Length	Width	Product
Maria's garden	24	6	4	6 × 4
A		7		7 × _____
B				_____ × _____
Any	Any	ℓ	w	ℓ × _____

Name _____

Area of Rectangles and Squares (continued)

The formula for the area of a rectangle is $A = \ell \times w$ or $A = \ell w$.

7. Reasoning Use the formula to find the area of a rectangle
that is 8 meters long and 5 meters wide.

$A = \qquad \ell \qquad \times \qquad w$

$A = (\text{_____}) \times (\text{_____}) = \text{_____}$ square meters

A square is a type of rectangle where all of the side lengths are equal.

Find a formula for the area of the square shown by answering 8
and 9.

8. Use the formula $A = \ell w$ to find the area of the square.

_____ × _____ = _____ mm^2

8 mm

9. If s equals the length of a side of a square,
how could you find the area of any square? $A =$ _____

Find the area of each figure.

10.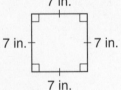

11.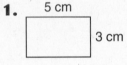

12.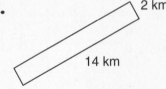

_____   _____   _____

Find the area of the rectangle with the given dimensions.

13. $\ell = 15$ mm, $w = 4$ mm   **14.** $\ell = 3$ cm, $w = 10$ cm

_____   _____

15. Reasoning The area of a square is 81 square feet.
What is the length of each side?   _____

16. Reasoning Using only whole numbers, what are all the possible
dimensions of a rectangle with an area of 12 square centimeters?

Name _____

Area of Irregular Figures

Materials crayons or markers

Find the area of the irregular figure on the right.

1. How many squares are there? _____

2. What is the area of the figure? _____ square meters

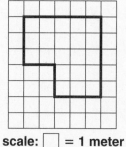

scale: ☐ = 1 meter

You can also find the area of the figure by breaking it into 2 rectangles and then finding the sum of the areas of the 2 rectangles.

3. What is the area of Rectangle 1?

$A = \ell \times w$

$A = 2 \times$ _____ = _____ sq meters

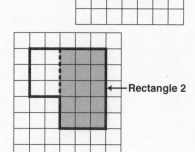

Rectangle 1→

4. What is the area of Rectangle 2?

$A = \ell \times w$

$A = 3 \times$ _____ = _____ sq meters

5. What is the sum of the two areas?

Area of Rectangle 1 + Area of Rectangle 2 = Total Area

        6   + _____   = _____ sq meters

6. Is the area the same as the one you found by counting? _____

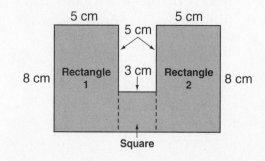

←Rectangle 2

Find the area of the shaded figure below by answering 7 to 12.

7. Divide the figure into 2 rectangles and a square.

8. What is the area of Rectangle 1?

5 × _____ = _____ sq cm

5 cm   5 cm

5 cm

8 cm   Rectangle 1   3 cm   Rectangle 2   8 cm

Square

Area of Irregular Figures (continued)

9. What is the area of Rectangle 2?   5 × _____ = _____ sq cm

10. What is the area of the square?   3 × _____ = _____ sq cm

11. Add the areas of the three smaller figures.

Rectangle 1   + Rectangle 2 +   Square   =   Total Area

_____ sq cm +   40 sq cm   + _____ sq cm = _____ sq cm

12. What is the area of the figure? _____ sq cm

13.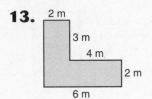

14.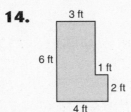

15.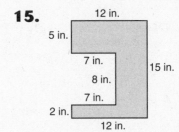

_____

_____

_____

16.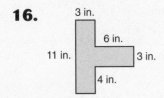

17.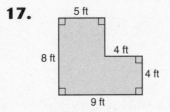

18.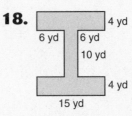

_____

_____

_____

19. Bob wants to carpet the room shown. How many square yards of carpet will he need? _____

20. Reasoning How could you use subtraction to find the area of the figure below?

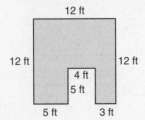

Rectangles with the Same Area or Perimeter

Materials colored pencils or crayons.

Ms. Arellano's class is making a sand box shaped like a rectangle for the kindergarten class. They have 16 feet of wood to put around the sand box. What length and width should the sand box be so it has the greatest area?

Each of the rectangles in the grid at the right has a perimeter of 16 feet. Find which rectangle has the greatest area by answering 1 to 3.

1. Complete the table. The formula for area of a rectangle is $A = \ell \times w$.

Rectangle	Length	Width	Area (square units)
W			
X			
y			
Z			

2. What are the length and width of the rectangle with the greatest area? _____

3. What length and width should Ms. Arellano's class use for the sand box? _____

4. **Reasoning** Tracy told Tomas that if a two rectangles have the same perimeter, they have the same area. Is Tracy correct? Explain your reasoning.

Mr. Katz has 30 carpet squares to make a reading area in his classroom. Each square is one foot on a side. He wants to make the area in the shape of a rectangle with the least possible border. How should he arrange the carpet squares?

Rectangles with the Same Area or Perimeter (continued)

Each of the rectangles on the grid at
the right has an area of 30 square feet.
Find which one has the least perimeter
by answering 5 to 8.

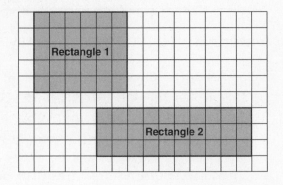

Rectangle 1

Rectangle 2

5. What is the perimeter of Rectangle 1?

$P = 2\ell + 2w = 2(_____) + 2(5)$

$= _____ + _____ = _____$ feet

6. What is the perimeter of Rectangle 2?

$P = 2\ell + 2w = 2(_____) + 2(3) = _____ + _____ = _____$ feet

7. What is the length and width of the rectangle with
the least perimeter?   _____

8. How should Mr. Katz arrange the carpet squares? _____

Draw a rectangle with the same area as the one shown.
Then find the perimeter of each.

9.   P = 12 in.

2 in.

4 in.

10.   P = 18 cm

3 cm

6 cm

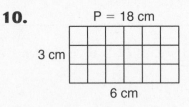

11.   P = 22 m

4 m

7 m

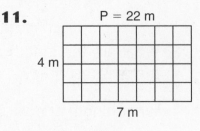

_____   _____   _____

_____   _____   _____

12. Reasoning Marco has 36 feet of fencing, what
is the greatest area that can he can fence?   _____

Area of Parallelograms

Materials grid paper, colored pencils or markers, scissors

Find the area of the parallelogram on the grid by answering 1 to 10.

1. Trace the parallelogram below on a piece of grid paper. Then cut
out the parallelogram.

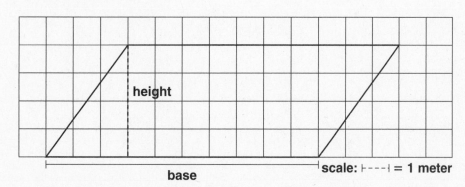

2. Cut out the right triangle created by the dashed line.

3. Take the right triangle and move it to the right of the parallelogram.

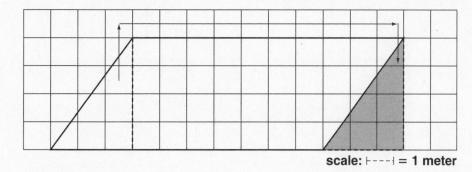

4. What shape did you create? _____

5. Is the area of the parallelogram the same as the area of the rectangle? _____

6. What is the area of the rectangle? $A = \ell \times w =$ _____ $\times 4 =$ _____ sq meters

7. What is the base b of the parallelogram? _____ meters

8. What is the height h of the parallelogram? _____ meters

9. What is the base times the height of the parallelogram? _____

10. Is this the same as the area of the rectangle? _____

Area of Parallelograms (continued)

The formula for the area of a parallelogram is $A = bh$.

11. Use the formula to find the area of a parallelogram with a base of
9 ft and a height of 6 feet.

$A =$ b $\times$ h

$A = (_____) \times (_____) = _____$ square feet

Find the area of each figure.

12.

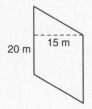

_____

13.

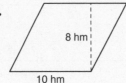

_____

14.

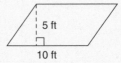

_____

15.

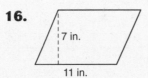

_____

16.

_____

17.

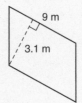

_____

18.

_____

19.

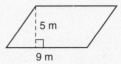

_____

20.

_____

21. Reasoning The area of a parallelogram is
100 square millimeters. The base is 4 millimeters.
Find the height.   _____

Name _____

Area of Triangles

Materials markers, crayons or colored pencils

Jerah is making a model of a sailboat. The sail of the boat is a triangle. The sail has a base of 4 inches and a height of 3 inches. What is the area of the sail? The triangle below. is a model of the sail.

Find the area of the sail by answering 1 to 5.

1. Color the triangle at the right.

2. How does the area of the triangle compare to the area of the rectangle?

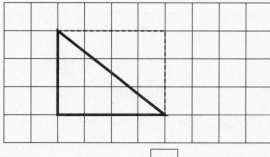

Area of the triangle = _____ × the area of the rectangle

$\square$ = 1 square inch

3. What is the area of the rectangle? _____ square inches

4. What is the area of the triangle? _____ square inches

5. What is the area of Jerah's sail? _____ square inches

Nina is making a model of a sailboat with a sail in the shape of a triangle like the one shown below. The base of her sail is 7 inches and the height is 4 inches. Find the area of the triangle by answering 6 to 10.

6. Color the triangle at the right.

7. How does the area of the triangle compare to the area of the rectangle?

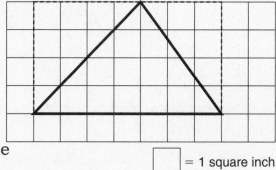

Area of the triangle = _____ × the area of the rectangle

$\square$ = 1 square inch

8. What is the area of the rectangle? _____ square inches

9. What is the area of the triangle? _____ square inches

10. What is the area of Nina's sail? _____ square inches

Area of Triangles (continued)

11. Complete the table.

Triangle	Base	Height	Area
Jerah's sail		3	
Nina's sail			
Any	b	h	$\frac{1}{2} \times b \times$ _____

The formula for the area of a triangle is $A = \frac{1}{2} \times b \times h$ or $A = \frac{1}{2}bh$.

12. Reasoning Use the formula to find the area of Jerah's sail.

$$A = \frac{1}{2} \times \quad b \quad \times \quad h$$

$$A = \frac{1}{2} \times \text{_____} \times \text{_____} = \text{_____ square inches}$$

13. Is the area the same as you found on the previous page? _____

Find the area of each figure.

14.

6 cm

7 cm

_____

15.

7 in.

16 in.

_____

16.

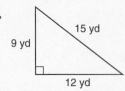

15 yd

9 yd

12 yd

_____

Find the area of the triangle with the measurements shown below.
Give the correct units.

17. $b = 22$ yd
   $h = 20$ yd

_____

18. $b = 8$ mm
   $h = 4$ mm

_____

19. $b = 12$ cm
   $h = 4$ cm

_____

20. The front of a tent is in the shape of a triangle with
a height of 6 feet and a base of 10 feet. What is the
area of the front of the tent?

_____

Circumference

Materials Round objects, at least 3 for each group; tape measure or
ruler and string for each student

Circumference (C) is the distance around a circle.

1. Complete the table for 3 different round objects.

Object	Circumference (*C*)	Diameter (*d*)	*C* ÷ *d*

The last column should be close to π, ≈ 3.14, every time.

If $C \div d = \pi$, then $C = \pi d$.

2. What is the relationship between the diameter (*d*)
and radius (*r*) of any circle?   *d* = _____

3. If $C = \pi d$ and $d = 2r$, what is a formula for
the circumference using the radius (*r*)? $C = 2\pi$ _____

Use a formula to find the circumference of each circle to the nearest
whole number.

4.

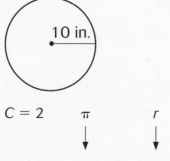

10 in.

$C = 2 \quad \pi \quad\quad r$

$\downarrow \quad\quad \downarrow$

$C \approx 2 \times 3.14 \times$ _____

$C \approx$ _____ inches

5.

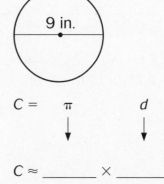

9 in.

$C = \quad \pi \quad\quad d$

$\downarrow \quad\quad \downarrow$

$C \approx$ _____ × _____

$C \approx$ _____ inches

Name _____

Circumference (continued)

Find the circumference of each circle to the nearest whole number.
Use 3.14 or $\frac{22}{7}$ for π.

6.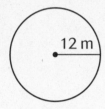
12 m

_____

7.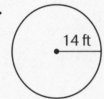
14 ft

_____

8.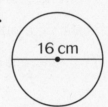
16 cm

_____

9.
28 yd

_____

10.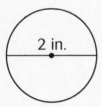
2 in.

_____

11.
13 mm

_____

12.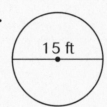
15 ft

_____

13.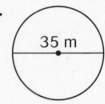
35 m

_____

14.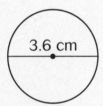
3.6 cm

_____

15.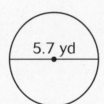
5.7 yd

_____

16.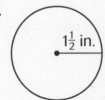
$1\frac{1}{2}$ in.

_____

17.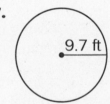
9.7 ft

_____

18. Miranda wants to sew lace around the outside of a pillow.
The pillow has a diameter of 35 centimeters. How much
lace does Miranda need?   _____

19. Reasoning Find the distance around the figure at the right.
Round your answer to the nearest whole number

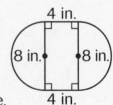
4 in.
8 in.   8 in.
4 in.

_____

20. Reasoning Write a formula for the circumference (C) of a semicircle.

_____

Name _____

Area of a Circle

Materials crayons, markers, or colored pencils, grid paper, compass

Sue places a water sprinkler in her yard. It sprays water 5 feet in every direction. What is the area of the lawn the sprinkler waters?

Find a formula for the area of a circle and find the area of the lawn by answering 1 to 8.

1. The sprinkler sprays in a circle.
What is the radius of the circle? _____

2. The grid at the right is a diagram of the sprinkler. Color all the whole squares within the circle one color. How many whole squares did you color?

_____ whole squares

3. Combine partial squares to estimate whole squares. Color the partial squares, using a different color. The partial squares make up about how many whole squares?

_____ whole squares

4. Add. What is a good estimate of the area of the circle?   _____ units

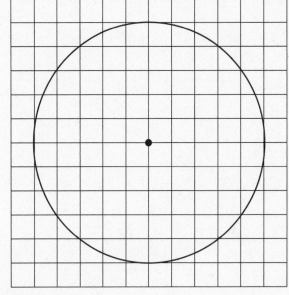

5. Draw circles on grid paper with each radius listed in the table. Estimate the area and complete the table. Use 3.14 for π. Round πr^2 to the nearest whole number.

Estimated Area	Radius (r)	r^2	πr^2
80	5	25	
	3		28
	6		

6. Is the estimated area close to πr^2 each time? _____

Name _____

Area of a Circle (continued)

The formula for the area of a circle is $A = \pi r^2$.

7. Use the formula to find the area of a circle with radius 5 feet by filling in the blanks at the right. Round to the nearest whole number.

$A = \pi \qquad r^2$

$\downarrow \qquad\qquad \downarrow$

$A \approx 3.14 \times$ _____

8. What is the approximate area of lawn watered by the sprinkler? Include the correct units.

$A \approx$ _____

about _____

Find the area of each circle to the nearest whole number.
Use either 3.14 or $\frac{22}{7}$ for π.

9.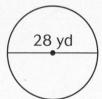
28 yd

_____

10.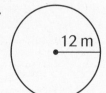
12 m

_____

11.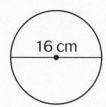
16 cm

_____

12.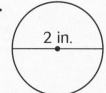
2 in.

_____

13.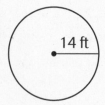
14 ft

_____

14.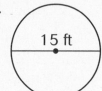
15 ft

_____

15.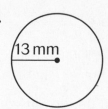
13 mm

_____

16.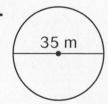
35 m

_____

17. A cement ring the shape of a circle surrounds a flag pole. The ring is 6 meters across. How much sod, to the nearest whole square meter, does it take to cover the area inside the ring?

_____

18. **Reasoning** Chase used 3.14 for π and found the circumference of a circle to be 47.1 feet. Find the area of the circle to the nearest whole number.

_____

Surface Area of Rectangular Prisms

Materials scissors, copy of nets for the square and rectangular prisms
from *Teaching Tool Masters*, for each student

The surface area of a rectangular prism is the sum of the areas of all
its faces.

How much wrapping paper does it take to cover the
box shown at the right, not counting overlap?

Find the surface area of the prism by answering 1 to 7.

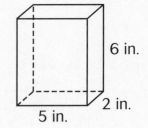

6 in.

2 in.

5 in.

1. Cut out and fold the net for a rectangular
prism. Use the folded prism to write
the length of each edge on the net.
Use lengths shown in the prism
above. Unfold the net and use it
to label the lengths of the edges
on the net at the right.

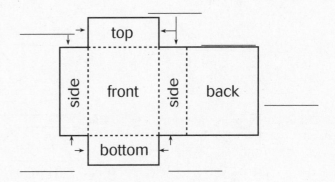

2. What is the area of the top
and bottom of the prism?

   $5 \times 2 =$ _____ in.²

3. What is the area of the side of the prism?

   _____ × _____ = _____ in.²

4. What is the area of the front and back of the prism?

   _____ × _____ = _____ in.²

5. Add the areas of all the faces to find the surface area.

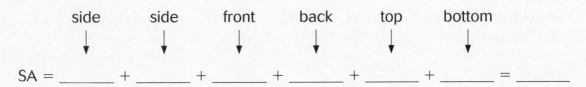

   side   side   front   back   top   bottom

   SA = _____ + _____ + _____ + _____ + _____ + _____ = _____

6. What is the surface area of the prism? _____ in.²

7. How much wrapping paper does it take to cover the box? _____

Surface Area of Rectangular Prisms (continued)

8. Cut out and fold the net for the square prism
and use it to find the surface area of the prism
at the right.

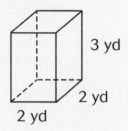

3 yd

2 yd

2 yd

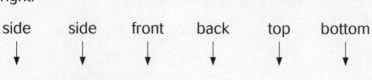

side   side   front   back   top   bottom

↓   ↓   ↓   ↓   ↓   ↓

SA = _____ + _____ + _____ + _____ + _____ + _____ = _____ yd²

Find the surface area of each figure.

9.

3 in.   4
10 in.

_____

10.

9 ft

2 ft
3 ft

_____

11.

5 in.   6 in.
4 in.

_____

12.

7 cm   4 cm
4 cm

_____

13.

4 in.
3 in.
8 in.

_____

14.

5 m
12 m
15 m

_____

15. What is the surface area of a rectangular prism that is 9 yards
wide, 10 yards long, and 11 yards high?

_____

16. How much wood does it take to make a storage box that is
4 feet square on the bottom and 3 feet high, with a lid? Do
not count overlap.

_____

17. Reasoning What is the surface area of the cube shown
at the right? How could you find the surface area with
out using addition?

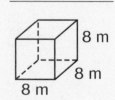

8 m

8 m

8 m

Surface Area

Materials scissors, copy of nets for the cylinder, square pyramid, and triangular prism from *Teaching Tool Masters*, for each student

How much aluminum does it take to make a juice can, not counting overlap, if the diameter is 6 centimeters and the height is 12 centimeters?

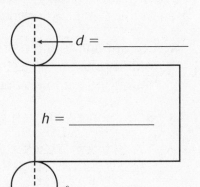

Find the surface area of a cylinder by answering 1 to 8.

1. Cut out and fold the net for a cylinder. Use the folded cylinder to write the diameter and height of the can, on the net. Unfold the net and use it to label those dimensions on the net at the right.

In any prism or cylinder, the top and bottom are bases. The remaining area is called the **lateral surface area**.

2. The lateral surface area of a cylinder makes a rectangle in the net. The width of the rectangle is the height of the cylinder. What is the length of the rectangle in the cylinder? Fold the net to see.

The length of the rectangle = the _____ of the base.

3. Use the formula for the circumference of a circle to find the length of the rectangle. Write the length in the net above.

$C = \pi d \approx$ _____ $\times$ _____ $\approx$ _____

4. What is the lateral surface area of the cylinder, to the nearest whole number?

_____ $\times$ 18.84 $\approx$ _____

5. What is the radius of the base of the cylinder? $r =$ _____

6. What is the area of each base of the cylinder, to the nearest whole number?

$A = \pi r^2 \approx$ _____ $\times$ _____ $\approx$ _____

7. What is the approximate surface area of the cylinder?

          base   base   lateral SA
          ↓   ↓   ↓

SA $\approx$ _____ + _____ + _____ $\approx$ _____ cm^2

Name _____

Surface Area (continued)

8. How much aluminum does it take to make a juice can?   _____

How much canvas does it take to make the pup tent shown, not counting overlap? Answer 9 to 12 to find the surface area of the triangular prism.

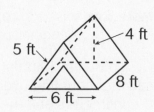

9. Cut out and fold the net for a triangular prism. Use the folded prism to write the lengths on the net. Unfold the net and use it to label the lengths on the net at the right.

10. Find the area of each face and write the areas below.

front   back   bottom   side   side
↓   ↓   ↓   ↓   ↓

SA = _____ + 12 + _____ + _____ + 40

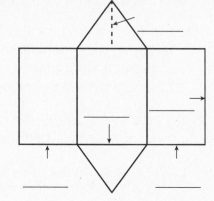

11. What is the surface area of the triangular prism?   _____ ft²

12. How much canvas does it take to make the tent?   _____

Answer 13 to 15 to find the surface area of the pyramid at the right.

13. Cut out and fold the net for a square pyramid to label the lengths on the net at the right.

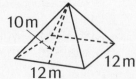

14. Find the area of each face and write the areas below.

bottom   side   side   side   side
↓   ↓   ↓   ↓   ↓

SA = _____ + 60 + _____ + 60 + _____

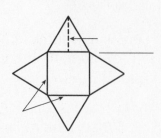

15. What is the surface area of the pyramid? _____   _____

Find the surface area of each solid. Use 3.14 for π.

16.

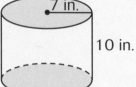

_____

17.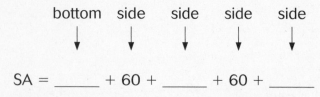

_____

18.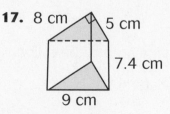

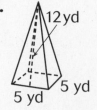

_____

Counting Cubes to Find Volume

Materials 28 unit cubes for each student

Answer 1 to 10 to learn how to find the volume of a prism.

1. Build the rectangular prism on the right.

2. How many cubes did you use?

3. Build a second layer on the rectangular prism.

4. How many cubes did you
use in the second layer?   _____

The **volume** of a figure is the number of
cubic units needed to fill it.

A **cubic unit** is a cube with edges that are 1 unit long.

5. Find the total volume of the rectangular prism.

cubes in 1st layer   +   cubes in 2nd layer   =   total cubes

_____   +   _____   =   _____

6. What is the total volume of the
rectangular prism?   _____ cubic units

7. Build a third layer on the rectangular prism by
putting a row of cubes on top of the back row.

8. How many cubes did you
use in the third layer?   _____

9. Find the total volume of the figure.

cubes in   +   cubes in   +   cubes in   = total cubes
1st layer   2nd layer   3rd layer

_____   +   _____   +   _____   =   _____

10. What is the total volume of the figure?   _____ cubic units

Counting Cubes to Find Volume (continued)

Find the volume of each figure in cubic units.

11.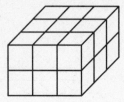

_____ cubic units

12.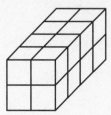

_____ cubic units

13.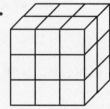

_____ cubic units

14.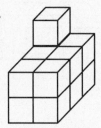

_____ cubic units

15.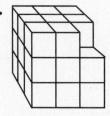

_____ cubic units

16.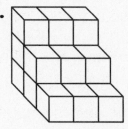

_____ cubic units

17. Reasoning Yao made a rectangular prism with
3 layers of cubes. He put 4 cubes in each layer.
What is the volume of the rectangular prism?

_____ cubic units

18. Reasoning Box *A* consists of 8 cubic units. Three
of Box *A* completely fills Box *B*. What is the volume
of Box *B*?

_____

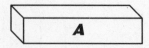

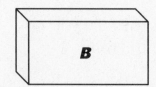

Measuring Volume

Materials 28 unit cubes for each student

1. Build the rectangular prism on the right.

2. How many cubes did you use?   _____

3. What is the volume?   _____ cubic units

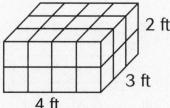

You can also find the volume (*V*) of a prism by multiplying the length (ℓ) × width (*w*) × height (*h*).

4. Find the volume if each cube is 1 cubic foot.

$V =$ ℓ   ×   *w*   ×   *h*

$V =$ _____ ft × _____ ft × _____ ft

$V =$ _____ cubic feet

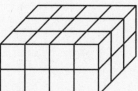

2 ft

3 ft

4 ft

1 cube = 1 cubic foot

5. Use cubes to find the volume of the prism at the right.

$V =$ _____ cubic units

6. Use multiplication to find the volume.

$V =$ ℓ   ×   *w*   ×   *h*

$V =$ _____ m × _____ m × _____ m

$V =$ _____ cubic meters

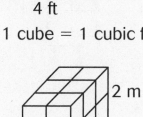

2 m

3 m

2 m

1 cube = 1 cubic meter

7. Find the volume of the prism at the right.

$V =$ ℓ   ×   *w*   ×   *h*

$V =$ _____ in. × _____ in. × _____ in.

$V =$ _____ cubic inches

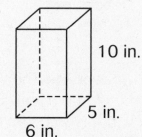

10 in.

5 in.

6 in.

Measuring Volume (continued)

Find the volume of each figure.

8.

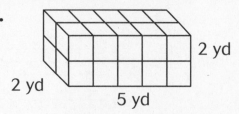

2 yd

2 yd

5 yd

_____ cubic yards

9.

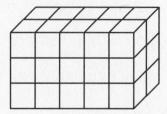

1 cube = 1 cubic centimeter

_____ cubic centimeters

10.

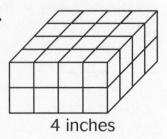

4 inches

_____ cubic inches

11.

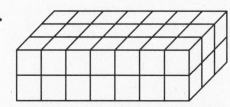

1 cube = 1 cubic millimeter

_____ cubic millimeters

12.

3 m

3 m

3 m

_____

13.

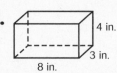

4 in.

3 in.

8 in.

_____

14.

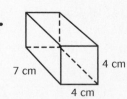

7 cm

4 cm

4 cm

_____

15.

3 yd

2 yd

2 yd

_____

16. Reasoning Find the volume of a storage unit
10 feet wide, 4 feet long, and 4 feet high

_____

17. Reasoning The volume of a rectangular prism
is 12 cubic feet. The length is 6 feet and the
width is 2 feet. What is the height?

_____ foot

Volume of Triangular Prisms and Cylinders

1. How many layers of cubes are
   in the prism at the right?   _____

2. Is the number of layers of
   cubes the same as the height?   _____

3. How many cubes are in each
   each layer?   _____

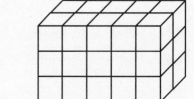

4. Is the number of cubes in each layer
   the same as the area of the base?   _____

5. Count the cubes. What is the volume of the prism?   _____ cubic units

6. Could you multiply the area of the base
   times the height to find the volume?   _____

For any prism or cylinder, the volume (V) equals the area of the base (B)
times the height (h), $V = Bh$.

Find the volume of the prism at the right by answering 7 to 11.

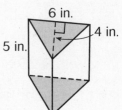

7. What is the shape of the base
   of the prism at the right?   _____

8. What are the base (b) and height
   or altitude (a) of the triangle? $b =$ _____ and $a =$ _____

9. What is the area of the base?

$$B = \frac{1}{2} \quad b \quad a$$

$$\qquad \downarrow \quad \downarrow$$

$$= \frac{1}{2} \times 6 \times \underline{\hspace{1cm}} = \underline{\hspace{1cm}}$$

10. What is the height (h) of the prism? $h =$ _____

11. What is the volume (V) of the prism?

$$V = B \quad h$$

$$\quad \downarrow \quad \downarrow$$

$$= 12 \times \underline{\hspace{1cm}} = \underline{\hspace{1cm}} \text{ in.}^3$$

Volume of Triangular Prisms and Cylinders (continued)

Find the volume of the cylinder at the right by answering 12 to 17.

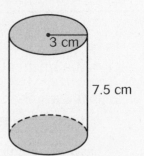

12. What is the shape of the base of the cylinder? _____

13. What is the radius (r) of the base? $r =$ _____

14. What units should be used for the volume?

_____

15. What is the approximate area of the base?

$B = \quad \pi \qquad r^2$

$\approx 3.14 \times$ _____ $\approx$ _____

16. What is the height (h) of the cylinder? $h =$ _____

17. What is the approximate volume (V) of the cylinder?

$V = \quad B \qquad h$

$\approx 28.26 \times$ _____ $\approx$ _____ cm^3

Find the volume of each prism or cylinder. Use 3.14 for π.

18.

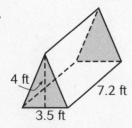

4 ft   7.2 ft
3.5 ft

_____

19.

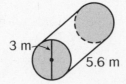

3 m   5.6 m

_____

20.

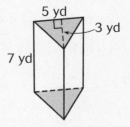

5 yd   3 yd
7 yd

_____

Carlos is making candles using the molds
shown at the right.

21. How much wax does Carlos need to make
a cylinder-shaped candle? Use 3.14 for π.

_____

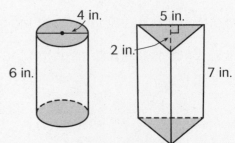

4 in.   5 in.
2 in.
6 in.   7 in.

22. How much wax does he need to make a triangular
prism candle?   _____

Comparing Volume and Surface Area

Materials 24 unit cubes for each student

Kira's dad is making her a toy box in the shape of a rectangular prism. The volume of the toy box is 24 cubic feet. He wants to know how much outside area of the box he will need to paint.

The area which needs to be painted is the surface area of the box. Find the surface area of a rectangular prism with a volume of 24 cubic feet by answering 1 to 5.

1. Use 24 cubes to make a rectangular prism like the one shown at the right. If each cube represents a cubic foot, what is the volume of the prism? _____

2. You can find the surface area of a figure by finding the sum of the areas of each face of the figure. Complete the first row of the table for the prism you made.

Length	Width	Height	Area of Front and Back	Area of Sides	Area of Top and Bottom	Surface Area
4	3	2				
	2	2				

3. If Kira's dad makes the toy box 4 feet by 3 feet by 2 feet, how much outside area of the box will he need to paint? _____ ft^2

4. Use the cubes to make a different rectangular prism with a volume of 24, a width of 2, and a height of 2. Use this prism to complete the second row of the table.

5 If Kira's dad makes the toy box 6 feet by 2 feet by 2 feet, how much outside area of the box will he need to paint? _____ ft^2

The area Kira's dad needs to paint depends on the dimensions he uses.

6. Reasoning Why is the volume of the toy box given in cubic feet and the surface area given in square feet?

Comparing Volume and Surface Area (continued)

Find the surface area and volume of each figure.

7.

_____

8.

_____

9.

_____

10.

_____

11.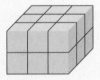

_____

12.

_____

13.

_____

14.

_____

15. Reasoning Janet needs to determine how much wrapping paper
she needs to wrap three presents of the same size. Will she need
to determine the surface area or volume of the present? Explain.

Recording Data from a Survey

Take a survey by asking, "What is your choice for a classroom mascot: a falcon, a cougar, a stingray, or a bear?"

1. Write each student's answer in the box below.

Choice of Classroom Mascot

2. Make a tally mark for each choice given. Remember, tallies are made in groups of 5 so that they are easier to count.

Sample of 12 Tally Marks

卌 卌 ||

Choice of Classroom Mascot		
Mascot	**Tally**	**Total**
Falcon		
Cougar		
Stingray		
Bear		

3. Count the tally marks. Record the total for each mascot choice.

4. How many students answered the survey? _____

5. Which mascot was chosen the most? _____

6. Which mascot was chosen the least? _____

Recording Data from a Survey (continued)

Favorite Season of the Year					
Summer	Fall	Summer	Winter	Spring	Fall
Winter	Summer	Spring	Fall	Fall	Spring
Summer	Winter	Winter	Winter	Summer	Winter

7. Complete the tally chart for the data above.

Favorite Season of the Year		
Time of Year	**Tally**	**Total**

8. What was the question for the survey?

_____

9. How many people answered the survey?   _____

10. Which season was the favorite of the most people?   _____

11. Which season was the least favorite of the people?   _____

12. How many more people chose Summer over Spring?   _____

13. Reasoning Write the seasons in order from least
favorite to most favorite.

_____

14. Reasoning How many more people would have to have
chosen Summer for it to be the most favorite season?   _____

Reading and Making Pictographs

The members of Tom's class voted for their favorite pizza toppings. The results are shown in the tally chart at the right. Answer 1 to 7 to help you make and use a pictograph of the data.

Favorite Pizza Toppings		
Toppings	**Tally**	**Number**
Sausage	||||	4
Vegetables	|||	3
Pepperoni	⌇⌇⌇⌇ ⌇⌇⌇⌇	10

1. In the first row of the chart below write a title that best describes the pictograph. Then list the three toppings in the first column.

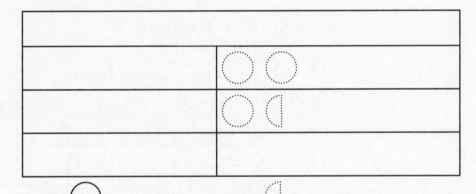

Each ◯ = 2 votes.   Each ◖ = _____ vote.

2. Complete the pictograph key.

3. Decide how many symbols are needed for each topping. Since sausage got 4 votes, draw 2 circles next to sausage. Since vegetables got 3 votes, draw 1 circle and 1 half-circle next to vegetables.

4. How many symbols are needed for pepperoni? _____

5. Draw 5 circles for pepperoni. Make sure you line up the symbols.

6. Which topping got the greatest number of votes? _____

7. Reasoning How can you tell which topping got the greatest number of votes by looking at the pictograph?

Reading and Making Pictographs (continued)

For Exercises 8 to 11, use the
pictograph shown at the right.

Number of Fish in the Aquarium

Silver Molly	◀‖• ◀‖• ◀‖• ◀
Black Neon Tetra	◀‖• ◀‖• ◀‖• ◀‖• ◀‖•
Angel Fish	◀‖• ◀

Key: Each ◀‖• = 2 fish. Each ◀ = 1 fish.

8. Which fish are there the
   most of in the aquarium?

   _____

9. How many Silver Molly fish are in the aquarium?   _____

10. How many more Black Neon Tetra fish
    are there than Angel Fish?   _____

11. Make a pictograph to display the data in the tally chart.

Favorite Drinks	
Fruit Juice	
Lemonade	
Milk	

Key: Each 🥛 stands for _____ votes.

Favorite Drinks		
Drinks	**Tally**	**Number**
Fruit Juice	ЖЖ |||	8
Lemonade	ЖЖ ЖЖ ||	12
Milk	||||	4

Use the pictograph you made in Exercise 11 to answer Exercises 12 to 15.

12. What does each 🥛 on the graph represent?

13. Which drink was chosen the least?   _____

14. How many more people chose lemonade over milk?   _____

15. **Reasoning** Do any kinds of drinks on the pictograph have
    the same number of votes? How do you know?

Name _____

Reading and Making a Bar Graph

Materials colored pencils, markers, or crayons, grid paper.

Robert's class voted for their favorite country, not including the United States. The results are shown in the table.

Make and use a bar graph of the data by answering 1 to 6.

1. Write a title above the graph. Label the axes: Country and Votes.

2. Complete the scale. Since the data go up to 11, make the scale by 2s.

3. Draw a bar for each country. Since Canada got 8 votes, color 4 squares above Canada, up to the 8 mark. For Japan, color one and a half squares because 3 is halfway between 2 and 4.

4. Which country got the least number of votes, that is, which has the shortest bar?

_____

5. Which country got the greatest number of votes, that is, which has the longest bar?

_____

6. **Reasoning** Which bar is twice as long as the bar for Great Britain? What does that mean?

| Our Favorite Countries ||
Country	Votes
Canada	8
Great Britain	4
Japan	3
Mexico	11

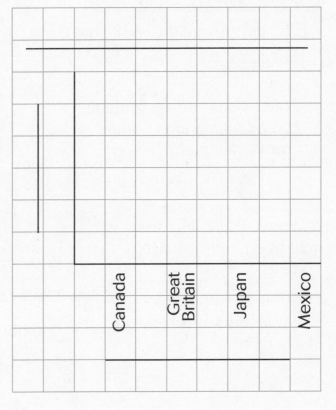

Reading and Making a Bar Graph (continued)

Use the grid on the right for Exercises 7 to 9.

7. Draw a graph of the data in the table.

Cities We Want to See	
City	**Votes**
Anaheim	5
Orlando	12
Chicago	2
Washington	7

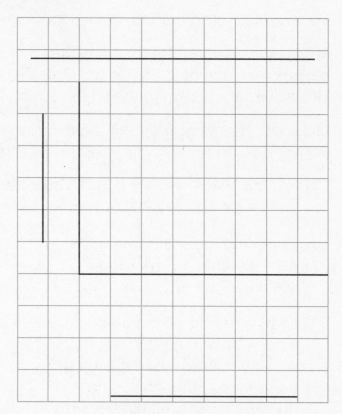

8. Which city got the most votes?

_____

9. Did twice as many students vote for Orlando as voted for Washington?

_____

Use the bar graph at the right to answer Exercises 10 to 12.

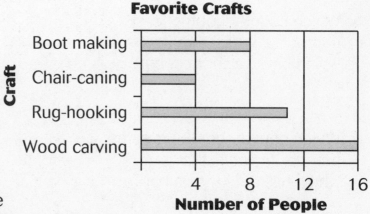

Favorite Crafts

10. Which craft did most students say was their favorite?

_____

11. How many students chose boot making as their favorite craft demonstration? _____

12. How many more students chose wood carving than chose chair-caning as their favorite crafts? _____

Name _____

Making Line Plots

A year is sometimes divided into quarters, as show at the right.

1st quarter: January to March
2nd quarter: April to June
3rd quarter: July to September
4th quarter: October to December

1. Take a survey by asking, "Which quarter of the year were you born?" Write the number of the quarter each person answers in the grid.

2. What are all of the possible quarters that can be said?

    _____

Quarter of the Year You Were Born					

Answer 3 to 7 to make and use a line plot of the data.

3. Draw a line. Below the line, list in order, all the possible quarters that could be said.

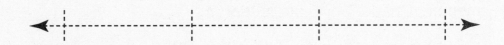

4. Write "Number of Birthdays by Quarter" below the line plot.

5. For each quarter that was said, mark an X above that quarter on the number line. If more than one X needs to be placed above a quarter, stack them in a single column.

6. Which quarter has the most number of birthdays?   _____

7. How many birthdays are after the 2nd quarter?   _____

Name _____

Making Line Plots (continued)

The nature club leader took a survey
of the number of birdfeeders each
member had made during camp.
The results are shown in the table.

8. Make a line plot to show the data.

Birdfeeders Made During Camp

Member	Made	Member	Made
Ivan	4	Luther	5
Chloe	4	Marco	5
Stacey	3	Victoria	6
Victor	6	Chi	7
Tony	5	Wesley	5
Manny	6	Wendy	5

9. How many members made 4 birdfeeders? _____

10. How many members made 2 birdfeeders? _____

11. What was the most number of
birdfeeders made by a member? _____

12. How many members made 5 or 6 birdfeeders? _____

13. How many members made less than 6 birdfeeders? _____

14. Did more members make more than
5 birdfeeders or less than 5 birdfeeders? _____

15. Reasoning By looking at the line plot, if one more person
attended camp, do you think that person would probably
make 4 birdfeeders or 5 birdfeeders? Explain.

Name _____

Interpreting Graphs

Use the bar graph at the right to answer 1 to 9.

1. What is this bar graph about?

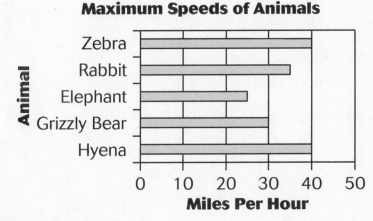

Maximum Speeds of Animals

The **scale** on a graph is the numbers used to describe the data.

2. The units used on this scale are miles per hour. What numbers does the scale use?

_____

The **interval** of the scale is the number you skip count by.

3. What is the interval of the scale? _____

4. Which animal has a maximum speed halfway between 20 and 30 miles per hour?   _____

5. What number is halfway between 20 and 30?   _____

6. What is the maximum speed of an elephant?   _____ miles per hour

7. Which animal has a maximum speed of 35 miles per hour?   _____

8. Which animal(s) has a maximum speed that is 15 miles per hour greater than an elephant?   _____

9. Reasoning Do any of the animals in the graph have a speed that is twice as fast as the elephant? How do you know?

Name _____

Interpreting Graphs (continued)

For 10 to 13, use the graph on the right.

10. What is the interval of the scale for this bar graph? _____

11. Which student made the most free throws? _____

12. How many free throws did Tawny make? _____

13. How many more free throws did Janet make than Ian? _____

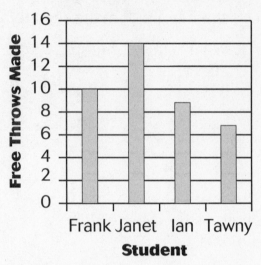

Free Throw Competition

For 14 to 18, use the graph on the right.

14. What is the interval of the scale?

_____

15. Which park received 275 votes?

_____

16. Which park received twice as many votes as Carlsbad Caverns? _____

17. How many fewer votes did Carlsbad Caverns receive than the Grand Canyon? _____

18. Reasoning Which two parks received the closest number of votes? Explain how you know.

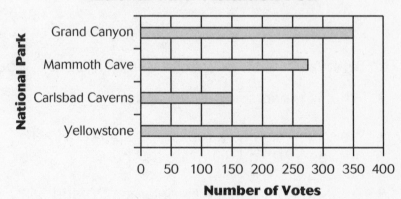

National Park Visitation Poll

Reading and Making Line Graphs

During a blizzard, a scientist measured the amount of snowfall every 30 minutes. The measurements are shown in the table. Make and use a line graph of the data by answering 1 to 6.

Snowfall Measurements

Time	Inches
Snowfall Begins	0
30 min	1
1 h	2
1 h 30 min	4
2 h	7
2 h 30 min	9

1. Write a title above the graph. Label the axes: Time and Inches.

2. Complete the scale. Since the data go up to 9, make the scale by 2.

3. Plot a point for each time. When the snowfall began there were 0 inches on the ground, so put a point at 0 along the line above Snowfall Begins. For 30 min, put a dot halfway between the 0 and 2, because 1 is halfway between 0 and 2. Do this for each time.

4. Draw a line from each point to the next.

5. What was the total snowfall after it had snowed for 2 hours?

_____

6. Reasoning How can you tell the total snowfall after it had snowed for 2 hours by only looking at the line graph?

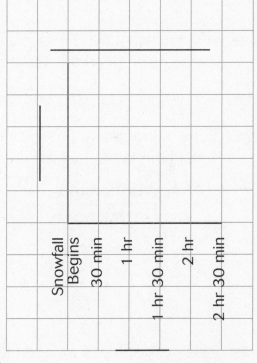

In a line graph, when the line goes up from left to right, there is an **increase** in the data. When the line goes down, there is a **decrease.** The increase or decrease indicates the **trend.**

The trend in the snowfall graph is for the snowfall to increase over time.

Name _____

Reading and Making Line Graphs (continued)

Use the line graph to answer
Exercises 7 to 10.

A cold front was expected to arrive
sometime during the day.

7. What is the trend in the data?

_____

_____

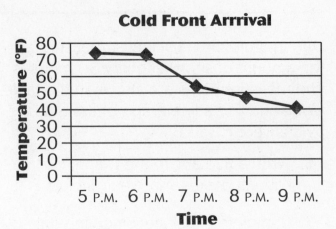

Cold Front Arrrival

8. About what time does it appear that the cold front arrived?

_____

9. Between what two times did the
temperature decrease the most?   _____

10. About how many degrees did it decrease? _____

11. Make a line graph to display the
data in the table.

Club Membership

Year	Members
2002	10
2004	15
2006	25
2008	40

Club Membership

Use the line graph you made in Exercise 11
for Exercises 12 and 13.

12. What was the trend?

_____

13. Reasoning How can you tell if the number of members increased
more between 2002 and 2004 or 2006 and 2008?

Stem-and-Leaf Plots

The number of points earned on a history project, by each of nine students, are:

12, 27, 10, 18, 29, 12, 23, 12, 19

Answer 1 to 12, to make and use a stem-and-leaf plot of the data.

Points Earned

Stem	Leaves
1	0
2	

$1 \mid 8 = 18$

Make the **stem** the first digit of each number.

1. What two stems are found in the data? _____

2. Write the stems, 1 and 2, in order from least to greatest under the heading Stem.

3. List all the numbers that have 1 as a stem. _____

4. Write the numbers that have 1 as a stem in order from least to greatest. _____

5. List all the numbers that have 2 as a stem. _____

6. Write the numbers that have 2 as a stem in order from least to greatest. _____

Make the **leaf** the second digit of each number. The leaves are listed in order from least to greatest after each stem.

7. Since 10 is the least number with a stem of 1, write a 0 after the stem 1. Since 12 is next, write 2 after the 0. Write the remaining leaves after the stem 1.

8. Since 23 is the least number with a stem of 2, write a 3 after the stem 2. Put this directly below the 0. Put 7 below the first leaf of 2 for 27 and 9 below the second 2.

9. What is the mode of the points earned data? _____

Stem-and-Leaf Plots (continued)

10. What is the median of the points earned data? _____

11. What is the range of the points earned data? _____

12. What is the mean of the points earned data? _____

For Exercises 13 to 17 make a stem-and-leaf plot and then answer the questions. For one-digit numbers, use a zero in the stem.

13. Organize the data below for the pounds of newspapers collected by the classes for recycling into a stem-and-leaf plot:
6, 18, 12, 13, 11, 12, 12

14. Find the mean of the data. _____

15. Find the range of the data. _____

16. Find the median of the data. _____

17. Find the mode(s) of the data. _____

Use the stem-and-leaf plot on the right for Exercises 18 to 22.

18. What is the mode(s)? _____

19. What is the median? _____

20. What is the range? _____

21. What is the mean? _____

22. Reasoning How would the recycling stem-and-leaf plot from Exercise 13 change if the class that collected 6 pounds had collected 26 pounds?

Length in Miles

Stem	Leaves				
2	2	4			
3	5	5	8	8	9

Circle Graphs

Circle graphs show parts of a whole.

Favorite Type of Exercise

The graph at the right shows the results of a survey of 8 people on their favorite type of exercise. Interpret the graph by answering 1 to 6.

1. The graph is divided into equal parts. How many equal parts are there? _____

2. How many of the equal parts are labeled Running? _____

3. What fraction of the graph is labeled Running? _____

This means $\frac{1}{8}$ of the people said that running is their favorite type of exercise.

4. What fraction, in simplest form, of the people said that hiking is their favorite type of exercise? _____

5. What fraction, in simplest form, of the people said that swimming is their favorite type of exercise? _____

6. Did a greater part of the people choose hiking or running combined than swimming? _____

Most circle graphs are not divided into equal parts. Use the benchmark fractions shown below to estimate.

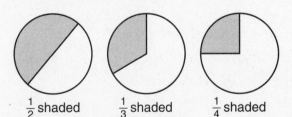

$\frac{1}{2}$ shaded $\frac{1}{3}$ shaded $\frac{1}{4}$ shaded

Where We Like to Go for Fun

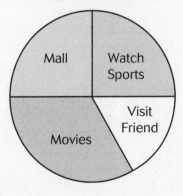

The graph at the right shows the results of a survey asking students where they most like to go for fun. Interpret the graph by answering 7 to 9.

7. Where did about $\frac{1}{3}$ of the students say they like to go for fun? _____

Circle Graphs (continued)

8. About what fraction of the students
said they like to watch sports?   about _____

9. What two categories combined were
chosen by about $\frac{1}{2}$ of the students?   _____ and _____

Use the graph at the right for Exercises 10 to 13.

Animals in a Pet Show

10. How many pets are entered?   _____

11. What fraction of the pets entering
the pet show are cats?   _____

12. What fraction of the pets entered
are *not* dogs nor guinea pigs?   _____

13. What fraction of pets entered have
fur or feathers?   _____

Use the graph at the right for Exercises 14 to 17

Favorite Sports of 10-Year-Old Boys

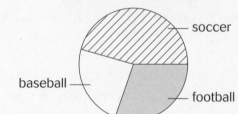

14. About what fraction of the
boys chose baseball?   _____

15. Almost half of the boys
chose which sport?   _____

16. Did more of the boys choose soccer or
baseball and football combined?

_____

17. Reasoning Thirty boys were surveyed and 10 of them said
the same sport. What fraction, in simplest form, of the boys
said that sport? Which sport would it have to be, based on
the graph? Explain your answers.

18. Reasoning Three-tenths of a circle graph is shaded blue.
How much of the circle graph is *not* shaded blue?   _____

Name _____

Making and Reading Circle Graphs

Materials colored pencils

A **circle graph** represents all of a set of data. Each part of the whole amount is shown by a wedge or sector of the circle.

Make a circle graph to show the data in the table by answering 1 to 13.

Favorite Type of Book	
Books	**Number of Students**
Adventure	3
Mystery	4
Biography	3
Poetry	2

1. How many students are represented by the data in the table? _____

2. Color 3 of the 12 sectors in the circle below red, to represent the number of students who chose Adventure books.

3. What fraction, in simplest form, of the graph is red? _____

4. What percent of the graph is red? _____

5. Write "Adventure" and the percent in the sector you colored red.

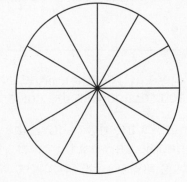

6. Color 4 sectors blue to represent the students who chose Mystery books. What fraction, in simplest form, of the graph is blue? _____

7. Write "Mystery" and 33% in the sector you colored red.

8. Color 3 sectors yellow to represent the students who chose Biography books. What fraction, in simplest form, of the graph is yellow? _____

9. What percent of the graph is yellow? _____

10. Write "Biography" and the percent in the sector you colored yellow.

11. Color 2 sectors green to represent the students who chose Poetry books. What fraction, in simplest form, of the graph is green? _____

12. Write "Poetry" and 17% in the sector you colored yellow.

13. Give your circle graph a title.

Making and Reading Circle Graphs (continued)

A survey had the results shown in the table. Use the table and the circle graph for Exercises 14 and 15.

14. Complete the table with fractions in simplest form and percent values.

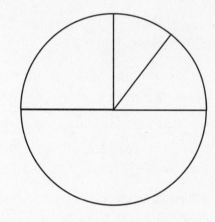

Favorite Type of Music			
	Number of Responses	Fraction	Percent
Pop	10		
Classical	5		
Oldies	2		
Jazz	3		

15. Color each section of the circle graph a different color and label each section with the correct category.

The graph at the right shows the results of a survey of 56 people on what they were wearing at a mall. Use the graph for Exercises 16 to 20.

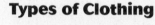
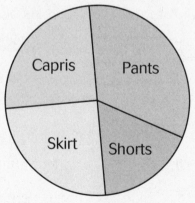

Types of Clothing

16. What percent of those surveyed were wearing capris? _____

17. What percent of those surveyed were not wearing a skirt? _____

18. About what fraction of those surveyed were wearing pants? _____

19. How many people were wearing pants or shorts? _____

20. Reasoning About how many people were wearing shorts? Explain how to estimate.

Histograms

Materials colored pencils

A **histogram** is a bar graph that has no space between the bars. A histogram has equal intervals on the horizontal axis.

The table shows the ages of 25 people who attended a play. Complete the histogram based on the data given in the table by answering 1 to 9.

Age	Frequency
0–14	3
15–29	12
30–44	5
over 44	5

1. List the age intervals in each blank along the horizontal axis.

2. Label the scale along the vertical axis. Make each interval the same.

3. Give the graph a title and label the axes.

4. How many people were 14 and under? _____

5. Color a bar of height 3 above 0–14.

6. How many people were 15 to 29? Color a bar that height above15–29. _____

7. How many people were 30 to 44? Color a bar that height above 30–44. _____

8. How many people were over 44? Color a bar that height above "over 44." _____

9. Did more people between the ages of 15 and 29 attend the play than people over 29? _____

Histograms (continued)

The histogram shows the time, in minutes, that people who were surveyed spend driving to work. Use the graph for Exercises 10 to 13.

10. How many people were surveyed?

_____

11. How much time did 20% of the people surveyed spend driving to work?

_____

12. How much time did the most people spend driving to work?

_____

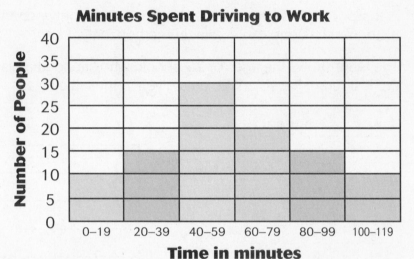

Minutes Spent Driving to Work

Number of People

Time in minutes

13. Reasoning Did twice as many of the people surveyed spend 40 to 59 minutes driving to work as spend 20 to 39 minutes? Explain how you can tell from the graph.

14. The table shows the results of a survey on the age of people visiting a restaurant. Use the data to complete the histogram.

Age	Frequency
0–19	12
20–39	18
40–59	10
60–79	4

Math Diagnosis and Intervention System

Intervention Lesson   **I69**

Choosing Appropriate Graphs

Some graphs are more appropriate to display certain types of data than other graphs.

A **line graph** shows changes over time.

A **line plot** compares data by showing clusters of information.

A **pictograph** best shows data that is multiples of a number.

A **bar graph** shows countable data and makes comparisons.

The following data lists the number of questions answered correctly on a quiz taken by 20 students.

4   7   5   9   6   4   2   8   7   6   10   5   8   6   4   3   10   8   6   6

Determine the most appropriate graph to display the data by answering 1 to 11.

1. Can a change in the quiz scores over time be determined by the data? _____

2. Is a line graph appropriate to display the data? _____

3. Are the data easily divided by a common number? _____

4. Is a pictograph appropriate to display the data? _____

5. Are there some numbers in the list that appear multiple times so that there are clusters of data? _____

6. Is a line plot appropriate to display the data? _____

7. Can you count the number of times each number appears in the list? _____

8. Is a bar graph appropriate to display the data? _____

9. What two types of graphs would be most appropriate to display the data? _____

10. How many different numbers appear in the list? _____

Choosing Appropriate Graphs (continued)

11. **Reasoning** If a bar graph is used to display the data, there would be 9 different bars. How could you avoid having so many bars in a bar graph that displays the data?

Tell what type of graph would be most appropriate to represent the data and why.

12. Every hour a lifeguard checks the level of water in the swimming pool as a new pool is being filled.

13. The teacher wants to show what percent of the students own each type of pet.

14. Marie has collected the following data. What would be the best way for her to display the data?

    The number of questions answered correctly on a quiz.

    4 5 8 3 4 5 6 9 4 6 9 8 7 3 2 8 7 8

Tell what type of graph you would choose to represent the data.

15.

Life Expectance of Animals	
Animal	**Years**
Bull Frog	16
Kangaroo	9
Lion	35
Sheep	15
Tiger	22

16. **Reasoning** The table shows the number of points made in a basketball game by individual players. Is a bar graph a good way to show the data? Explain.

Player	Points
Devin	8
Seth	12
Immanuel	10
Ricardo	18

Double Bar Graphs

Materials colored pencils

A **double bar graph** uses two different-colored or shaded bars to compare sets of data that can be counted.

Make a double bar graph for the data in the table by answering 1 to 6.

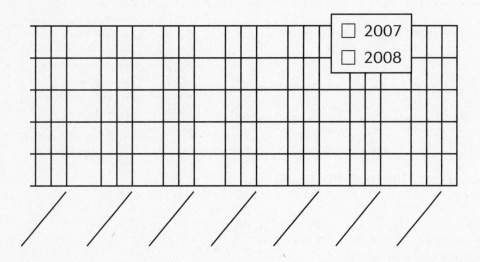

☐ 2007
☐ 2008

1. List the days of the week in each blank along the horizontal axis in the order in which they appear in the table.

2. What is the greatest number in the table? _____

3. Label the scale along the vertical axis. Choose numbers so that each interval is the same and the scale reaches to at least 9.

4. Label the horizontal axis "Days," the vertical axis "Attendance (in thousands)," and title the graph.

**State Fair Attendance
(in thousands)**

Day	2007	2008
Friday	5.5	6.5
Saturday	6.5	9
Sunday	8	9
Monday	5	6
Tuesday	2	5
Wednesday	2.5	5.5
Thursday	3	6

5. Use a yellow pencil to color in the square in the key that is labeled 2007. Color the first bar for each day yellow. Make the height of each bar according to the values in the 2007 column of the table.

6. Use a red pencil to color in the square in the key that is labeled 2008. Color the second bar for each day red. Make the height of each bar according to the values in the 2008 column of the table.

Name

Math Diagnosis and
Intervention System

Intervention Lesson   I70

Double Bar Graphs (continued)

Use the double bar graph you created on the previous page for
Exercises 7 and 8.

7. Was attendance generally higher in 2007 or 2008? _____

8. Which two days of the week had higher attendance than the other
days, both years?

_____ and _____

Use the graph at the right to answer Exercises
9 to 13.

9. What does each pair of bars represent?

_____

_____

10. For which item were the most boxes sold?

_____

11. How many more caramels did 5th graders
sell as compared to 6th graders?

12. Which type of box had the most sales for 5th graders? _____

13. Which type of box had the most sales for 6th graders? _____

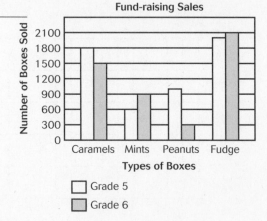

Use the graph at the right to answer
Exercises 14 to 18.

14. Reasoning For which subject is the
difference in choice the greatest?

_____

15. Which subject was chosen as favorite the most?

_____

16. What was the total number of students who
chose Math as their favorite subject?

_____

17. Which subject was least popular with 5th graders? _____

18. Which subject was least popular with 6th graders? _____

© Pearson Education, Inc.

Finding the Mean

Materials color tiles: 5 red, 12 blue, and 7 yellow for each
student or group

The **mean,** or average, is the sum of all the numbers in a set of
data divided by the total number of data.

Carlos made 5 baskets in his first basketball game of the season,
12 baskets in the second game, and 7 in the third game. What
is the mean number of baskets that Carlos made during the first
three games?

Find the mean by answering 1 to 3.

1. Use tiles to represent the number of baskets that Carlos
   made. Make one stack of 5 red tiles to represent the baskets
   in the first game, one stack of 12 blue tiles to represent the
   baskets in the second game and one stack of 7 yellow tiles
   to represent baskets in the third game.

2. Move tiles from one stack to another until there are three
   stacks of equal height.

3. How many tiles are in each stack?   _____
   This number represents the average number of baskets
   in each game or the mean.

Find the mean without using tiles by answering 4 to 6.

4. What is the total number of baskets that Carlos
   made in all three games? $5 + 12 + 7 =$ _____

5. If 24 tiles are divided between three stacks,
   how many tiles are in each stack? $24 \div 3 =$ _____

6. Because there were 3 games, the total number of baskets
   was divided by 3. This is the mean. Is this number the
   same as the mean found when using the tiles?   _____

7. **Reasoning** Carlos scored no points in the fourth game of
   the season. What effect does that have on the mean?

Finding the Mean (continued)

Find the mean for each data set.

8. $120, $280, $410, $300, $180

_____

9. 175 ft, 136 ft, 157 ft, 112 ft

_____

10. 23 in., 37 in., 67 in., 93 in., 25 in.

_____

11. 5,341 km, 6,780 km, 2,543 km

_____

12. 89 weeks, 37 weeks, 27 weeks, 12 weeks, 86 weeks, 97 weeks

_____

13. 3 runs, 5 runs, 8 runs, 4 runs, 10 runs, 5 runs, 4 runs, 1 run

_____

14. $991, $759, $610, $967, $733

_____

15. 36 lb, 53 lb, 25 lb, 14 lb

_____

16. 76 bulbs, 36 bulbs, 98 bulbs, 25 bulbs, 38 bulbs, 27 bulbs

_____

17. 1,664 books, 2,533 books, 1,267 books, 7,668 books

_____

18. $67, $44, $32, $86, $12, $11

_____

19. 379 points, 255 points, 116 points

_____

20. $1,561; $2,689; $1,442; $3,522; $1,756

_____

21. 4 h, 1 h, 0 h, 5 h, 7 h, 0 h, 5 h, 2 h

_____

22. Dale worked 7 days and made $350. What was the average amount he made each day? _____

23. Reasoning Mrs. Hernandez's math class made the following scores on a quiz: 5, 7, 8, 7, 9, 10, 2, 2, 3. If 2 points are added to everybody's score, how is the mean affected?

Median, Mode, and Range

Materials 40-50 color tiles, counters or other small object
placed in a clear container

How many items are in the container? Collect your classmates'
guesses and find the median, mode, and range of the data by
answering 1 to 7.

1. Ask 9 people in your class to guess the number of items
in the container. Write the 9 guesses in the blanks below.
These numbers are the data.

_____ _____ _____ _____ _____ _____ _____ _____ _____

The **median** is the middle number when the data are listed in order.

2. List the data in order from least to greatest. If there are
some data that are the same, list those multiple times.

_____ _____ _____ _____ _____ _____ _____ _____ _____

3. Circle the number that is in the middle of the list.
What is the median of your data? _____

The **mode** is the data value that occurs most often. If there is
more than one number that appears the most often, it is possible
to have more than one mode. If each number appears only
once, then there is no mode.

4. How many modes are there for your data? _____

5. What is the mode of your data? _____

The **range** is the difference between the greatest and least data values.

6. What is the difference between the greatest
and the least data values? _____

7. Count the number of items in the container.
Was the median, mode, or range closest to the
actual number of items? _____

Median, Mode, and Range (continued)

Find the median, mode and range of each data set.

8. 2, 5, 1, 8, 8, 12, 6   **9.** 25, 60, 20, 45, 25   **10.** 54, 54, 60

median _____   median _____   median _____

mode(s) _____   mode(s) _____   mode(s) _____

range _____   range _____   range _____

11. 4, 1, 1, 8, 8, 12, 8   **12.** 35, 23, 15, 23, 24   **13.** 15, 11, 12, 18, 14, 11, 9, 14, 13

median _____   median _____   median _____

mode(s) _____   mode(s) _____   mode(s) _____

range _____   range _____   range _____

14. If the number 8 were removed from the data in Exercise 11, what two numbers would be in the middle of the data? _____

The average, or mean, of 4 and 8 is the median. What is the median of the data after removing the number 8? _____

15. Reasoning If the number 100 is added to the data in Exercise 12, how does that affect the mean, median, mode, and range?

16. Brandi's scores on math exams were as follows: 96, 96, 89, 84, 25. Find the mean, median, and mode for Brandi's quiz scores.

17. Reasoning Which of the measures that you found in Exercise 16 best represents a typical exam score for Brandi? Explain.

Sampling Methods

Materials an alphabetical roster of students in the class—one for each
student, scissors, small container

A **population** is an entire group of people or things about which
information is sought. A **sample** is a part of the population. Many times
a sample is used to represent a population when it is too difficult to
study the entire population.

What is the percent of students in your class who like yogurt?
Find different ways to answer this question by answering 1 to 8.

1. What is the population you wish to study?   _____

2. What are three examples of a sample of this population?

Convenience sampling uses any convenient method to form
the sample. Many times convenience sampling is **biased** or not
representative of the entire population.

3. Ask 5 of your classmates near you if they like
yogurt. How many of the 5 like yogurt?   _____

Systematic sampling uses a pattern to identify members
of the sample.

4. Using the class roster, choose a name on the list.
Make a mark next to this name and every third name
after it until you have chosen 5 names. If you reach
the bottom of the list before 5 names are chosen,
start over at the top of the list. Ask these 5 people
if they like yogurt. How many of the 5 like yogurt?   _____

Random sampling is a method in which each member
of the population has an equal chance of being chosen.

5. Cut out each name on the class roster, fold the
names and put them in a container. Choose 10 of
the names and ask these 10 people if they like
yogurt. How many of the 10 like yogurt?   _____

Sampling Methods (continued)

6. Fill in the table below and compare the results.

Sample	Number who like yogurt	Number Polled	Percent who like yogurt
Convenience			
Systematic			
Random			

A larger sample is usually more representative of the population.

7. Which sample do you think is more representative of the population? Explain.

8. Ask the entire class if they like yogurt and find the percent who say yes. Were your samples representative of the population? Which sample had results the closest to the population?

Identify each as a population or a sample. If a sample is used, identify the type: convenience, systematic, or random.

9. A volunteer agency contacts every 20th agency in their directory to find out the number of hours volunteers work at their agency.

_____

10. When students enroll at Jefferson Middle School, they are asked to tell their method of transportation to school. The results are tallied.

_____

11. Raul is running for class president. He stands outside his classroom and asks students whom they plan to vote for.

_____

Using Statistics

A **biased sample** is a sample that is not a good match for the entire population.

A student group is making a decision about the type of fundraiser they would like to hold. To help in their decision, they polled 20 students arriving at school near the sixth grade classrooms. They asked students if they would be more likely to buy petunias, flowers, or popcorn. What are the possible biases in this study and could they have been avoided?

Find the biases by answering 1 to 6.

1. Are there biases in the sample?

2. Who is the target population, that is, who would most likely be buying the product sold during the fund raiser? _____

3. Does the sample represent the target population? _____

4. How could the student group get a better representation of the target population?

5. Are there biases in the choices offered in the survey?

6. How could the choices be improved and biases avoided?

Using Statistics (continued)

The student group decided to ask parents the following question:
"Would you buy flowers to support our student organization?" Answer 7
to 9 about this survey question.

7. Would most parents want to support a school organization?   _____

8. Would some parents say yes to this question, even if they
would not actually buy the flowers?   _____

9. Is this a good question to gather the information the
students need?   _____

A government study wants to find the average family size in a
community. For Exercises 10 and 11 tell whether each sample might
be biased and why.

10. Survey people who are home on Monday morning

11. Survey people whose children attend the elementary school

12. Byron has a jar of 500 marbles. He wants to know how many of
them are blue. He takes a handful of the marbles as a sample
and finds that 10 of the 50 marbles in the sample are blue and
concludes that 20%, or 100 of the total jar, is blue. He later
counts all the blue marbles and finds that 200 of them are blue.
Was Byron's sample biased? What could have made it biased?

13. Which question do you think is most fair? Explain.

     A. Do you want your neighborhood to be safer?

     B. Are you in favor of a Neighborhood Watch program in your area?

     C. Do you think other people should invade your privacy?

How Likely?

Materials 1 yellow and 5 blue color tiles in a small paper bag,
for each child or pair

1. What are the possible color tiles
you could pull out of your bag?   _____ or _____

Each possible result is called an **outcome**. Pulling a tile from
your bag is called an **event**. The possible outcomes are getting
yellow or blue. Below are 4 ways to describe how likely an event is.

certain: It is sure to happen.	**likely**: It will probably happen.
impossible: It will never happen.	**unlikely**: It probably will not happen.

Draw a line to match the event with the likelihood for your bag.

2. Pulling a blue tile out of the bag.   Certain

3. Pulling a yellow tile out of the bag.   Impossible

4. Pulling a red tile out of the bag.   Likely

5. Pulling a colored tile out of the bag.   Unlikely

Below are 3 ways to compare the chances of two outcomes.

Outcomes with the same chance of happening are **equally likely**.
The outcome with a greater chance of happening is **more likely**.
The outcome with a lesser chance of happening is **less likely**.

6. Which color tile do you have more of?   _____
Getting blue is *more likely* than getting yellow.

7. What outcome is *less likely* than blue?   _____

8. Reasoning How many yellow tiles would you need
to make the outcome of getting a yellow tile
equally likely as getting a blue tile?   _____

How Likely? (continued)

Use the spinner for Exercises 9 to 12.
Tell whether each event is likely,
unlikely, certain, or impossible.

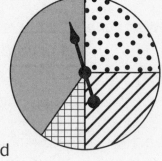

9. checked

_____

10. red

_____

11. gray or dotted

_____

12. gray, striped, dotted, or checked   _____

For Exercises 13 to 16, use the spinner above.

13. What outcome is more likely than dotted?   _____

14. What outcomes are equally likely?   _____

15. What outcome is less likely than striped?   _____

16. What outcomes are less likely than gray?

_____

17. Reasoning Draw a spinner for which the
chance of spinning A, B, or C is equally likely.

18. Reasoning Draw a spinner for which the chance
of spinning A is more likely than spinning B or C.

19. Reasoning How can you tell by looking at a
spinner that one outcome is less likely than
another outcome?

Outcomes and Experiments

Materials transparent spinner, for each pair or group; red, yellow, blue crayons

A **prediction** tells what may happen using information you know.

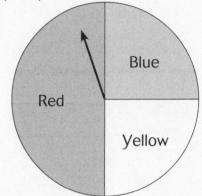

1. Color the spinner at the right.

If you spin the spinner 20 times, how many times would you **predict** spinning each color? Answer 2 to 10 to make and test your predictions.

2. How many of the 4 equal parts of the spinner is each color?

_____ part yellow   _____ part blue   _____ parts red

So, if you spin the spinner 4 times you would predict that it would land on yellow 1 time, blue 1 time, and red 2 times.

3. Complete the spinning prediction table.

4. How many times do you predict the spinner will land on each color, if you spin the spinner 20 times?

Yellow	1	2		4	
Blue	1		3		
Red	2	4			
Total Spins	4	8	12	16	20

yellow _____ times   blue _____ times   red _____ times

5. Place the transparent spinner on the spinner above so the centers match. Spin the spinner 20 times. Make a tally chart of your results.

Result	**Tally**	**Number**
Yellow		
Blue		
Red		

Outcomes and Experiments (continued)

6. How many times did you spin each color in 20 spins?

yellow _____ times   blue _____ times   red _____ times

7. Reasoning How do your predictions compare to your actual spin results?

8. How many times do you predict the spinner will land on each color, if you spin the spinner 40 times?

yellow _____ times   blue _____ times   red _____ times

9. Spin the spinner 20 more times. Add the results to the tally chart above. How many times did you spin each color in 40 spins?

yellow _____ times   blue _____ times   red _____ times

10. Reasoning Are your predictions closer to your actual spin results with 20 spins or with 40 spins? _____

11. Complete the table to predict the results of pulling a shape from the bag and returning it, each number of times.

Triangle	7	14	21	28	42	84
Circle	2		6		12	24
Square	1	2				12
Total Picks	10	20		40	60	

12. Complete the table to predict the results of spinning the spinner, each number of times.

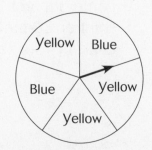

Yellow	3	6				48
Blue	2					32
Total Spins	5	10	15	20	40	

Line Plots and Probability

Materials 2 cubes, each numbered 1, 1, 2, 2, 3, 3 per pair

1. Toss the two number cubes. Find the sum of the two cubes. Record the sum in a box in the grid. Do this until all 30 boxes are filled.

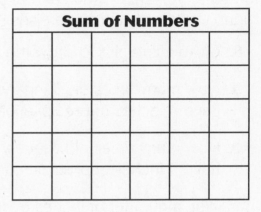

2. Find, then list all the possible outcomes for the sum of the two number cubes.

$1 + 1 =$ _____ $1 + 2 =$ _____

$1 + 3 =$ _____ $2 + 2 =$ _____

$2 + 3 =$ _____ $3 + 3 =$ _____

_____

Answer 3 to 7 to make and use a line plot of the results.

3. Draw a line. Below the line, list the possible outcomes in order from least to greatest.

4. Write a title below the line plot.

5. For each sum that was rolled, mark an X above that sum on the number line. If more than one X needs to be placed above a sum, stack them in a single column.

6. Which outcome has the most number of Xs? _____

7. **Reasoning** Predict the next sum most likely to be rolled and least likely to be rolled. Explain.

Line Plots and Probability (continued)

Larry recorded the total January precipitation (to the nearest inch) for the past 30 years in the chart at the right. Use the data for Exercises 8 to 14.

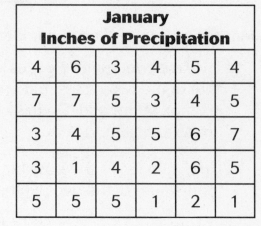

January Inches of Precipitation					
4	6	3	4	5	4
7	7	5	3	4	5
3	4	5	5	6	7
3	1	4	2	6	5
5	5	5	1	2	1

8. Make a line plot to show the data.

9. How many times did January have 4 inches of precipitation? _____

10. How many times did January have 5 inches of precipitation? _____

11. Which number of inches occurred 4 times in the 30 years? _____

12. Which numbers of inches occurred the same number of times?

_____

13. **Reasoning** Why was 0 not included on your line plot?

14. **Reasoning** How many inches of precipitation do you predict Larry's area will have next January? Explain.

Making Bar Graphs to Show Outcomes

Materials 3 index cards (cut in half vertically), bag

1. Write each letter in the word "MUMMY" on an index card. Use the extra index card to make a tally chart for the possible outcomes: M, U, and Y.

2. Place the letters in a bag. Shake them and without looking pick a letter. Tally the letter. Replace the letter, shake, pick, and tally. Do this 20 times.

Answer 3 to 8 to make and use a bar graph of the results.

3. Write the title: Letters Picked from Bag above the graph and label the axes: Outcome and Number of Times.

4. Complete the scale. Make the scale by 2s.

5. Draw a bar for each letter. For every 2 tally marks for the letter M, color in one square above the letter M. After coloring a square for every 2 tallies, if you have a tally left over, color half of a square. Do this for U and Y.

6. Which two letters were picked about the same number of times?

   _____

7. Which bar is the longest? _____

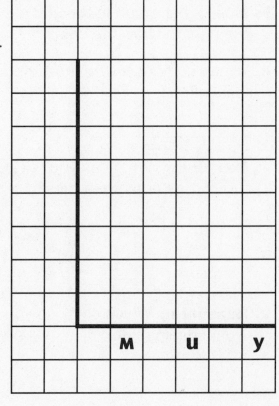

Since the bar above M is the longest, M is the outcome that occurred most often.

8. **Reasoning** Predict the next letter picked. Explain how you made your prediction.

Making Bar Graphs to Show Outcomes (continued)

Kendra spun a spinner 20 times. She recorded the number of
times each color was spun. Use the data for Exercises 9 to 13.

Spinner Results		
Outcome	**Tally**	**Number**
Purple	卌 卌 I	11
Green	IIII	4
Orange	IIII	4
Yellow	I	1

9. Make a bar graph in the grid on
the right to show the data.

10. Which color occurred most often?
least often?

_____

11. Reasoning What can you tell from
the orange and green bars?

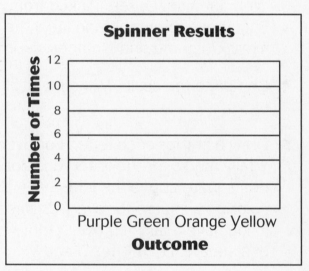

12. Reasoning Which color do you predict
would be spun next?

_____

13. Reasoning Draw what you think the spinner
looked like that Kendra used.

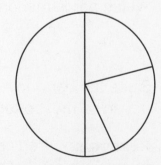

Probability as a Fraction

Probability is the likelihood that an event will happen.

Find the probability of getting an even number when spinning
the spinner at the right, by answering 1 to 6.

1. List the possible outcomes.

_____

2. How many possible outcomes are there?   _____

3. What are the favorable outcomes, the even numbers?   _____

You can describe the probability (*P*) of an event by writing a
fraction with the number of favorable outcomes over the number
of possible outcomes.

4. How many favorable outcomes are there?   _____

5. Probability $= \dfrac{\text{number of favorable outcomes}}{\text{number of possible outcomes}}$

$P = \dfrac{\text{number of even numbers}}{\text{total numbers}}$

$P = \dfrac{5}{10}$ or $\dfrac{1}{2}$

6. What is the probability of spinning an even number?   _____

Probability can be described in 4 ways.

Certain events are sure to happen and have a probability of 1.

Impossible events never happen and have a probability of 0.

Likely events probably will happen and have a probability
between $\frac{1}{2}$ and 1.

Unlikely events probably will not happen and have a probability
between 0 and $\frac{1}{2}$.

Probability as a Fraction (continued)

For Exercises 7 and 8 use the spinner at the right.

7. How likely is it that a 12 will be spun? _____

8. What is the probability that a 12 will be spun? _____

For Exercises 9 to 13, use the spinner at the right.
Write the probability of spinning each.

9. circle

10. octagon

_____

_____

11. not a triangle

12. star, circle, or triangle

_____

_____

13. Reasoning To have a probability of 1, what would the spinner have to land on?

For Exercises 14 to 19, write the probability and tell whether it is likely, unlikely, impossible, or certain that a triangle will be picked.

14.

15.

16.

_____

_____

_____

17.

18.

19.

_____

_____

_____

Name _____

Outcomes and Tree Diagrams

Each possible result of an event is called an **outcome.**

How many outcomes are possible when you spin the spinner
once and pick a marble once? Solve by answering 1 to 3.

1. List all the possible outcomes for each.

_____ _____ _____ _____   _____ _____

2. Complete the tree diagram to show all the possible outcomes.

Spinner	Bag	Possible Outcomes

A — Black ——— A Black

A — Gray ——— A Gray

B — Black ——— [   ]

B — [   ] ——— B Gray

[ ] — [   ] ——— C Black

[ ] — [   ] ——— [   ]

[ ] — [   ] ——— [   ]

[ ] — [   ] ——— [   ]

3. How many possible outcomes are there? _____

© Pearson Education, Inc.

Outcomes and Tree Diagrams (continued)

You can also multiply the possible outcomes.

4.

_____ × _____ = _____

number of possible   number of possible   total possible
outcomes of the spinner   outcomes of the marbles   outcomes

There are 8 possible outcomes.

For Exercises 5 to 8, use the spinners on the right.

5. Make a tree diagram to list all the possible
outcomes of spinning Spinner 1 once and
spinning Spinner 2 once.

Spinner 1   Spinner 2

6. How many possible outcomes are there?   _____

For Exercises 7 and 8, multiply to find the number of possible
outcomes.

7. tossing a coin and
spinning Spinner 1

_____

8. tossing a number cube numbered
1 though 6 and spinning Spinner 2

_____

Finding Combinations

Materials nickel, dime, and penny, equilateral triangle, pentagon,
and square power polygon for each student

You can pick one coin and one shape. Find how many different
combinations you can choose by answering 1 to 5.

1. Put the nickel next to each shape and list each combination below.

nickel and _____   nickel and _____   nickel and _____

2. Do the same with the dime and penny.

dime and _____   dime and _____   dime and _____

penny and _____   penny and _____   penny and _____

3. How many different combinations can you choose from? _____

You can also make a table to find all the combinations.

4. Draw the coin in the bottom part of each box in its row, and
the shape in the top part each box in its column.

	Triangle	Pentagon	Square
Nickel			
Dime			
Penny			

5. How many combinations can you choose from? _____

Finding Combinations (continued)

For Exercises 6 and 7, complete the table to find all the combinations.

6. Choose one shoe and one hat.

	Cowboy Hat	Cap	Visor	Top Hat
Boot	Cowboy Hat Boot			
Sneaker				
Sandal				

7. How many different combinations are listed in the table? _____

For Exercises 8 to 12, use objects, pictures, or a table to find the number of possible combinations.

8. Choose one vehicle (car, truck, van, or motorcycle) and one color (silver, white, black, or red)

_____

9. Choose one movie (science fiction, comedy, or cartoon) and one time of day (afternoon or evening)

_____

10. Choose one painting (Picasso, or Monet) and one frame (wood, or metal)

_____

11. Choose one meat (ham, turkey, chicken, bologna, or salami) and one bread (white or wheat)

_____

12. Reasoning If a third kind of bread was offered in Exercise 11, how many combinations would there be? _____

Predictions and Probability

Maureen counted the colors of cars that were in one section of the school's parking lot. The table at the right shows the data that she recorded. If there are 200 cars in the entire parking lot, predict the total number of green cars.

A **prediction** is a statement about a future or unknown event. Use the data in the table and answer 1 to 5 to make a prediction about the number of green cars in the entire lot.

Car Colors	
red	ЖНТ ЖНТ II
blue	ЖНТ ЖНТ ЖНТ II
black	ЖНТ II
green	ЖНТ ЖНТ
gold	IIII

1. How many green cars did Maureen count?   _____
   This value represents the number of favorable outcomes.

2. How many total cars did Maureen count?   _____
   This value represents the number of possible outcomes.

3. Complete to find the probability that a car in the parking lot is green.

   $$\frac{\text{number of favorable outcomes}}{\text{total number of outcomes}} = \frac{10}{\boxed{}} = \frac{1}{\boxed{}}$$

   So, 1 out of every 5 cars in the parking lot is green. Use this probability to predict how many cars are green if there is a total of 200 cars.

4. Find $200 \times \frac{1}{5}$.   _____

5. If the parking lot has 200 cars, predict the number of cars that are green.   _____

The table shows the number of cell phones that sold in one week. If 250 total phones are sold, predict the number of phones that are Model X. Answer 6 to 10.

Model	Number Sold
X	12
Y	20
Z	8

6. How many Model X phones were sold in one week?   _____

7. How many total phones were sold in one week?   _____

8. Find the probability that a customer will buy a Model X phone.   _____

   So, 3 out of 10 customers will buy a Model X phone.

9. Find $250 \times \frac{3}{10}$.   _____

10. If 250 phones are sold, predict the number of Model X phones.   _____

Predictions and Probability (continued)

A bag has beads of 3 colors: orange, purple, and pink.
Beads are drawn from the bag and replaced. The results
are recorded in the table shown.

Orange	IIII IIII II
Purple	IIII IIII III
Pink	IIII IIII IIII IIII IIII

Use the table to answer Exercises 11 to 15.

11. How many bead were drawn?   _____

12. What is the probability that the next bead drawn will be orange? _____

13. What is the probability that the next bead drawn will be pink?   _____

14. If there are 300 beads in the bag, predict the number that are pink.   _____

15. If there are 150 beads in the bag, predict the number that are purple.   _____

Veronica conducted a survey in which she asked 35 people to choose
their favorite food category: 10 chose Mexican, 15 chose Italian, and
10 chose Chinese.

Use the survey results to answer Exercises 16 to 21.

16. How many people were surveyed?   _____

17. What is the probability that the next person surveyed will
choose Mexican as their favorite food category?   _____

18. What is the probability that the next person surveyed will
choose Italian as their favorite food category?   _____

19. Predict how many people out of 70 would choose Chinese
as their favorite food category.   _____

20. Predict how many people out of 140 would choose Italian
as their favorite food category.   _____

21. Reasoning Predict how many people out of 7 would choose
Mexican as their favorite food category.   _____

Name _____

Counting Methods

A fruit snack can be made with one choice of fruit and one choice of yogurt. There are 4 different kinds of fresh fruits: strawberries, banana slices, pineapple chunks, and orange slices. The flavors of yogurt are lemon or vanilla. How many different fruit snacks are possible?

Draw a tree diagram and make an organized list to find all the possible combinations by answering 1 to 4.

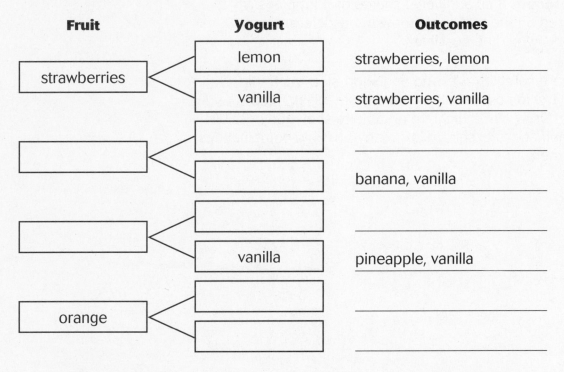

Fruit	Yogurt	Outcomes

1. Write each of the four fruit choices in the four boxes under the fruit column in the tree diagram above.

2. Write each of the two yogurt choices in each pair of boxes under the yogurt column in the tree diagram above.

3. Use the tree diagram to help you make an organized list of all the possible combinations in the outcome column.

4. Count the number of outcomes. How many different fruit snacks are possible? _____

You can also use the **counting principle** to find the total number of fruit snack choices. See how by answering 5 to 8.

Counting Methods (continued)

5. How many different choices for fruit are possible?

6. How many different choices of yogurt are possible?

7. What is the product of 4 × 2?

8. How many different fruit snacks are possible?

9. Reasoning If an additional choice of 3 toppings is offered on the fruit snack, how many different fruit snacks would be possible?

     $4 \times 2 \times \boxed{} =$ _____

10. A store sells long-sleeved and short-sleeved T-shirts. The T-shirts come in the colors white, black, yellow, and gray. Draw a tree diagram or table to show the possible combinations of shirts. How many possible combinations are there?

_____

Use the table to answer Exercises 11 and 12.

Juices	Eggs	Breads
orange	scrambled	bran muffin
grapefruit	hard-boiled	whole wheat toast
apple		bagel

11. Find the number of possible outcomes for a juice drink and eggs.

_____

12. Find the number of possible combinations for a juice drink, eggs, and a bread.

_____

Permutations and Combinations

Salvador wants to take two of the following five classes next year:
Spanish, Music, Gym, Art, or Band. Find the number of class
arrangements Salvador can choose by answering 1 to 5.

1. Complete the table to find all the possible arrangements of classes.
Note: SM stands for Spanish-Music.

	Spanish	**Music**	**Gym**	**Art**	**Band**
Spanish		SM	SG	SA	SB
Music			MG		
Gym	GS				
Art		AM			
Band				BA	

2. How many different arrangements are listed in the grid?   _____

When the order of items in an arrangement is important, each
possible arrangement is called a **permutation**. In the table, there
are 20 different arrangements of classes.

3. Is the order in which Salvador takes the classes important?   _____

The selection of items in which the order of items does *not* matter
is called a **combination**.

4. Each pair of classes is listed in the table twice, because each
pair of classes can be arranged 2 ways. Since order does not
matter, and SM and MS are the same, divide the number of
permutations, 20, by 2 to find the total number of combinations. $20 \div 2 =$ _____

5. How many class arrangement choices does Salvador have?   _____

Salvador wants to take one of the five classes in the table above during 1st
period and another class during 4th period. Use the table and answer
6 to 11 to find the number of ways Salvador can arrange his schedule.

6. Is the order in which Salvador takes the classes important?   _____

7. Since the order is important, are the arrangements
a permutation or a combination?   _____

Name _____

Permutations and Combinations (continued)

8. How many classes does Salvador have to choose
from for his 1st period class?   _____

9. How many classes are remaining for Salvador to
choose from for his 4th period elective?   _____

10. The number of arrangements is 5×4.
How many arrangements are possible?   _____

11. How many different ways can Salvador arrange
his class schedule?   _____

12. Reasoning The number of permutations found for Salvador's
electives was twice as many as the number of combinations.
How can the combinations listed be used to find the number of
permutations?

Decide whether order matters in each situation. Write Yes or No.

13. Choosing a line up of 10 band members to march
in the front row from 25 band members   _____

14. Choosing 3 room monitors from 18 students in the class   _____

15. A combination to a school locker   _____

Find the number of possible arrangements. State whether it is a
permutation or combination.

16. Holly is choosing 2 books to read from a shelf of
6 books.   _____

_____

17. A club is choosing a president and vice-president,
from 10 club members.   _____

_____

18. Tito is arranging 3 toys on a shelf from a box of 10 toys. _____

_____

Representing Probability

The **probability** of an event describes the likelihood that an event will occur. The probability of an event can be any number from 0 to 1. You can represent probability as a faction, decimal, or percent.

Falisha spins the spinner shown. Find the probability that the spinner will land on 1. Answer 1 to 6 to represent the probability as a fraction, decimal, and percent.

1. How many sections of the spinner have a 1?   _____

2. How many total sections are on the spinner?   _____

3. Complete to write the probability as a fraction in simplest form.

$$P = \frac{\text{number of favorable outcomes}}{\text{total number of outcomes}} = \frac{\boxed{}}{8} = \frac{\boxed{}}{4}$$

4. To write $\frac{1}{4}$ as a decimal, divide 1 by 4. $1 \div 4 =$ _____

5. To write 0.25 as a percent, move the decimal point two places to the right and add the % sign.   _____

6. So, the probability that the spinner will land on 1 is:

$\frac{1}{4} = 0.$_____ $=$ _____%.

Find the probability that Falisha will spin a number less than 4. Answer 7 to 12 to write the probability as a fraction, decimal, and percent.

7. How many sections on the spinner have a number less than 4?   _____

8. How many total sections are on the spinner?   _____

9. Complete to write the probability as a fraction in simplest form.

$$P = \frac{\text{number of favorable outcomes}}{\text{total number of outcomes}} = \frac{\boxed{}}{8}$$

10. To write $\frac{5}{8}$ as a decimal, divide 5 by 8.   _____

11. To write 0.625 as a percent, move the decimal point two places to the right and add the % sign.   _____

12. So, the probability that that spinner will land on a number less than 4 is: $\frac{5}{8} = 0.$_____ $=$ _____%.

Name _____

Representing Probability (continued)

A **complement** of an event is the probability that the event does **not** happen. To find the probability of a complement, subtract the probability of the event from 1.

Find the *complement* of Falisha spinning the spinner and it landing on a number less than 4 by answering 13 and 14.

13. Previously, you found that the probability of the spinner landing on a number less than 4 was 0.625.

What is 1 − 0.625?   _____

14. So, what is the probability of the spinner NOT landing on a number less than 4?   _____

A marble is chosen from the jars without looking. Find each probability as a fraction, a decimal, and a percent.

Jar 1   Jar 2

15. *P*(black from Jar 1)   **16.** *P*(black from Jar 2)

_____   _____

17. *P*(gray from Jar 1)   **18.** *P*(not gray from Jar 2)

_____   _____

19. *P*(not white from Jar 1)   **20.** *P*(gray or white from Jar 1)

_____   _____

21. Reasoning Are you more likely to get a black marble from Jar 1 or Jar 2? Explain.

Experimental Probability and Predictions

Materials 8 yellow, 7 red, and 5 blue color tiles in a small paper bag,
for each student or pair

Do not look in the bag of tiles Use it
to help answer 1 to 12.

1. Do the following experiment. Pull
out one tile from the bag without
looking, and record the color in
the tally chart. Place the tile back
into the bag. Repeat this process
40 times.

Tile Experiment		
Color	**Tally**	**Number**
Yellow		
Red		
Blue		

Experimental probability is based on
the results of an experiment.

2. How many times did you get a yellow tile?

3. How many trials were there, that is how many times did pull a tile? _____

4. Complete to find the experimental probability that the next tile
pulled from the bag will be yellow.

$$P = \frac{\text{Number of Yellow Tiles Pulled}}{\text{Total Number of Trials}} = \frac{\boxed{}}{40}$$

5. Complete to find the experimental probability that the next tile
pulled from the bag will be red.

$$P = \frac{\text{Number of Red Tiles Pulled}}{\text{Total of Number of Trials}} = \frac{\boxed{}}{40}$$

6. Complete to find the experimental probability that the next tile
pulled from the bag will be blue.

$$P = \frac{\text{Number of Blue Tiles Pulled}}{\text{Total of Number of Trials}} = \frac{\boxed{}}{40}$$

7. Find the sum of the experimental probability of randomly selecting
a yellow tile, a red tile, or a blue tile.

_____ + _____ + _____ = _____

The probability of an event can be any number from 0 to 1. So the sum
of each event occurring in an experiment should equal 1.

8. Does the sum of the probabilities equal 1? _____

Experimental Probability and Predictions (continued)

You can use the experimental probability of an event to make predictions.

9. There are 20 tiles in the bag. Use the results of your experiment to predict how many tiles of each color are in the bag.

_____ yellow, _____ red, and _____ blue

10. Look in the bag. Were your predictions close to the actual number of each color of tiles in the bag?   _____

11. Predict how many tiles would be yellow, if a tile was pulled from the bag 200 times.

Multiply the experimental probability from item 4 by 200.   _____

12. Predict how many tiles would be red, if a tile was pulled from the bag 200 times.   _____

The table at the right shows the number of times Jeffrey's school bus has been early, on time, and late to pick him up over the past 10 days. Use the table to answer Exercises 13 to 17.

Jeffrey's Bus		
Early	On Time	Late
2	5	3

13. What is the experimental probability that the bus will be early the next time Jeffrey rides it?   _____

14. How many times can Jeffrey expect the bus to be early over the next 20 school days?   _____

15. What is the experimental probability that the bus will be late the next time Jeffrey rides it?   _____

16. How many times can Jeffrey expect the bus to be late over the next 20 school days?   _____

17. What is the sum of the experimental probabilities of the bus being early, the bus being on time, and the bus being late?   _____

18. A manufacturer sampled 100 screws and found that 5% were defective. Predict how many screws, out of 500, you would expect to be defective,   _____

19. Reasoning A craft store recorded the colors of yarn they sold. After 50 packages were sold, they found there was a 20% chance that a shopper buying yarn would buy a red color. How many of the 50 packages sold were red?   _____

© Pearson Education, Inc.

Adding Probabilities

Materials index card, scissors, and a small bag for each student or group

Cut an index card into 12 pieces and label each with a number 1 to 12. Place the card pieces into a bag. Draw one card at random from the bag. Answer 1 to 9 to determine the probability that the number drawn is a prime number or a 6.

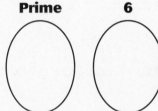

Prime   6

1. Write the prime numbers from 1 to 12 in the circle at the right labeled Prime. Write the number 6 in the circle labeled 6.

   Are any of the numbers in both circles? _____

Mutually exclusive events are events that cannot happen at the same time.

2. Can you randomly draw a card that is both a prime number and the number 6? _____

3. So, are the events "drawing a prime number or a 6" mutually exclusive? _____

If events are mutually exclusive you can add their probabilities to find the probability of either event happening.

4. How many favorable outcomes are there for randomly drawing a prime number? _____

5. What is the probability of drawing a prime number? _____

6. How many favorable outcomes are there for randomly drawing a 6? _____

7. What is the probability of drawing a 6? _____

8. Find the sum of the two probabilities.

   P(prime number) $+ P$(6) $= P$(prime or 6)

   $$\dfrac{5}{\boxed{}} + \dfrac{\boxed{}}{12} = \dfrac{\boxed{}}{12} = \dfrac{1}{\boxed{}}$$

9. So, what is the probability of choosing a prime number or a 6? _____

Adding Probabilities (continued)

You have a bag containing tiles with numbers labeled 1 to 20. Tell whether the events are mutually exclusive. Write Yes or No.

10. P(odd or 13)

_____

11. P(odd or 14)

_____

12. P(even or odd)

_____

13. P(even or prime)

_____

14. P(2 or less than 12)

_____

15. P(14 or greater than 18)

_____

16. P(multiple of 3 or multiple of 5)

_____

17. P(divisible by 2 or 7)

_____

You toss two number cubes each labeled with the numbers 1–6. Tell whether the events are mutually exclusive. Then, find the probability.

18. P(3 or 4)

_____

19. P(1 or number less than 3)

_____

20. P(even or 3)

_____

21. P(number less than 3 or number greater than 3)

_____

22. Reasoning The probability that it will rain today is 25%. The probability that it will rain tomorrow is 75%. Mark concludes that the probability it will rain in the next 2 days is 100%. Is he right? Why or why not?

Independent Events

In a game, players spin the spinner at the right twice and
record their results.

Answer 1 to 7 to find the probability of the spinner landing on 5
both times.

1. List the possible outcomes of the spinner.   _____

2. What is the probability of spinning 5 on the first spin? $P(5) =$ _____

3. What is the probability of spinning 5 on the second spin? $P(5) =$ _____

4. Does the outcome on the first spin affect the outcome of the
second spin?   _____

If the outcome of the first event does not affect the outcome of the
second event, the two events are **independent events**.

5. Are the two events, spinning a 5 and then spinning a 5,
independent events?   _____

To find the probability of two independent events, you find the
probability of each event and then multiply.

6. Multiply. $P(5) \times P(5) = P(5, 5)$

$$\frac{1}{\boxed{}} \times \frac{\boxed{}}{5} = \frac{\boxed{}}{25}$$

7. What is the probability of the spinner landing on 5 both times?   _____

Answer 8 to 12 to find the probability of the spinner landing on a 1
or 2 and then a number other than 3.

8. What is the probability of spinning a 1 or 2 on the first spin?   _____

9. What is the probability of spinning a number other
than 3 on the second spin?   _____

10. Are the two events independent?   _____

11. So, multiply the probabilities of each event.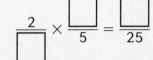

Independent Events (continued)

12. What is the probability of the spinner landing on a 1 or 2 and
then a number other than 3?   _____

Find each probability using the spinner at the right.

13. $P(2, 3)$ **14.** $P(1, \text{not } 1)$ **15.** $P(3, 3)$

_____   _____   _____

16. $P(1, 6)$ **17.** $P(\text{not } 5, \text{not } 5)$ **18.** $P(\text{not } 3, 3)$

_____   _____   _____

Players pick a letter from the bag without looking. They
record it and put it back. Then they pick another letter
in the same way. Find the probability of the following.

19. $P(A, A)$ **20.** $P(X, y)$ **21.** $P(A, \text{not } X)$

_____   _____   _____

22. $P(A, \text{not } A)$ **23.** $P(C, y)$ **24.** $P(\text{not } C, \text{not } y)$

_____   _____   _____

25. Reasoning If the probability of spinning red twice on a spinner
is $\frac{9}{25}$, then what is the probability of spinning red just once?   _____

26. Reasoning The probability of choosing a 7 from a bag of cards
is $\frac{1}{10}$. What is the probability of choosing a 7 and then not choosing
a 7?   _____

Name _____

Dependent Events

Materials index card, scissors, and small bag for each student or group

Cut an index card into 8 pieces. Write the following numbers, one on each card: 1, 3, 2, 2, 4, 4, 5 and 5. Place the card pieces into the bag.

If you draw one card without looking, record its value, replace the card, and then select another card and record its value, what is the probability that you draw a 5 both times? Answer 1 to 5 to find the probability.

1. How many favorable outcomes are there for getting
    a 5 on the first draw?   _____

2. What is the probability of getting a 5 from the bag on the
    first draw?   _____

If the outcome of the first event does not affect the outcome of the second event, the two events are **independent events**.

3. Are the events of getting a 5 on the first draw and getting a 5 on
    the second draw independent?   _____

4. What is the probability of getting a 5 from the bag on the
    second draw?   _____

To find the probability of two independent events, you find the probability of each event and then multiply.

$$P(5) \times P(5) = P(5, 5)$$

5. Multiply to find the probability of drawing a 5,
    replacing the card, and then drawing a 5 again.

$$\frac{1}{\boxed{}} \times \frac{\boxed{}}{4} = \frac{\boxed{}}{16}$$

If you draw one card without looking, do NOT replace the card, and then select another card, what is the probability that you draw a 5 both times? Answer 6 to 12 to find the probability.

6. What is the probability of getting a 5 from the bag on the first
    draw?   _____

7. Assume the card you got on the first draw was a 5. Take a card
    with 5 on it out of the bag. How many cards are left in the bag? _____

8. How many of the cards that are left in the bag have a 5?   _____

9. What is the probability of getting a 5 from the bag on the second
    draw if you get a 5 on the first draw and do not replace it?   _____

Dependent Events (continued)

10. Does the outcome of the first event affect the outcome
of the second event? _____

If the outcome of the first event affects the outcome of the second
event, the two events are **dependent events**.

11. Are the events of getting a 5 on the first draw and getting a 5 on
the second draw when the first card is not replaced dependent? _____

To find the probability of two dependent events, you find the
probability of each event and then multiply.

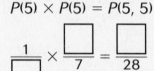

12. Multiply to find the probability of drawing a 5 and
then a 5 again if the card is NOT replaced.

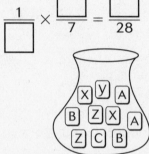

Players pick a letter from the bag without looking. They
record it and put it back. Then they pick another letter
in the same way. Find the probability of the following.

13. $P(A, A)$ **14.** $P(X, y)$ **15.** $P(A, \text{not } X)$

_____   _____   _____

Players pick a letter from the bag without looking. They record it and do
not put it back. Then they pick another letter in the same way. Find the
probability of the following.

16. $P(A, A)$ **17.** $P(X, y)$ **18.** $P(A, \text{not } X)$

_____   _____   _____

19. Reasoning The probability of choosing a 7 from a bag of cards
is $\frac{3}{10}$. What is the probability of choosing a 7 and then a 7 again if
the card is not replaced? Explain.